INTERHEMISPHERIC RELATIONS AND CEREBRAL DOMINANCE

INTERHEMISPHERIC RELATIONS AND CEREBRAL DOMINANCE

edited by

Vernon B. Mountcastle, M.D.

The Johns Hopkins University School of Medicine
Baltimore, Maryland

The Johns Hopkins Press
Baltimore

Printed in the U.S.A.
Library of Congress Catalog Card Number 62–15311

Originally published, 1962
Second printing, 1967

Preface

This book contains the papers and the formal discussions presented at a conference on interhemispheric relations and cerebral dominance held at the Johns Hopkins University School of Medicine, April 23–25, 1961. The conference arose from a suggestion of Dr. R. L. Masland of the National Institutes of Health. It was planned by a committee of the faculty of the School of Medicine made up of Dr. John E. Bordley, Chairman, Dr. David B. Clark, Dr. Vernon B. Mountcastle, Dr. Thomas B. Turner, and Dr. A. E. Walker. The committee began its deliberations with the intent of planning a conference on the problem of cerebral dominance, alone. Early in our survey it became clear that presently the most active segment of the field is that concerned with the functional relations between the hemispheres, a subject which at once encompasses and is larger than that of cerebral dominance, as classically defined. The large share of the papers presented at the conference and contained in this book are concerned with this subject, and not with that of cerebral dominance, *per se*.

The conference centered on this simple question: "Why do we have two brains?" The reader of this volume will perceive at once that to this question only very simple answers can be given. What he may also see is that a better understanding of it will surely depend upon a synthesis of the efforts of many investigators, laboring in diverse fields, and that studies now under way promise important advances. Thus an approach from the evolutionary point of view provides new hypotheses concerning interhemispheric function, while the use of the methods of physiological psychology to study the behavior of animals after section of the intercerebral commissures provides many new experimental observations. While these, for the present, fit no generalization, they have given the first measures of the learning and behavioral deficits which supervene when an animal is forced to operate with what can be termed, for certain functions, two separate brains. I hope this volume will serve also to emphasize the continuing need and the great importance of detailed studies of human beings after brain lesions, and several papers included here illustrate the important results which can be obtained when such studies are carried out under controlled conditions. The advantage of the human being as a verbally reporting observer need hardly be emphasized. It is of special significance, I believe, that no paper is included here which describes results obtained by the electrophysiological method, though it is to be expected and hoped that this powerful tool will also be brought to bear upon the problems of interhemispheric relations.

The members of the Medical Faculty of the Johns Hopkins University wish to express their appreciation to those colleagues who took time from busy lives and traveled from distant places that we might have the pleasure of their company and the benefit of their learning. Our gratitude is due also to those whose sponsorship made the conference possible, the National Institute of Neurological Diseases and Blindness, and the Association for the Aid of Crippled Children.

VERNON B. MOUNTCASTLE, M.D.
Professor of Physiology,
The Johns Hopkins University

Baltimore, Maryland
July 31, 1962

■ □

Contributors

Arthur L. Benton
State University of Iowa College of Medicine, Iowa City, Iowa

David Bodian
The Johns Hopkins University School of Medicine, Baltimore, Maryland

Macdonald Critchley
The National Hospital, London, England

Derek Denny-Brown
Harvard University Medical School, Boston, Massachusetts

John L. deC. Downer
University College, London, England

George Ettlinger
The National Hospital, London, England

H. Hécaen
Les Hopitaux Psychiatriques de la Seine, Paris, France

Richard Jung
University of Freiburg, Freiburg, Germany

Henricus G. J. M. Kuypers
University of Maryland School of Medicine, Baltimore, Maryland

John C. Lilly
Communication Research Institute, Miami, Florida

Brenda Milner
McGill University, Montreal Neurological Institute, Montreal, Canada

Mortimer Mishkin
National Institute of Mental Health, Bethesda, Maryland

Ronald E. Myers
The Johns Hopkins University School of Medicine, Baltimore, Maryland

Walle J. H. Nauta
Walter Reed Army Institute of Research, Washington, D.C.

William D. Neff
Psychophysiology Laboratory, Bolt, Beranek, & Newman, Inc., Cambridge, Massachusetts

James L. O'Leary
Washington University School of Medicine, St. Louis, Missouri

Karl H. Pribram
Stanford University School of Medicine, Stanford, California

Arnold B. Scheibel
University of California Medical Center, Los Angeles, California

Madge E. Scheibel
University of California Medical Center, Los Angeles, California

Roger W. Sperry
California Institute of Technology, Pasadena, California

Hans-Lukas Teuber
Massachusetts Institute of Technology, Cambridge, Massachusetts

Gerhardt von Bonin
Mount Zion Hospital and Medical Center, San Francisco, California

Sidney Weinstein
Albert Einstein College of Medicine, New York, New York

Harold G. Wolff
Cornell University Medical College, New York, New York

J. Z. Young
University College, London, England

Contents

I

Anatomical Asymmetries of the Cerebral Hemispheres

by GERHARDT VON BONIN

Professor Emeritus, Medical School, University of Illinois and Mount Zion Hospital and Medical Center, San Francisco, Calif.

IN THE BOOK of Judges, chapter 20, verse 16, we read that in the army of the children of Benjamin there were 700 left-handed soldiers who formed a group of their own in the army. But even that did not help them: "and the Lord smote Benjamin before Israel . . . " (Verse 35)

This is probably the oldest reference to left-handedness for it dates from about 1100 B.C.

Philologic evidence, namely that the word for "ten" and for "right" have the same stem both in Greek and in Latin, seems to indicate that our early forefathers started counting with the left hand and then went over to the right hand. It has also been said that, since the heart was on the left side, warriors held the shield in the left hand, and, therefore, fought with the spear or sword in the right hand, and that that was the origin of right-handedness (Stier, 1911).

Before I discuss the brain, I should like to point out that asymmetries of paired organs are the rule, rather than the exception, in the human body. Thus the limbs as well as the clavicle are asymmetrical, the right arm is a little longer than the left one, and for the bones of the leg the opposite is true; those on the left are slightly longer than those on the right side (Ingelmark, 1947). Also, the left clavicle is longer than the right one (Martin, 1957).

In the case of the clavicle, it is clearly the heart which causes the asymmetry, in the case of the arm and leg, we are not nearly as certain, but it should be kept in mind that we are (generally) right-handed and left-footed. The curious reversal of the asymmetry of the femur makes a simple explanation difficult. But this is not our problem here.

	R	*L*	*R*>+, *L*>−
Clavicle	142 mm	145 mm	
Humerus			6–12 yrs. + 3.79 mm 13–20 yrs. + 5.73 mm
Femur			6–12 yrs. + 2.03 mm 13–20 yrs. − 3.10 mm

The individual bones of the skull were measured by Woo (1931) in the long series of Egyptian skulls at the Biometric Laboratory in London. He found that, in the frontal and parietal region, the right bone was consistently the larger one.

The study of the anatomical asymmetries in the brain which started about 1860 soon got tangled up with physiology and questions of cerebral dominance, particularly after it became clear that language was generally bound up with the left hemisphere.

The whole idea appears to go back to Dax, who, as we will hear in detail from Dr. Critchley, showed in 1830 that aphasia was generally associated with a lesion of the left hemisphere, if a right-handed person was involved. He felt sure that this would manifest itself in physical characters, although he himself made no measurements.

A pre-eminence of the left hemisphere was claimed by Boyd (1861) and Ogle (1871) in England and by Broca (1875) in France. Boyd published brain weights in 1861, from which a slight preponderance of the left hemisphere seems to emerge. The difference in favor of the left hemisphere was a little more than 5 grams, which might be considered sufficient to establish left hemispheric superiority, if it were not for the fact that very soon afterwards several authors found the right one heavier. Thus Wagner (1864) measured 18 brains. In this short series, he found the right hemisphere the heavier one, (570.5 against 569.8 gm.) and Thurnam (1866) came to the same result, on the strength of 257 male and 213 female brains (511.1 against 510.8 gm.). Broca (1875) found the following weights in two series which he measured:

	N	R	L
Bicêtre	19	531.3	530.8
St. Antoine	18	575.8	574.4

The preponderance of the left hemisphere was proclaimed by Ogle (1871). It is not always clear what he means. He starts out by citing

Boyd's (1861) paper on the weight of the two hemispheres and then goes on to Bastian's (1866) determination of the specific gravity of the two sides, in which he found the left side somewhat heavier. Bastian's (1866) figures (for 27 brains) are:

Average of Specific Gravity of Gray Matter

	Left	Right
Frontal	1.0291	1.0276
Parietal	1.0300	1.0296
Occipital	1.0320	1.0316

Since the gray matter is supposed to be somewhat lighter than the white, it would seem that the left hemisphere had a higher concentration of cells in its cortex than the right one, or that the errors of Bastian's (1866) determination are of the order of .004. We prefer the latter explanation. Ogle (1871) made no measurement himself; he concludes by saying:

> Seeing, however, that we know, if the argument I have used in the earlier part of this paper be valid, that some or other anatomical differences between the two sides must precede the right-handedness and moreover that this difference must be somewhere in the brain (for how otherwise can the facts which I have brought forward about aphasia be explained?) it appears to me only rational to suppose, when one finds such an anatomical difference between the two hemispheres as that now revealed, that this anatomical difference is the antecedent for which one was searching.

He feels that it is in the vessels of the brain, particularly in the larger size of the left carotid artery, that one has to look for the reason for the superiority of the left hemisphere.

Braune (1891) measured 100 brains, and obtained a slight preponderance of the right hemisphere and an equally slight preponderance of the left cerebellar hemisphere, which is what one would expect.

	Cerebrum	Cerebellum
Right	551.23	78.93
Left	549.66	79.76

We will pass by some more modern papers, since they do not add anything new, and go directly to a paper by Hoadley and Pearson (1929). They measured the right and left internal length of the skull in 729 male Egyptian skulls. These were originally sent to Pearson (1929) by Sir Flinders Petry, who had found them. They belong to the 26–30th Dynasty. The data obtained were: R: 171.0, L: 170.1 mm. Hoadley and

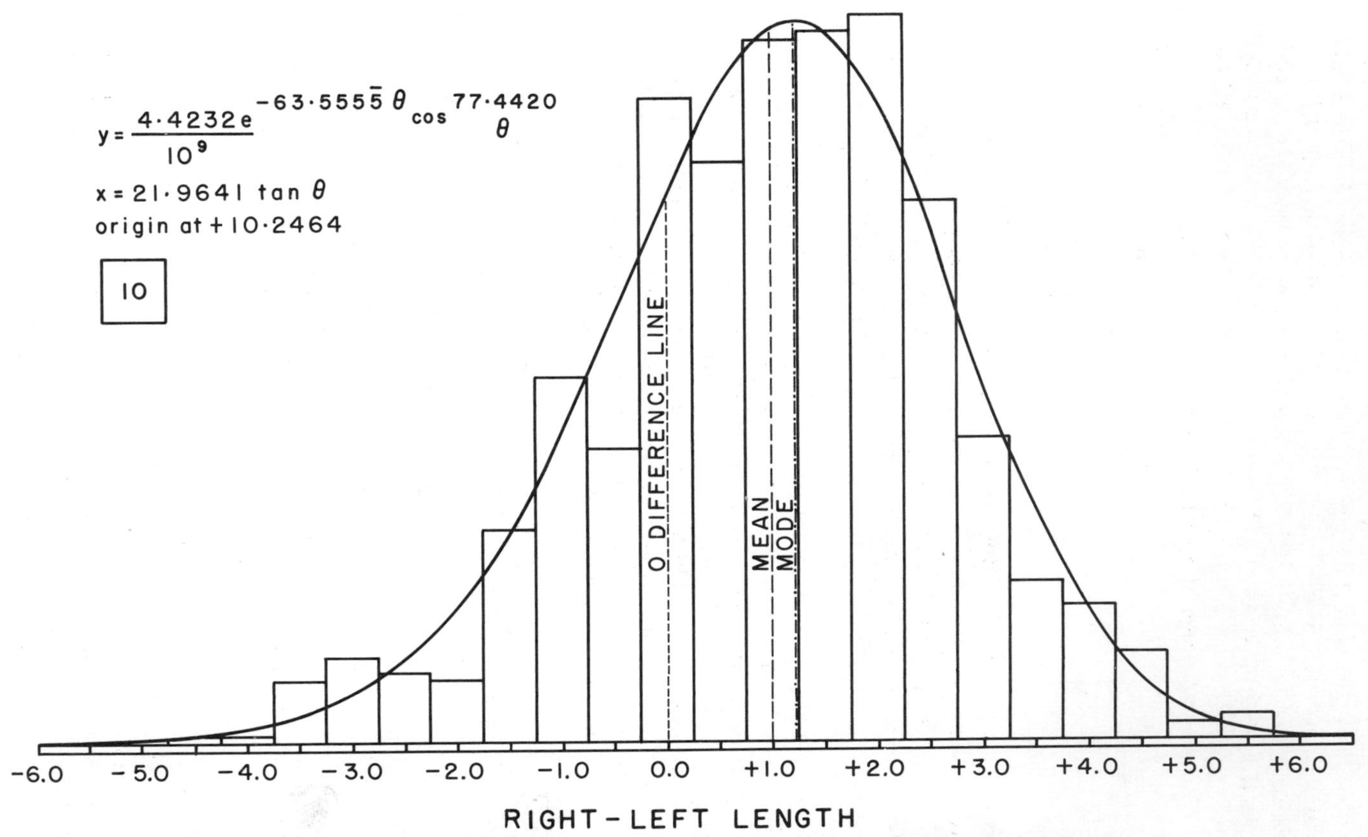

Fig. 1. A graph illustrating the differences between the internal lengths of the two sides of the skull. (from Hoadley, M. F. & Pearson, K. *Biometrika*, **21:** 94–123, 1929)

Pearson (1929) discuss at great length the possible pitfalls of their measurements but finally come to the conclusion that the right hemisphere is slightly larger than the left one, thus confirming Braune (1891) and Broca (1875), who both weighed hemispheres. The former found the right one heavier by 1.57 gm., the latter by 1.97 gm. Figure 1 illustrates their findings once more.

We have a few measurements of the volume of the gray substance of the brain, separately for right and left side. Aresu (1914) measured the surface of the brain by depositing silver on it, and then determining the amount of silver used for this purpose. From these data he computed, first, the area covered and, then, the volume of the cortex, assuming it to have a thickness of 3.5 mm. This is, of course, a very time-consuming and laborious process, and it is, therefore, not surprising that he only subjected 12 brains to this procedure. His results are:

volume of right side 360 cm^3.
volume of left side 364 cm^3.

This is based on 4 males, 4 females, and 4 children, in ages between 1 year and 4 months and 4 years and 8 months.

The interesting thing here is that the left side appears to be larger than the right one, in contrast to what we found for the weight and the size of the hemisphere as a whole. Of course, 12 determinations against over 700 do not carry too much weight, and Aresu's (1914) measurements have certainly large inherent errors, but it is still possible that both determinations are close to the truth. In other words, the fissures in the left hemisphere are slightly deeper than on the right side. It has to be admitted, though, that this is unlikely, particularly since it involves additional assumptions about the size of the basal ganglia, or the thickness of the myelin sheets, all of which are very far-fetched.

The probable error of Aresu's (1914) determination is about 8 grams; the difference which he found is insignificant. Weil (1929) measured the surface of the cerebral and cerebellar hemispheres planimetrically and came to the conclusion that "the measurements of the cerebral surface do not support the theory of a marked asymmetry of the hemispheres in higher forms."

A somewhat different picture emerges when we turn our attention to details of the fissures. We begin with the Sylvian fissure. According to Eberstaller (1884), this fissure is 58.2 mm. long on the left and 51.8 mm. long on the right side. A single anterior ramus is more frequent on the right than on the left side. It goes with the greater length of the left posterior ramus, that Kodama (1934) found that the left insula is 56.4

mm. long and 38.1 mm. high, while the right one is only 52.8 mm. long and 37.5 mm. high. Unfortunately, nothing is known about the size of the basal ganglia.

The sulcus cinguli shows an interruption more frequently on the left side in Eberstaller's (1884) material, but Retzius' (1896 & 1902) figures, obtained from Swedes, do not substantiate this. Weinberg (1905) found, in Poles, a doubling of the sulcus cinguli in its anterior part more frequently on the left side than on the right side.

In the calcarine fissure, Wen (1933) found, in Chinese brains, a hook more frequently on the left than on the right side.

The occipital and the parietal part of the intraparietal sulcus are fused in Cunningham's material (1892) in 87.5 percent on the right, but only in 58.4 percent on the left side. The difference (29.1 $\pm$ 11.2 percent) is just about significant.

The doubling of Heschl's gyrus appears to be more frequent on the right than on the left side according to Pfeifer (1936), but no figures are given. Economo & Horn (1930) found the same in 6 brains which they investigated in great detail, but it appears that they examined for side differences only macroscopically.

On the basis of a few brains, Gans (1922) asserted that, in Europeans, the left ascending parietal gyrus is broader and better developed than the right one, and later (1923) pointed out, again on the basis of only a few cases, that just the reverse holds good for the Chinese, in which I (1924) confirmed him—with 2 (!) brains.

The left hemisphere has a slightly greater specific gravity than the right one. This would mean that there is little more cortex on the left side. That fits in with the fact that the left Sylvian fissure is a little bit longer, that the insula is longer and higher on the left side, that there is a doubling of the sulcus cinguli more frequently on the left side, and that the calcarine fissure has a hook more often on the left than on the right side.

But all these morphological differences are, after all, quite small. How to correlate these with the astonishing differences in function, such as the speech function on the left side, is an entirely different question, and one that I am unable to answer.

■□ II

Why Do We Have Two Brains?

by J. Z. YOUNG

University College, London, England

THIS PAPER is an attempt to bring together evidence from various sources about the influences that have determined the condition that we have paired cerebral hemispheres but can often dispense with one of them or with the commissure between them. Briefly the evidence suggests (1) that bilaterality was originally a necessity for nervous systems that operate by means of a map-like analogue system. (2) In the visual system in particular, the inversion produced by the lens requires to be corrected; and this was a prime function of the optic chiasma system, which, in turn, perhaps determined all the other crossings in the brain. (3) The more complex computing sections of nervous systems, such as the human one, are less dependent on topographic mapping and, therefore, bilaterality becomes less important.

I suspect that you may try to dismiss the method of enquiry used as "unscientific." You may label it with the hate word "teleological," because I ask, "What have been the causes that have produced the present state of the brain?" Yet I hope that in the end you will agree that this is a perfectly direct scientific problem. Physical factors must have determined that some animals have paired brains and others do not. The trouble is that this was determined long ago. Yet as evidence of how and why it happened, we have surviving today many animals with conditions most different from our own, and to these we shall often refer. We cannot at present make new types of animals experimentally to test hypotheses about how they have been produced. But all these various species are available as evidence for us, natural experiments in how to live under various conditions. And if you say, "Why should we trouble with these relics and with all this past history?" then I will say that in order to understand the correct functioning of the nervous system and its pathology, we need to know the evolutionary and embryological processes that have made it what it is. How else should we expect to learn how to control and heal it?

In order to arrive at a satisfactory explanation of any condition, it is often useful to look first at its opposite, to find a state in which it is not present. We are fortunate in that there are many animals provided with only one median eye and brain; we need think no further than the crustacean *Cyclops,* named for this very condition. If we can find the significant differences between the way of life of such animals and those with paired eyes and brains, then I believe we shall be able to answer our question. But in order to specify "significant differences," we have to think about the whole problem of the way in which an organism makes a fit or match with its environment.

Every living thing maintains itself distinct from its surroundings, only merging with them after death. Yet no organism is cut off from its environment; the two interchange continuously. Thus, we have the paradox that each creature is able to maintain its difference from the environment only because it "mirrors" or "represents" that same environment. It remains unlike it by virtue of the very fact that it resembles it. This is the paradox of the concept of "representation," one of the most central and subtle problems of epistemology and, of course, art.

The organism maintains a steady state of homeostasis because its structure and actions are appropriate to match those that go on around it. Such a homeostat must contain instructions that appropriately represent all relevant features of the environment. By means of these instructions, it is ensured that the system takes suitable actions and survives. These instructions lie, of course, mainly in two systems, first in the deoxyribosenucleotides, which make the genetic code, and secondly, in animals, the nervous system, which controls much of behavior. These are the systems of instructions that represent the environment, and it is in them that we should expect to find especially explicit the isomorphism or matching with the surroundings. Why is it, then, that a nucleus and a nervous system seem so different and, our particular problem, why has the nervous system, but not the genetic system, right and left sides?

In order to see the sense in which such apparently disparate systems both "represent" the same environment, we must consider the whole question of coding and representation. A code may be defined as a set of physical events that is part of the communication system of a homeostat. It has been decided during the construction of the system that these physical events shall stand for a set of events in the world around. The internal code of events may or may not have any physical resemblance to those that it represents. Thus, it may have been decided that the instructions in the computer of a guided missile shall be in the form of magnetized points on a metallic tape. When this tape is in a suitable machine, it is able to ensure that the missile arrives at its destination in spite of wind changes or even, perhaps, enemy counteraction. The magnetized tape only "represents" wind in the very sophisticated context of the whole missile, its detectors and its fins or other "means of expression." We might say that such a code is a very abstract representation. It is in this sense that the DNA molecules of the genes represent the environment. They ensure, in their context, the proper development and operation of a particular homeostat. Moreover, by the instructions that they contain for their own periodic reshuffling from time to time, they ensure the astonishing continuity of animal life that is made possible by the relatively slow changes that we call evolution.

Such "abstract" representations are highly efficient for long-term forecasting. It is because the DNA molecules are not themselves enzymes, still less eyes or kidneys, that they can be shuffled and assorted to provide the material for natural selection. We may compare such an "abstract" code with the binary code of a digital computer. Such codes are efficient for doing really difficult jobs of forecasting. Given sufficient time (or great speed, which comes to the same thing), general purpose computers can solve any problem. For example, living matter considered as one whole system, has solved the problem how to remain alive for a thousand million years or more.

The point for us is to contrast these abstract codes with those of the nervous system which must make "decisions" about quite complex matters in a short time. If carbon compounds provided components as reliable as metals, this would be less of a problem. We could have ultra high speed digital computers in our heads and make accurate forecasts about the best courses of action in the light of what our eyes, ears, and nose report and have reported in the past. It is not beyond possibility that there are homeostats with such computers elsewhere in the universe. They would seem to us to be as wise and farseeing as we, perhaps, to a flatworm. But the operations of the carbon compound machines of which we are made are slow, relative to the events in the world about which they must make forecasts. In order to deal with these events, the nervous system, therefore, operates on a different principle. It contains a memory that is much more closely isomorphic with the world, that which it represents, than are the genes or the elements of a computer.

To put it bluntly, there is in the brain of simpler animals at least, a sort of map of the world, in which certain visual features are represented in approximately the same relative positions as they occupy in the outside world.

The advantage of this system is that it ensures speed of decision by neglecting all items of information that do not fit with the map. The receptors pass on only information about those sorts of change that can be anticipated by "consulting" the map.

The presence of such maps is not hypothetical; there is plenty of evidence that they are there. They are perhaps most conspicuously map-like in the visual system of animals of an intermediate level of neural complexity, such as a frog or an octopus. In mammals and man, although the receptor and motor fields are elaborately mapped on the cortex, it may be that the information contained in these areas is not so closely limited to a naturalistic model isomorphic with the surroundings. The mammalian brain uses so many special tricks that it begins to approach the condition of a general purpose computer. Nevertheless, we have been evolved from homeostats whose neural memories contain maps of the surroundings. I believe that we can show that such maps require two brains and that this is at least one of the reasons why so many tracts are crossed in the nervous system.

If the representation in a brain is a map, then those events that have important spatial relations must be represented the same way "up" on the map. Many of the occurrences that are signalled by the eyes, gravity receptors, and touch receptors have such important spatial characteristics. During the movement of an animal downward, while following prey with the eye, the indication from the gravity receptors must track across the map in the same direction as that from the eye. Because of the inversion produced by the lens, the information from these two systems, light and gravity, would proceed in opposite directions over any map to which it was isomorphically transferred from the two receptor surfaces, unless on one of the pathways there is a reinversion. It is, therefore, very interesting to find that there are elaborate arrangements in many animals to ensure just this correction, and their presence alone is strong evidence that in these animals, at least, the brain contains a map with spatial organization similar to that of the world itself.

In an octopus or other cephalopod, Kopsch (1899) and Cajal (1917) showed that there is behind the retina a chiasma such that fibers from the dorsal retinal surface go to the ventral surface of the optic lobe and vice versa (Figure 1). This chiasma is not in any way concerned with transmitting information from one side of the body to the other. It is strictly on one side (there are in addition mid-line commissures that

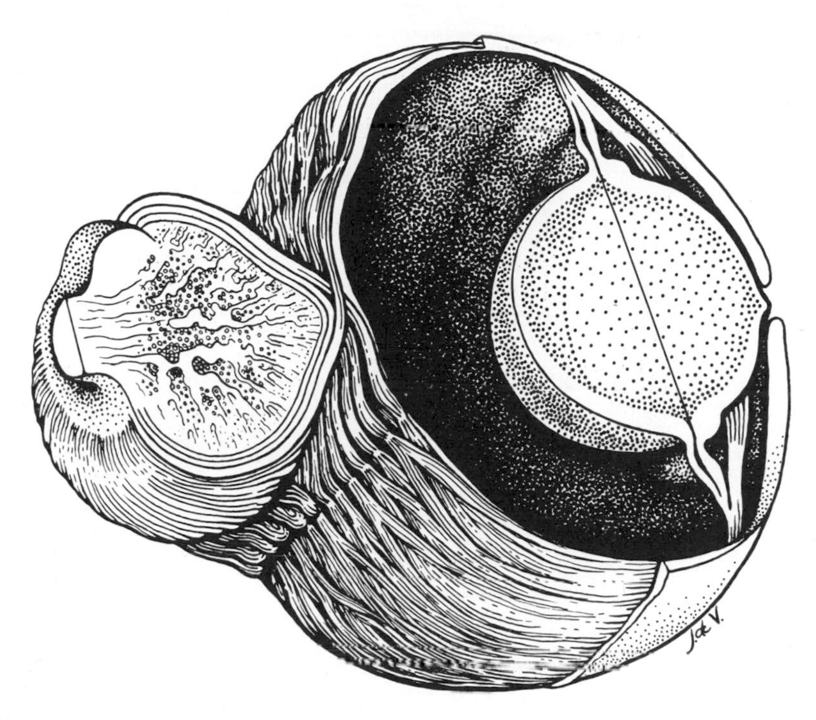

Fig. 1. Diagram of the eye and optic lobe of an octopus to show how the chiasma of the optic nerves behind the retina produces a reinversion of the retinal image in the dorsoventral sense.

connect the two sides and transfer information from one side to the other). The postretinal chiasma can have no other function but to reinvert the display on the retina in the dorsoventral direction. Notice that it does not do this in the anteroposterior direction.

In the many discussions of the significance of the vertebrate chiasma system, no one seems to have considered the implications of this dorsoventral reinversion in cephalopods. Cajal, in his 1917 paper, promised that he would do so and even went so far as to give us the title of his proposed paper, "Considerations on the significance of the optic chiasmas of the insects, crustacea, and cephalopods, with various sketches." So far as I can discover, this paper never appeared. Perhaps that was because he could not reconcile the cephalopod condition with his own theory of the significance of the vertebrate sensory and motor chiasmata, published in 1899. This theory, you will remember, supposes that the chiasma serves to unify the two halves of the panoramic field that is provided by two separate eyes, "the decussation of the optic

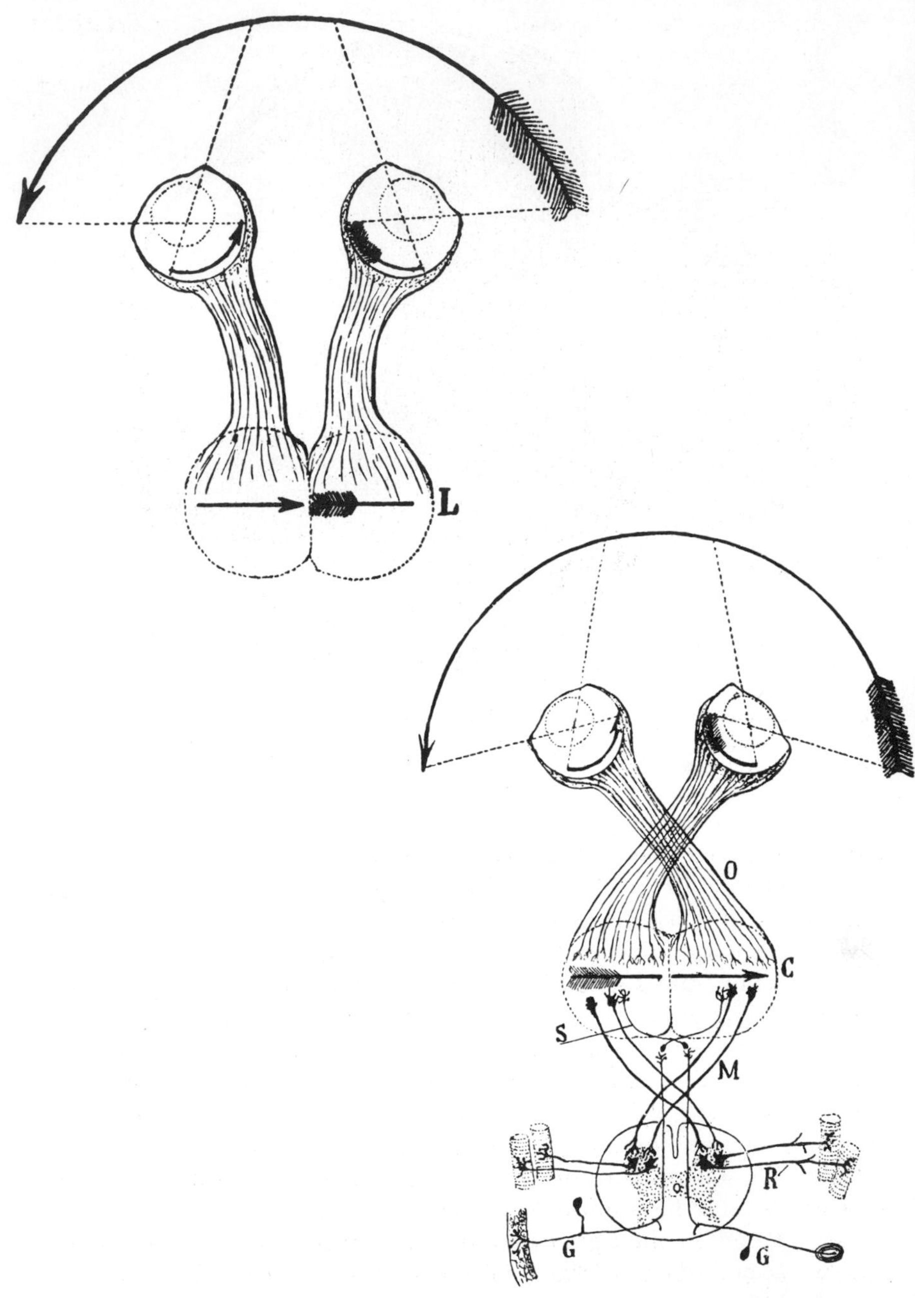

Figs. 2 and 3. Cajal's diagrams to show how a panoramic visual field would be broken up by the inverting action of the lenses and how this is avoided by a chiasma.

nerves is motivated by a necessity to restore the lateral inversion of the two images caused by the action of the lenses" (Figures 2 and 3).

In the few words he gives in his 1917 paper "anticipating" the never-published theoretical discussion, Cajal says that he will try to establish that the cephalopod chiasma, like that of vertebrates, also corrects lateral inversion, the fact that it is actually horizontal, being imposed, as he rather mysteriously puts it, "by the dominant orientation of the ocular axis of the animal which, in its actions and movements of progression and pursuit of the prey, reflects preferentially the space on either side of its home."

This will not do. In these animals, reinversion of the image is in the vertical not the lateral plane, and I propose to explore the suggestion that it is related to gravity, not to the panorama. Polyak (1957), in his discussion of the chiasma problem, also ignores the cephalopods and dismisses the suggestion of Wundt (1919) that a vertical correction is involved in the vertebrate chiasma as "positively naïve."

The cephalopod chiasma might, of course, be necessitated for other reasons, for instance, to allow eye movements. It might be an embryological accident, but if so, it is an expensive one, for it increases the length of the optic nerves. Moreover, during development, special morphogenetic processes must exist to ensure that when fibers reach the equator they continue to advance across the pathway of their fellows proceeding in the opposite direction.

The condition in arthropods may throw light on the problem. Here the connections cannot be influenced by eye movements, since the retina and optic lobe move together, if at all. Moreover, no inverted image of the panorama is formed, although there may be inversion within each ommatidium. It is interesting to find from the work of Cajal and Sanchez (1915) and others that there are numerous miniature chiasmata between the axons of the retinal cells themselves, immediately behind the retina. Then follows a series of three lobes connected by pathways that first cross and then cross back again. Moreover, the two chiasmata may lie in different planes (Hanstrom, 1928).

With all these complications, it is difficult to interpret the arthropod condition. That there is crossing at all, in a system with no inverted image formation, shows that chiasmata may serve some other purpose than inversion. Indeed, with the two of them, the orientation of the information is left as it was on the retina.

It may be that these further mysteries finally deterred Cajal from publishing his paper. Perhaps he was wise. Let us nevertheless leave the arthropods for the future and press on with trying to interpret the relatively simple dorsoventral chiasma of cephalopods and draw lessons from it that may be applicable to vertebrates. For both of these groups of animals, we are fortunate in having much experimental evidence that was not available in 1917.

Recognition of shape by an octopus depends upon the maintenance of the correct position of the head in space. The animals can be taught to distinguish between many shapes, for instance, between vertical and horizontal rectangles (Boycott & Young, 1956; Sutherland, 1957, 1958). From an animal that has learned, say, to attack a horizontal but avoid a vertical rectangle, the statocysts are now removed. The eyes are normally held with the slit-like pupil horizontal. After the operation, however, the position of the eye will depend upon that of the head (Figure 4). When the animal sits on the bottom of the tank, the eyes

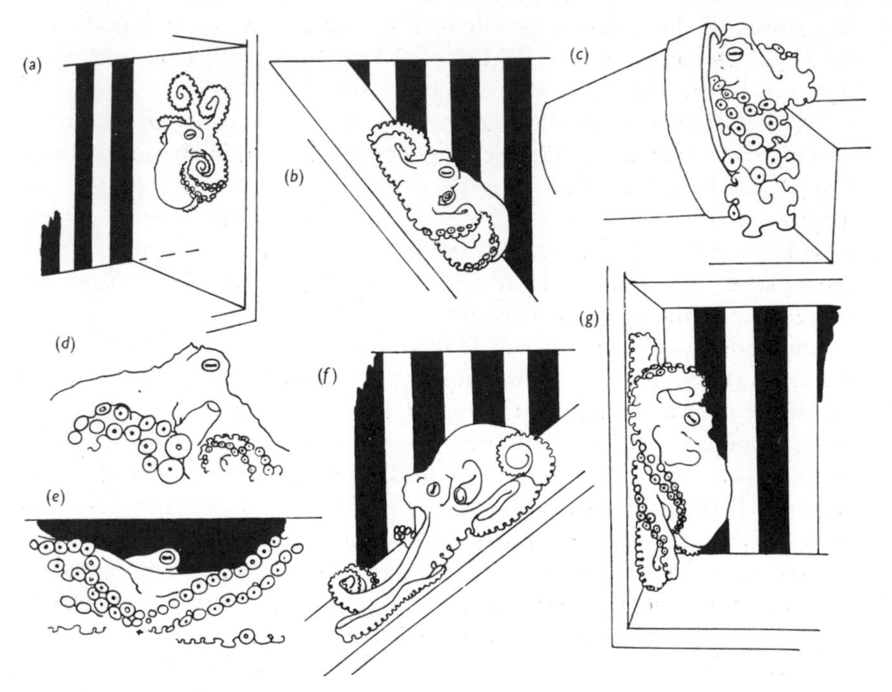

Fig. 4. Drawings from photographs of octopuses in various positions. A–C normal animals; the pupil is always horizontal. D–G, after removal of the statocysts, the eye is oblique or nearly vertical, except when the animal sits on the bottom of its tank. (from Wells, 1960)

will be as they were before operation, and the discrimination will be correctly performed. But when he sits on the side of the tank, the pupil will be vertical or nearly so, and he will now attack the vertical rectangle and avoid the horizontal one (Wells, 1960).

That there is anatomical basis for such discrimination is further shown by the fact that the retinal elements are arranged in an approximately rectangular array, with the axes horizontal and vertical (Figure 5). Moreover, in the optic lobes, the dendrites of the cells that form

Fig. 5. Portion of the retina of an octopus cut tangentially. The black objects are the bodies of the retinal cells filled with pigment. Between these are the "rhabdomes, composed of masses of fine tubules (not stained). The rhabdomes are mostly arranged approximately in horizontal and vertical planes, as the eye is usually held.

the next link in the chain have mainly a horizontal-vertical orientation (Figure 6). It is suggested that these dendritic fields serve to encode the horizontal and vertical extents of the figures. The horizontal cells that are active when food is concurrently present will become "conditioned," "switched," or "typed," so that when activated again they tend to produce an attack (Young, 1960). Further mechanisms ensure generalization, so that cells are conditioned in other parts of the lobe and in the opposite lobe. The "map" is thus a very crude one, but it has certain essential spatial features, and therefore spatial limitations. For example, Sutherland (1957) showed that rectangles shown at right angles to each other, but set obliquely at 45° to the horizontal, cannot be discrimi-

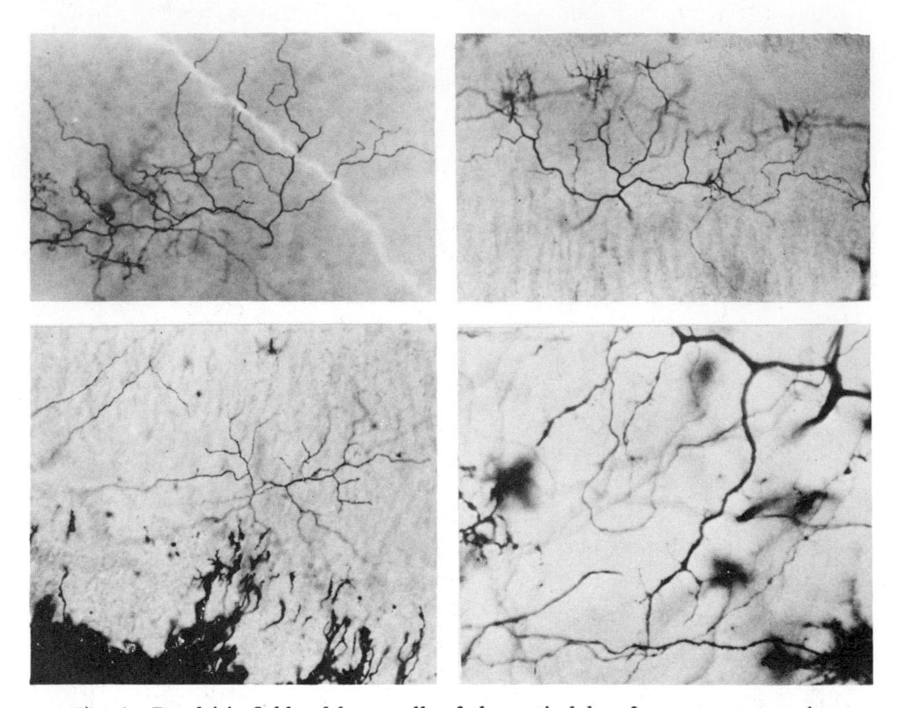

Fig. 6. Dendritic fields of large cells of the optic lobe of an octopus seen in thick sections tangential to the surface, stained with the Golgi method. The optic nerve fibres end in contact with these dendrites. The dendritic fields are mainly oval, with the long axis horizontal.

nated; the system does not provide for differentiating in those directions.

These invertebrates thus provide us with reason to believe that bilaterality is associated with a system for representing in their correct spatial relations in the memory, the features of the environment that are signalled by various receptors. It is interesting to consider whether the necessary inversion could be achieved by a chiasma behind a median eye. It is difficult to see how this could accurately sample the field in all directions (unless it scanned very fast). In fact, we find that median eyes in crustacea or insects and the pineal eyes of lampreys or lizards have poor dioptric apparatus (Figure 7). They do not record the direction of visual changes but serve to signal general levels of illumination for such purposes as activation to flight (this is the function of the median ocelli of insects), color change of lampreys (Young, 1935), or temperature regulation in lizards (Stebbins & Eakin, 1958).

There are other possibilities besides median and paired eyes. One could get, presumably, a suitable reinversion with, say, five eyes

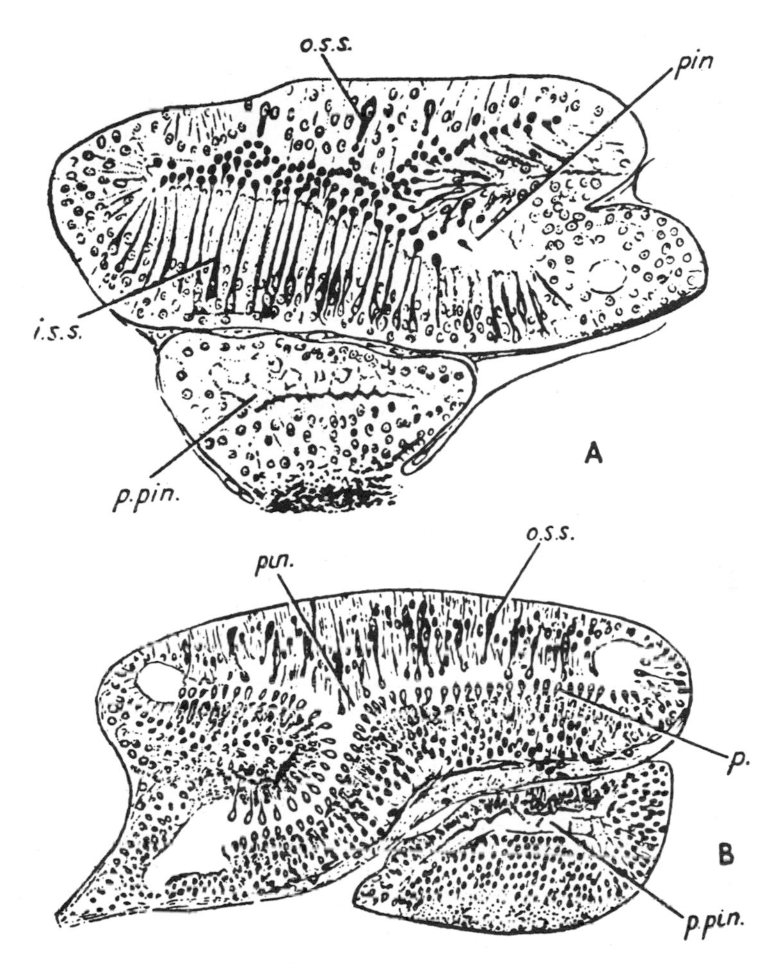

Fig. 7. The "median" eyes of a lamprey seen in transverse (A) and sagittal section (B). i.s.s., inner sensory cell, o.s.s., outer sensory cell, pin. pineal, p. pin, parapineal. (After Trètjakoff)

(Echinoderms), or many, as in the scallops *Pecten*. But it is difficult to see how an effective system could be built with multiple memories and representations of spatially organized visuostatic-tactile information. Two eyes seem to provide the best opportunity to search a large visual field and reinvert the display. But so long as the computing system depends upon topologically correct mapping, two eyes involve two brains. At least for systems with relatively simple codes and mapping operations, one in the middle would not do.

I have discussed the problem so far mainly with reference to cephalopods, but the principles elicited apply strikingly well to vertebrates. Paired eyes are found only in the higher members of the phylum, whose behavior is controlled by reference to a spatial map. The simplest chordates alive today do not have them, and we may provisionally conclude that they were not a feature of the first chordates to be evolved. Perhaps the simplest present day animals, with an indubitably chordate organization, are the tadpole larvae of sea squirts (Figure 8). The

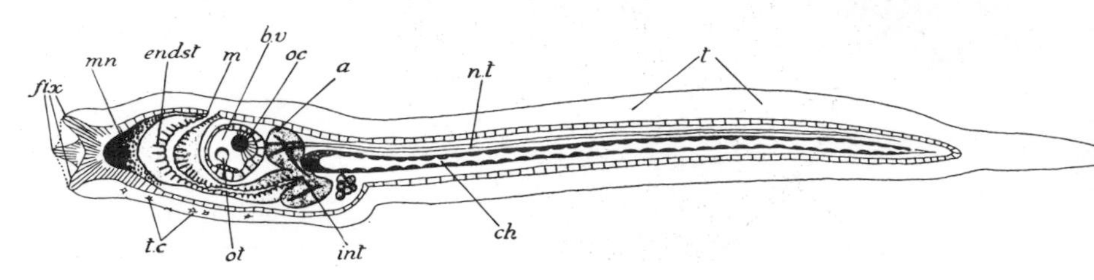

Fig. 8. Tadpole larva of the sea-squirt *Ciona*. a, anus; b.v. brain vesicle; ch. notocord, endst. endostyle, fix., processes by which the larva ultimately becomes fixed; int. intestine; m. mouth; m.n. mental process; n.t., nerve tube; oc. ocellus (a lens and a few receptor cells) ; ot. static organ of a single otolith cell with receptor at its base; t. test.; t.c. test. cells. (from MacBride after Kowalevsky)

nervous system of these consists of an unpaired brain vesicle containing two unpaired receptors, a statoreceptor composed of one cell, and a photoreceptor with a few. The information provided by these ensures that the larva goes first to the sea surface for a few hours and then reverses its tropisms and descends to the bottom to become a sessile sea squirt. Although the receptors are unpaired, the animals have a bilateral organization, including paired bands of muscles on either side of an incompressible notochord. This motor arrangement is indeed the basic vertebrate locomotor system and perhaps the main significance of their bilaterality. The receptors nevertheless remain unpaired; they can direct the organism toward or away from light, or the earth's center, without any elaborate map.

Amphioxus, though somewhat more complicated, has no paired eyes (or statoreceptors). The light receptors are cells of the central nervous system, protected by asymmetric pigment cups. They serve to guide the organism as it swims on a spiral course. They probably steer it mainly away from the light and ensure that it remains buried.

The lampreys show us a critical experiment, for their photoreceptors are unpaired in the larval stage, but the adult has fully developed paired eyes (Figure 9). The larva lives and feeds in the mud. It avoids

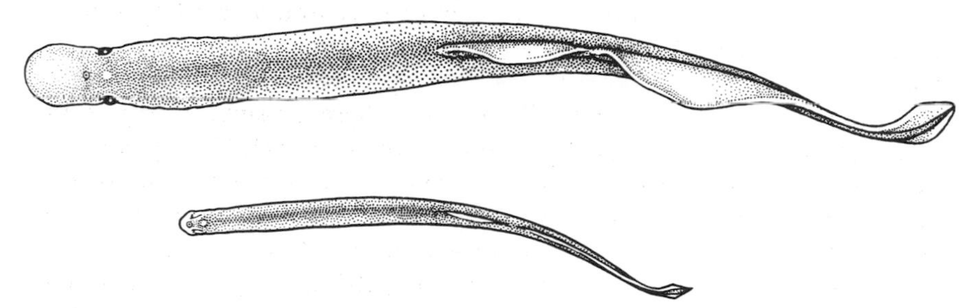

Fig. 9. Ammocoete larva (below) and adult lamprey to show the median pineal present in both, but the paired eyes only in the adult.

the light by a simple photokinesis; whenever it is illuminated, it swims head downward and so continues until it is buried. The photoreceptors mainly concerned are not even in the head but in the skin of the tail (Young, 1935). Pineal eyes are present, however, arising as diverticula of the roof of the diencephalon and possessing a very simple retina and dioptric apparatus (See Figure 7). As already explained, their main function is to regulate the color and possibly feeding and internal activities as well, so that these conform to the day and night rhythm. They do this by control of the pituitary.

It is interesting that the pineal organs originally develop as paired structures, the pineal and parapineal, but these differentiate unequally until one lies above the other in the mid-line. The initial bilaterality is presumably a reflection of the paired nature of morphogenetic processes in the diencephalon, related to the formation of paired eyes later in life, but for the simpler photoreceptor functions of the larva, a more economical median packing is adopted, beneath a single clear patch on the surface of the head.

When a lamprey undergoes metamorphosis, its paired eyes, which have already formed but have lain deeply buried, come to the surface and begin to play their part in hunting for prey, presumably using a map in the midbrain roof. The pineal persists in the adult, continuing its previous functions. Stensiö and other paleontologists have described several types of early chordate in which the pineal eye was well developed, and lampreys are a surviving relic of this group.

If the paired eyes serve to project a map upon the tectum, there must, according to our principles, be a reinversion of the information, and this indeed occurs. The optic nerves of *Salmo,* for example, cross completely, and each contains two bundles. One consists of fibers originating in the dorsal and anterior quadrants of the eye and ending in the ventral and lateral quadrants of the opposite tectum. The other bundle has the reverse course (Ströer, 1940). The existence of this distribution has been confirmed by physiological and degeneration studies (Buser & Dussardier, 1953). Ströer (1940) claimed that there is a similar projection in amphibians, reptiles, and birds, but, as Armstrong (1950) has pointed out, for lizards the situation is more complicated. There is, however, abundant evidence in frogs that the projection from the retina to the colliculus is arranged in a well organized and inverted map (Gaze, 1958 & 1960; Lettvin *et al.,* 1959; Maturana *et al.,* 1960). The posterior retina projects to the anterior pole of the optic lobe, the anterior retina to the posterior pole. The fibers from the dorsal side of each retina end "tucked round the lateral edge of the lobe," the ventral fibers near the dorsal mid-line (Gaze, 1960) (Figure 10). Moreover, this tectum receives

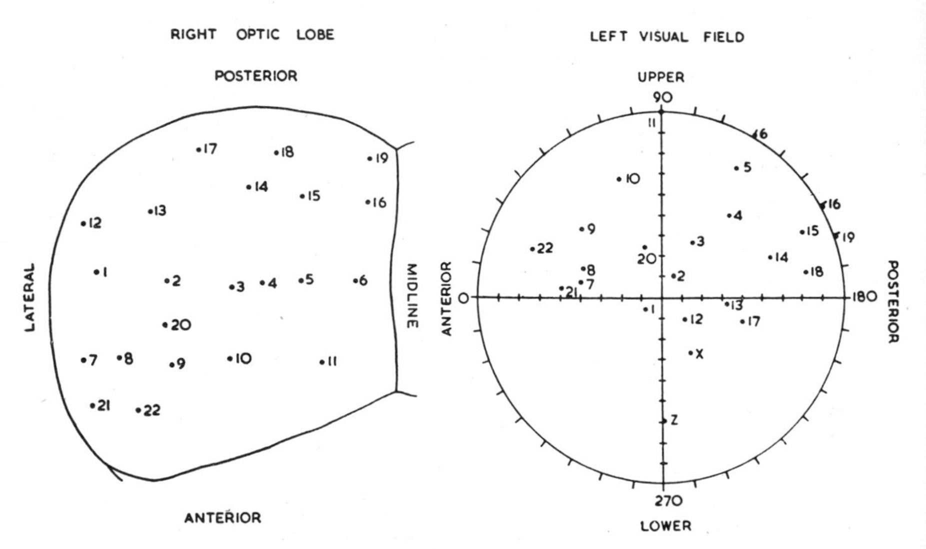

Fig. 10. Maps to show the positions where activity was recorded in the optic tectum of the frog, following stimulation with spots of light at the places numbered in the visual field. (from Gaze, 1958)

a large component from the eighth nerve centers and is indeed ideally placed and connected to make a map with combined optic and stato-acoustic information.

The fact that the visual projection is inverted in these lower vertebrates, as in cephalopods, makes it very difficult to doubt that the inversion is of significance, especially since it is produced by different morphogenetic operations in the two groups. In vertebrates, the fibers, of course, pass through a mid-line chiasma below the brain. The suggestion is that the function of this chiasma is to produce the inversion (Figure 11). Gaze (1960) discusses this possibility as follows: "The

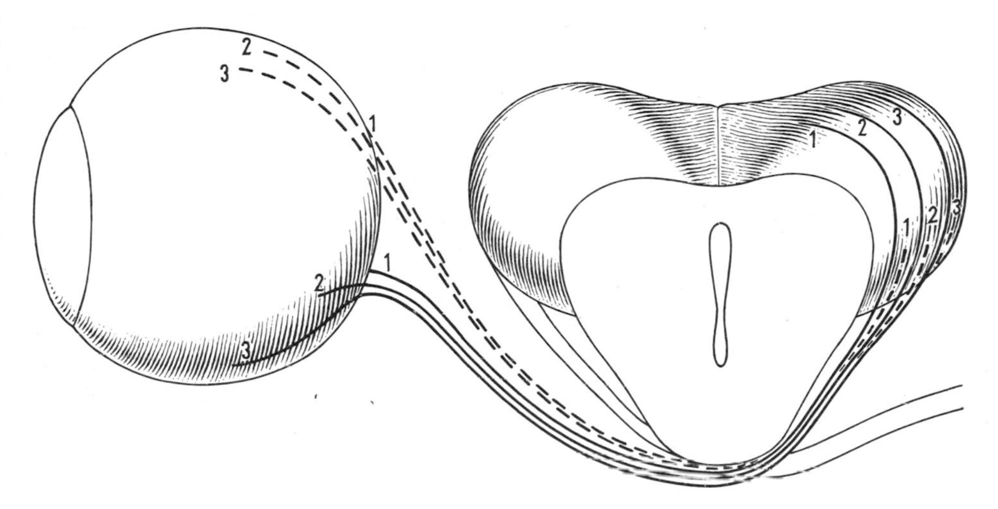

Fig. 11. Diagram to show how a vertebrate optic chiasma can serve to produce image inversion.

orderly termination of fibers from different parts of the retina is an expression of the time sequence of events during fiber growth." He points out that the optic axons enter the lobe from the anterior end, and that it is known that during development a wave of differentiation passes over the lobe from in front, backwards. There is not enough evidence to show exactly how this would produce the inversions, but if the fibers have different distances to travel, it clearly might do so. Thus, the fibers from the ventral part of the retina may reach the tectum first and continue over its surface to the mid-line. If they occupy the sites there, the later arrivals must end more laterally, and so an orderly inverted projection would be produced. Vertebrates have thus achieved this inversion not by inventing a mechanism to direct separate bundles in opposite directions where they cross behind the eye, as in cephalopods, but by a device that avoids the detailed crossing by use of a different topological principle. However, the whole question of how the pattern of optic connections with the tectum is arrived at during development and regeneration is most complicated and cannot at present be understood in terms of any one known set of determining factors.

There have been many theories of the significance of the optic chiasma (Jacobsohn–Lask, 1924). Cajal's suggestion that it serves to bring together features of the external field on the tectal map has plausibility. It is a suggestion of the same type as the present one, in that it depends on the assumption that the system operates through the presence in the brain of a map that is spatially isomorphic with the outside world. However, it is not clear that the continuity of the map across the mid-line is really a necessity. Cajal speaks, for example, of the danger of losing prey, if it leaves one field in crossing the mid-line. Would this danger necessarily be greater than with two distinct fields? It clearly depends on the mechanism that is used to "scan" the map. An octopus has two distinct maps and attacks in the appropriate direction whenever an object moves in any part of either of them. However, it may be that vertebrates make use both of the advantages of a chiasma suggested by Cajal and of that here proposed. Perhaps there are other advantages as well. It is difficult to say which factor came first, but the ensuring of correspondence with the mapping of the gravity receptors was probably a necessity for the usefulness of any map at all.

The details of the mesencephalic projection in the frog provides the most beautiful example of mapping (Gaze, 1958; Lettvin *et al.,* 1959; Maturana *et al.,* 1960). The retinal information is coded by the ganglion cells, so that five types of fiber can be recognized in the optic nerve, and each of these projects to make an accurate map in the tectum. For each locus on the retina there is a corresponding point on the tectum (Gaze, 1958), and contiguous loci on the retina are contiguous on the tectum. Each type of fiber ends at an appropriate depth. Two end at the same depth and there are thus four maps, fully in register. Together they provide a system by which the visual image is "analyzed" at every point in terms of four arbitrary contexts (local variations of intensity, moving edge curvatures, and standing contrasts) together with a general measure of illumination. Certain combinations of these "contexts" presumably allow the tectal cells to extract what the authors call the "universals," such as prey or enemies, to which the frog responds.

The details of this analysis are fascinating, but the important point for us is that the map is upside down compared to that of the retina. It thus corresponds to whatever map may be provided by the gravity receptors, from which fibers are known to reach the tectum. If a fly moves "up" in the visual field, the retinal projection also moves "up," as presumably do signals from the eighth nerve and probably also from the proprioceptors and skin.

Such isomorphic maps can clearly operate as analogue computers, allowing the animal rapidly to extract certain relevances from the visual image and rapidly combine them with other information to produce correct predictions.

In mammals, the projections to the superior colliculus preserve the same inverted relations as in lower vertebrates. These "lower" optic centers are presumably concerned in orientating and eye movements that involve co-operation of information from visual and gravitational sources, and the topographical map is strictly conserved here. In the cortex, the situation is more complicated. The projection is there, but it is not concerned simply with being a map congruous with that from the gravity receptors. It has no specific orientation in relation to the plane of the animal. Nevertheless, the methods of coding and computing may well depend, in part, on a spatially arranged analogue. Microelectrode recording from the visual cortex of the cat shows that each cerebral cell "looks at" a particular, small retinal field, usually an oval with its axis horizontal, vertical, or oblique (Figure 12), (Hubel & Wiesel, 1959). The presence of a point-to-point projection from retina to cortex and the congruence of the two maps are, of course, well known. This alone strongly suggests an analogue mapping. But as the coding system becomes more refined, wider departures from strict isomorphism are found. The "picture" becomes more "abstract," more impressionistic. All the information reaching the cortex is separated from the receptors at least by a relay in the thalamus at which recoding may take place. Both visual and static information now perhaps have their directions indicated by more subtle features than being "up" or "down" on a map. Elaborate dynamic mechanisms, such as the thalamocortical and reticular circuits, may serve to measure delays and match inputs along the various afferent channels in ways impossible for an octopus or frog, which has no such subtleties. Correspondingly, we find, for example, that a man wearing inverting spectacles learns, after an initial confusion, to compensate. He has other ways of organizing his responses besides the strictly topographical map. Through the use of words, for instance, he can describe relations of position and movement.

Nevertheless, the two sides of the cortex are there, even in man. This suggests that the isomorphic map is still of much importance. In a sense, however, we have given up bilaterality, for we can do at least moderately well without the nondominant hemisphere or the callosum between the two. If we have correctly interpreted the significance of "analogue" and "abstract" coding, this is what we should expect. With the increase in number of peripheral and central pathways, the brain begins to lose its analogue characteristics. By the multitude of sets and

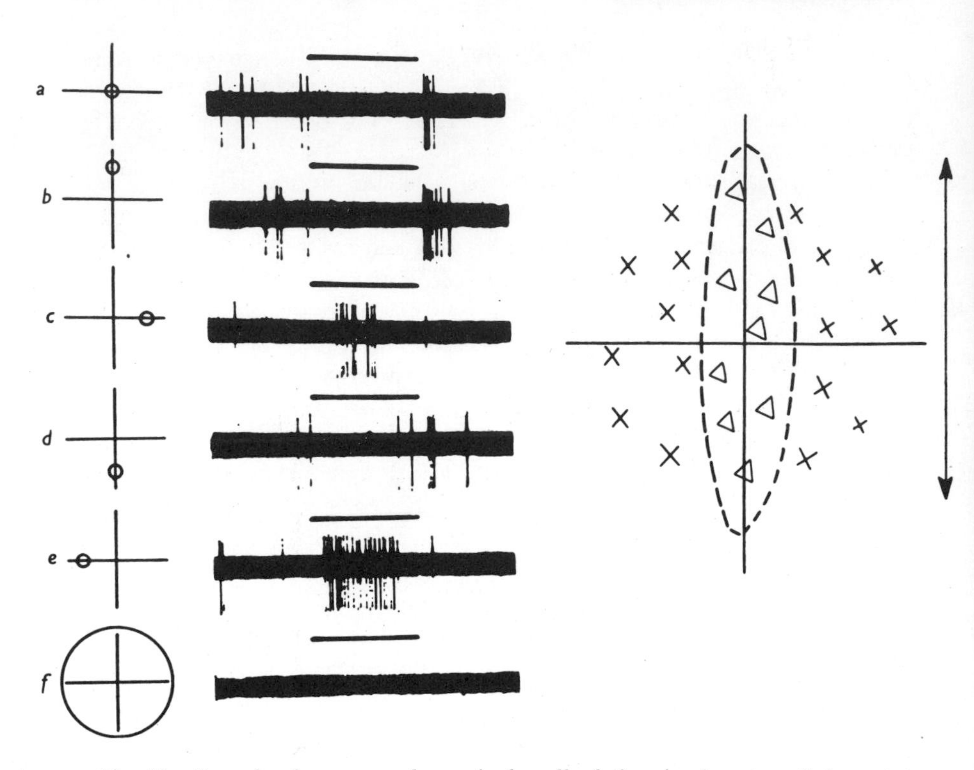

Fig. 12. Records of responses by a single cell of the visual cortex of the cat to illumination of various parts of the visual field, as shown at the left. When the light is in the center of the field of the cell, the discharge is inhibited (a, b and d). When it is more peripheral and at the sides, the firing is accentuated. The line above each oscillograph record shows the duration of illumination. (from Hubel & Wiesel, 1959)

subsets into which it classifies the information and the freedom with which these are combined, it begins to acquire powers like those of a general purpose computer. Yet it has its limitations. It is derived from systems that not many millions of generations ago functioned as rather simple isomorphic analogues. It still demands some degree of isomorphism and can only secure the appropriate organization of the fields by developing as a paired structure, even though one side later becomes dominant over the other. Perhaps the nondominant one is a vestige, but personally I would rather keep mine than lose it. Maybe it is the two together that serve to make the most truly useful representation of the world, partly map-like, partly abstract.

Discussion First Session

A.

DAVID BODIAN

The Johns Hopkins University School of Medicine, Baltimore, Maryland

I HAVE no work of my own to present to this Conference, but could not resist Professor Bordley's invitation to comment briefly on the opening papers of two so distinguished students of the nervous system.

Professor von Bonin has given us a review, both critical and suggestive, but in addition to offering a slight ray of hope for the morphological approach, he has reaffirmed, in no uncertain terms, the point of view that comparisons of hemisphere size, like comparisons of whole brain size among individuals of a single species, are largely unrewarding. The main contribution of evidence of gross asymmetry may be to suggest that differences at another order of magnitude may be present, namely the microscopic level. To the pessimist, who is not willing to accept the significance of the one percent or less variation of weight from side to side, his discussion provokes perhaps a more serious implication, namely that those who seek for anatomical correlates of unilateral hemispheric dominance may be up against the possibility that the anatomy of the hemispheres is entirely irrelevant to this problem. To an anatomist, this unhappy heresy is quickly replaced by the reflection that, in spite of many decades of great contributions to the anatomy of the hemispheres, the quantitative analysis of the internal structure has hardly begun. I think Professor von Bonin rightly pointed this out. Before we abandon ourselves to an ultimate pessimism, I know that most of us would prefer the hope that the development of microscopic and electron microscopic skills will make possible a rational quantitative approach to the cellular organization of the cortex. I am glad to say that there are some who are still willing to embark on this rather formidable enterprise, including Dr. Van der Loos in our department at Johns Hopkins. It certainly is one of the great challenges in neuroanatomy.

Professor Young continues to remind us that comparative neurology is still a fertile source of neurological theory, especially to one of his gifts. He has emphasized problems of bilaterality and of decussation of tracts, rather than the problem of unilateral dominance, but has skirted the crucial problem of the adaptive significance, if any, of decussations or of unilateral dominance. The comparative approach evokes the thought that unilateral cerebral dominance in human beings must have evolved, at least within the primates, because of some selective advantage, and this suggestion would be reinforced by evidence of genetic tendencies in unilateral dominance. Professor Young's discussion of theories of decussation also serves to remind us of one of the simplest explanations of decussations, namely Coghill's. You may recall that Coghill pointed out that a unilateral stimulus in the tadpole produces a response which involves contraction of the muscles of the opposite side of the body—a simple defensive reflex. This version of the origin of decussations introduces, as a basic concept, the idea of an adaptive advantage for a crossed connection in the central nervous system.

I feel sure that as the Conference progresses, Professor Young's comparative cue may provoke other thoughts concerning both evolutionary and ontogenetic aspects of unilateral control of muscular activity.

B.

ARNOLD B. SCHEIBEL and MADGE E. SCHEIBEL

University of California Medical Center, Los Angeles, California

THE INVITATION to discuss this admirable contribution of Professor Young comes as a privilege and a responsibility. The basic problems surrounding the twinned brain can scarcely be more easily approached today than three-quarters of a century ago, when Hughlings Jackson gave them his attention. Yet, not only has our speaker come to grips with the problem, marshaling data from his own extensive experience and that of others, but he has chosen to work within the more difficult frame of the Aristotelian query. Almost anything else along this line would be anticlimactic.

Professor Young suggests that a bilateral neural apparatus arose as a necessary correlate to analogical mapping techniques. Further, he adduces that as cortical levels of representation become more complexly symbolic—more digitalized—bilaterality becomes relatively less significant, remaining important chiefly in the extent to which isomorphic vestiges continue to play a role. We wish to raise an alternative hypothesis to his second point, suggesting that continued development of the two hemispheres with emergence of dominance represents not a system in obsolescence, but rather a powerful new means for appreciation of the immediate environment.

Briefly, the argument runs as follows. The characteristic neuropil pattern, in those locales where some type of representation of the environment is involved, invariably includes presynaptic bushy arbors which enclose within their fields the postsynaptic array. Originally direct efferent components, these elements gradually become substituted by short axoned cells as the phyletic scale is ascended. With telencephalization and further massive stepwise increases in cell population (especially short axoned cells) and fiber connections, there is an increased opportunity for both structural and functional variability and, as one consequence, increased possibilities for interhemispheric differences. Since awareness of spatial position may well depend on asymmetry of the perceiving system, our paired brain becomes, rather than a holdover from an isomorphic past, an increasingly useful mechanism for appreciation of the environment along a new axis of orientation.

The presence of bushy arbor terminals for axons carrying data to fields where representation is involved is remarkably consistent. Simple versions of this theme are shown by Cajal (1917) for the optic apparatus of the cephalopod, and by Cajal & Sanchez (1915) for the optic lobes of the arthropod. The pattern achieves richer expression in Herrick's (1948) figures of the tiger salamander. In mammalian vertebrates, monkey, and man, they are known to all neurologists to occur at lower and intermediate sensory relays, such as the dorsal horn, the gracile and cuneate nuclei, the colliculi, and specific thalamic relays. Elaborations of the bushy arbor at cortical (sensory) stations involving representation and localization are figured prominently by Cajal (1955), Lorente de No (1943), O'Leary (1941), and others.

In contrast, afferents to nonrepresentational systems, such as the brain stem reticular core, are sparsely branched, spread over large and overlapping sectors of the receptive field, and, by virtue of their discrete bouton apparatus, achieve low intensities of postsynaptic innervation at any one site. Such patterns, expressed by the overlapping termini of many dissimilar systems projecting on the core, are well suited to the extraction of integrates by postsynaptic reticular neurons. Specific spatio-temporal patterns and the individual modalities of the converging afferent systems are lost in the interaction. Short axoned cells are apparently not involved in this process (Scheibel & Scheibel, 1958).

The bushy arbors in representational systems are formed by intensive reduplication of the terminal fibers feeding the neuropil field. Such arbors envelop limited numbers of postsynaptic elements. The complex thus formed seems to remain the framework for neural representation at all phyletic levels and, in itself, is apparently sufficient to form crude neural analogues for some types of sensory experience. With phylogenetic development comes change in the nature of the elements involved and progressive addition to the basic complex, enriching possibilities inherent in this kind of circuity.

In lower forms, these postsynaptic elements are usually part of the direct outflow to effector areas and receive a relatively uncontaminated version of the input. With increasing complexity of the organism, the basic neuropil complex is enriched by increased numbers of afferents of simpler terminal patterns from "projection" or "non-specific" systems. These project upon occasional units of the postsynaptic array, adding information, modulating thresholds, and thereby fractionating previously "simple" fields.

Simultaneously, afferent elements tend to become separated from efferents, with the appearance of increasing numbers of short axoned, Golgi type II cells which become the receptive elements in the afferent neuropil field. This steady enhancement in number of short axoned cells, as the vertebrate scale is ascended, was commented upon by Cajal (1955) and by subsequent workers, and though their relationship to higher levels of neural activity is mainly inferential, the studies of the Vogts give some substance to this position. These workers observed a marked increase in thickness of the short axoned cell-bearing layers 2 and 4, in specific cortical areas in cases where the individual had appeared especially gifted during life. Thus one patient, who remained sensitive to eidetic images into adult life, showed unusual thickness in second and fourth layers of visual cortex, while another, a musician known for his unusually perfect sense of pitch, showed increased thickness of granule cell layers in the auditory receptive area (Vogt & Vogt).

The dramatic increase in number of short axoned cells epitomizes the growth of the entire brain cell population. Computations recently reported by Bok (1959), after comparison of isocortical surface area to body weight in a number of mammals, indicate that human isocortex contains approximately 2^5 times as many cells as would be indicated by linear extrapolation from lower forms (i.e., rodents). These findings closely parallel those of Dubois (1914) who used somewhat different parameters in his calculations. Both workers have suggested five crucial jumps in forebrain or isocortical development from rodent to man; each jump characterized by one more complete cell division; each jump characterizing another level of species development. Apparently it is the last complete division, that separating monkeys and other primates from man, which is responsible for so many of the higher symbolic operations characteristic of man. And appearing now, perhaps for the first time, is a concomitant cerebral characteristic—dominance—the demonstrable, functional nonparity of the hemispheres.

Even if we assume with Bok (1959) and Dubois (1914) that rather clear-cut, stepwise increases in cell population have occurred, the reason why one of our two hemispheres begins to demonstrate at least functional priority over the other is not clear. Perhaps by the time of the last complete division or two, we are coming to a point where definitive genetic control is less effective, and ultimate structurofunctional patterns depend increasingly on cytoplasmic and local environmental factors (Gruneberg, 1935).

We still have to face the main question: Does the emerging functional (and perhaps structural) dominance of one hemisphere herald the obsolescence of the two-brained system? Here we must take issue with Professor Young and maintain a more hopeful view. In *The Analysis of Sensation,* Ernst Mach (1959) suggests that ". . . right and left appear to us to be similar, in contrast to before and behind, and to above and below." That we can differentiate at all between these two modes of horizontal orientation may well depend on some kind of proprioceptive, ". . . and possibly in the last resort upon a chemical difference," between the two sides. Tschirgi (1958) suggests, with Mach (1959), that an animal whose brain is bilaterally symmetrical cannot differentiate between stimuli arriving at homologous points, being limited to mirror image responses upon homologous right and left stimulation. "Awareness of spatial position is, therefore, dependent upon asymmetry of the perceiving system, and evolution consists of increasing that asymmetry." Tschirgi (1958) traces the development of the organism from hypothesized, archaic states of complete (i.e., spherical) symmetry, through progressively more asymmetric stages (i.e., radial, bilateral, complete asymmetric), showing that with each increase in asymmetry, more can be known about the surface of the body and its environment. Man is presumed to be approaching that final category of asymmetry "because he can distinguish right from left, but he frequently makes mistakes.

His brain has only just begun to develop a functional difference between the two hemispheres and his universe has only dimly achieved three dimensions." (Tschirgi, 1958).

Consideration of such an hypothesis does not necessarily conflict with Professor Young's attempt to relate brain bilaterality to isomorphic maps, although we see difficulties in the position, as does he. It would not be the first time that neural mechanisms, planned for one use, later served other ends. Rather, it seems difficult to conceive that the evolution of a dominant–nondominant relation, between two such highly engineered entities as the hemispheres, bears within itself the seeds of its own decay; that somehow, as before, a greater richness might not lie within.

C.

HENRICUS G. J. M. KUYPERS

University of Maryland School of Medicine, Baltimore, Maryland
(present address: University of Western Reserve School of Medicine, Cleveland, Ohio.)

MR. CHAIRMAN, in his present paper, Dr. Young seems to express his belief in the overall presence of an "isomorphic" coding in primitive brains .This type of coding, he assumes, would facilitate the rapid processing of data. Isomorphic coding seems to represent a double-faced concept. It seems to imply: (a) a spatial coding, i.e., separate events being coded in separate places; and (b) that the central units carrying the code maintain a spatial arrangement, mirroring that of the units in the receptive surface and even that of the environment, the source of the information to be coded.

In regard to the first aspect, the overall presence within the nervous machinery of a spatial type of coding seems rather striking indeed. This holds true especially since even information not immediately reflecting spatial features of the environment, at least in part, appears to be coded spatially. This is exemplified by the coding of the olfactory (Adrian, 1953, 1954; Mozell & Pfaffman, 1953) and auditory (Rose, Galambos, & Hughes, 1959; Ades, 1959) information in the brain stem. However, in spite of the striking presence of spatial coding in the central nervous system, so impressive to me as an anatomist, this type of coding is not the only one. Even in some rather primitive parts of the mammalian brain stem, e.g., the reticular formation, some sensory information seems to be subjected in part to temporal coding (Amassian & Waller, 1958). This is obviously most discouraging to us anatomists, for the investigation of short-lasting, temporal changes is not our strongest point, to say the least. Nevertheless, it seems of importance to incorporate this temporal coding into our concepts, in order to avoid having them crippled from the beginning by irreparable shortcomings.

After this introduction, let us turn to the second aspect of the isomorphic coding: the isomorphism between the environment and the receptive surfaces, on the one hand, and the population of central units carrying the code, on the other hand. This aspect has been illustrated in a versatile fashion by Dr. Young, using the optic system as an example. He appears to have been rather successful in this matter. However, if I understand him correctly, I am forced to confess that the extremes of this concept of isomorphism are not appealing to me. I refer specifically to the parallelism between the spatial *orientation* of the optic map and the general *orientation* of the animal. Moreover, I gained the impression that this aspect of the "isomorphism" is rather limited, in that what is "up" in the environment is actually "medial" on the map, suggesting a rotation of less than 90°.

However, aside from these points of disagreement, I am truly fascinated by some of the suggestions presented by Dr. Young in connection with the present problem. I was fascinated especially by the suggested correlation between the orientation of the retinal elements and that of the dendrites of the cells in the optic lobe. This is so striking to me since we found a somewhat analogous arrangement in the nuclei of the posterior funiculus of the cat, where the cells, with small and large receptive fields respectively, seem to maintain different dendritic trees (Figure 1). The suggestion that the information from the gravity receptors, the skin receptors, and the optic receptors probably would track over the same map in the same direction is likewise a very remarkable point of view. Whether this represents the "reason" for the elaborate crossings in the optic system, however, is difficult to decide. I would suggest that a further insight into this "reason" could possibly be obtained from looking at the other side of the optic lobe, that is to say, the organization of its motor outflow.

Mr. Chairman, unfortunately enough, my acquaintance with many of the animals discussed by Dr. Young, tends to be exclusively culinary in nature. Therefore, I feel somewhat reluctant to penetrate deeper into the problems which are connected with this part of the animal kingdom.

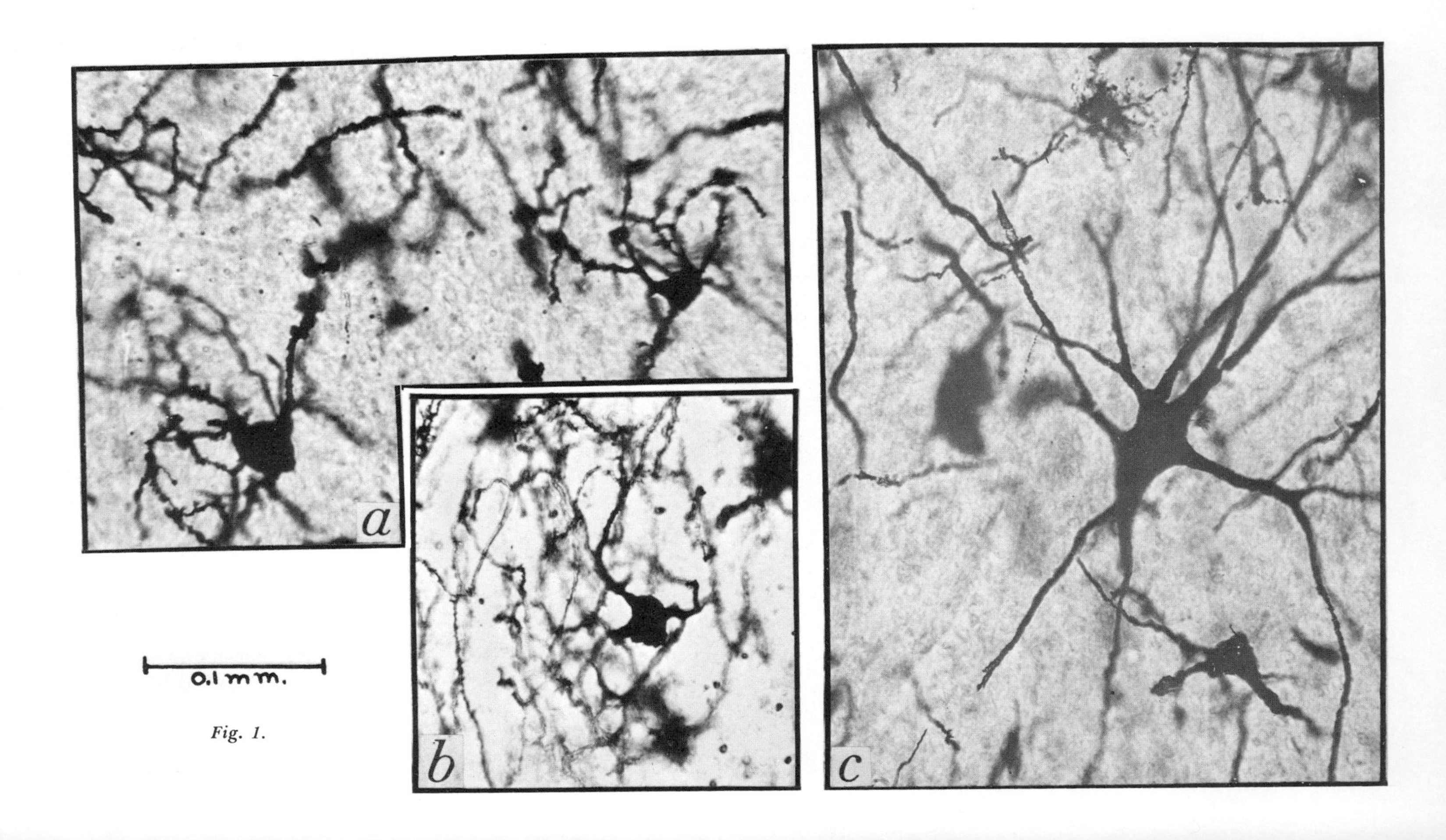

Fig. 1.

Allow me, therefore, to turn to Dr. Young's statement, at the end of his discussion, about the octopus. Here he observed that "the principle of isomorphic coding and the presence of two eyes almost inevitably involves two brains." The two eyes are directed towards the sides. As a consequence, each of these two brains codes information obtained from one half of the environment. Strikingly enough, this arrangement is maintained in the mammalian series in that, in each of the superior colliculi, one-half of the environment is coded (Apter, 1945). This appears to represent a true continuation of the previous line of organization, for this coding of one-half of the environment is maintained independently of the position of the eyes, which may differ as much as that between the rabbit and the monkey (Whitteridge, 1960). Furthermore, again, what is "up" in the environment is "medial" on the collicular map. However, Dr. Young tends to de-emphasize this point of similarity between the optic lobe and the mammalian superior colliculus. This, I assume, is due to the fact that, classically, the optic function of the mesencephalon is thought of as being limited to motor adjustment mechanisms. On the other hand, recent experiments, such as those of Blake (1959), Sprague, Chambers, & Stellar (1961), and others, seem to indicate that, in the cat and in the chimpanzee, the deeper parts of the superior colliculus may play a very important role in the visual perception and recognition of the contralateral half of the environment. This would make the other similarities between the optic lobe and the superior colliculus even more striking.

The same general line of organization found in the optic lobe and the mammalian superior colliculus, also can be distinguished in the cerebral cortex, in that, in general, each of the hemispheres seems to code optic information derived primarily from the contralateral half of the environment (Talbot & Marshall, 1941). The same holds true for the cutaneous tacticle information (Woolsey, Marshall, & Bard, 1942) and, to some extent, also for the auditory information (Rosenzweig, 1954). Each of the hemispheres seems to see, to listen to, and to feel, primarily, the contralateral half of the environment. This is most strikingly illustrated by some aspects of the parietal syndrome (Critchley, 1953). This general trend is not limited to the sensory systems, but can be distinguished also in some hemispheric motor systems, which influence primarily the contralateral extremities (Woolsey, Settlage, Meyer, Sencer, Hamuy, & Travis, 1950) and thus act primarily in the contralateral half of the environment. Finally, each of these hemispheres directs the eye toward the contralateral half of the environment (Crosbey, Henderson, & Yoss, 1952; Crosbey & Henderson, 1948; Wagman, Krieger, & Bender, 1958), thus mimicking the motor organization of the corresponding superior colliculus (Apter, 1945).

However, Dr. Young tends to de-emphasize these similarities between the superior colliculus and the cerebral cortex. If I understand him correctly, this is prompted by the fact that the isomorphism between the map and the environment presumably decreases, e.g., due to the discontinuation of the parallelism between the *orientation* of the map and that of the animal and, furthermore, due to the loss of strict unilateral representation. As I have been forced to confess before, the first point has very little convincing power to me. However, the loss of unilaterality strikes closer to home. In regard to this latter point, at least the anatomical (Polyak, 1957) and the physiological macroelectrode studies of the optic system (Talbot & Marshall, 1941) do not substantiate this entirely. As a matter of fact, such studies appear to emphasize the unilaterality, thus suggesting that the macular sparing, following cortical lesion in man, has to be explained on a different basis. Furthermore, the comparison of the macroelectrode studies of the superior colliculus and the optic cortex seem to reveal more gross similarities than dissimilarities. On the other hand, in regard to the auditory system, Dr. Young's statement seems to hold true, in that the tonal elements, numerous at lower levels, become less dominant in the cerebral cortex, thus making the picture a more impressionistic one (Ades, 1959). However, even at cortical levels a certain tonal organization is maintained, and a certain isomorphism between the receptive surface and the map is undeniable (Woolsey & Walzl, 1942; Rose & Woolsey, 1949). In the somatosensory system (S1) another trend prevails. The tactile sensory information, obtained with maximal resolution by way of the distal parts of the extremities, seems to be coded almost exclusively unilaterally and in great detail (Woolsey, Marshall, & Bard, 1942). This somatosensory map actually becomes increasingly more detailed in higher mammals (Lende & Woolsey, 1956; Woolsey, Marshall, & Bard, 1942). The same holds true for the motor map (Lende & Woolsey, 1956; Woolsey, Settlage, Meyer, Sencer, Hamuy, & Travis, 1950). Here, this increase in detail appears to be brought about by the appearance of direct cortico-motoneural connections (Figure 2) in the primates (Kuypers, 1958). These connections become increasingly more numerous in higher primates, thus further increasing the resolution of the system.

Mr. Chairman, in view of this, I would suggest to Dr. Young, that at least in some systems, the cortical coding becomes more isomorphic, thus shifting to a more surrealistic, rather than to an impressionistic, interpretation of the environment. This seems to fit the general rule that whatever the cortex does, the subcortex can do also, but in a less sophisticated manner and in less detail. The subcortex may be able to distinguish tone, but the cortex seems necessary for the distinction

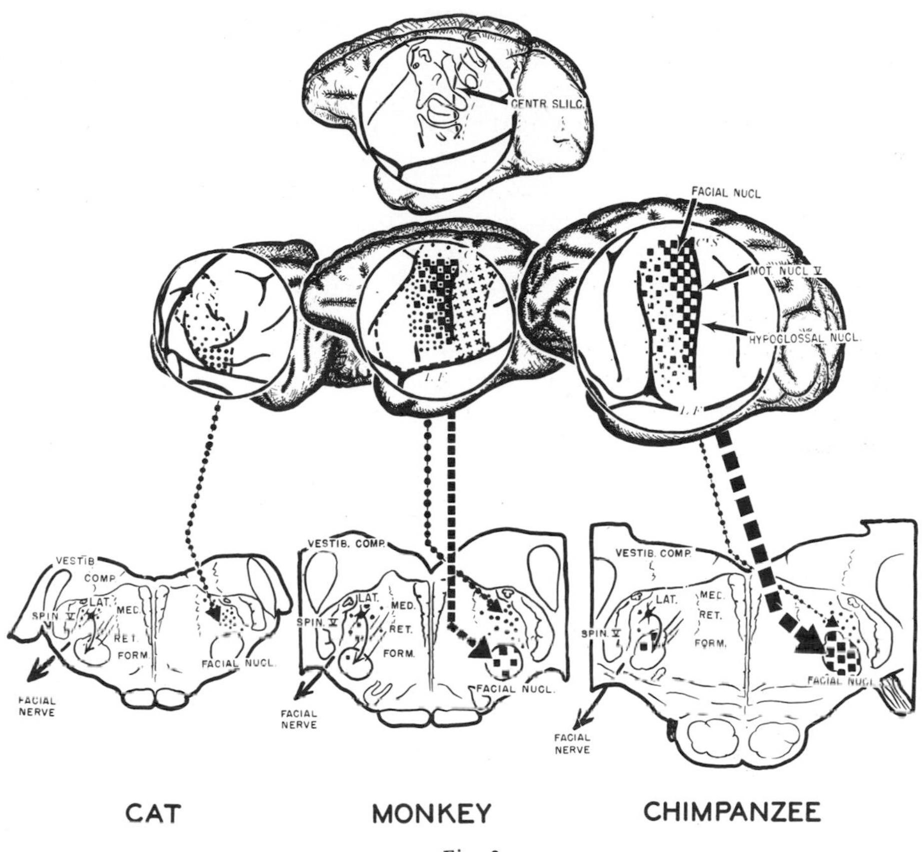

Fig. 2.

between tonal patterns (Ades, 1959). The subcortex may be able to distinguish differences in density of luminous flux (Klüver, 1941), but the cortex seems necessary for visual discrimination (Klüver & Bucy, 1939). The subcortex seems able to produce general movements, but the cortex seems necessary for the finer detail, e.g., individual finger movements (Travis, 1955). The latter point may well be a reflection of the fact that the cortex (Figure 3) influences the motor neurons directly, as well as through internuncial elements (Kuypers, 1960), whereas the subcortex appears to influence motor neurons almost exclusively through internuncial elements (Kuypers, Fleming, & Farinholt, 1960). However, in spite of these differences in emphasis between Dr. Young and myself, Dr. Young ultimately may well be right, for on the sensory side, the loss of strict unilaterality in the cerebral cortex is indicated by the fact that only one temporal lobe seems necessary in order to maintain a certain degree of visual discrimination, even in the absence of the ipsilateral occipital lobe. In addition, this seems to contrast the "mesencephalic agnosia," following undercutting of the superior colliculus, which agnosia apparently is rather unilateral in nature. Furthermore, on the motor side, in man, one of the extremities does not limit itself to its proper territory but seems to lead the entire operation. In other words, at this point the motor cortex, as an instrument, seems to be played upon in a different manner. In these respects, the picture becomes more impressionistic or even abstract indeed. However, then we have reached the threshold of a higher level of organization within the nervous system, as compared to the motor and sensory cortices. At these higher levels we might have one brain rather than two. In view of the abstract characteristics of this one brain, I would prefer to end here my comments.

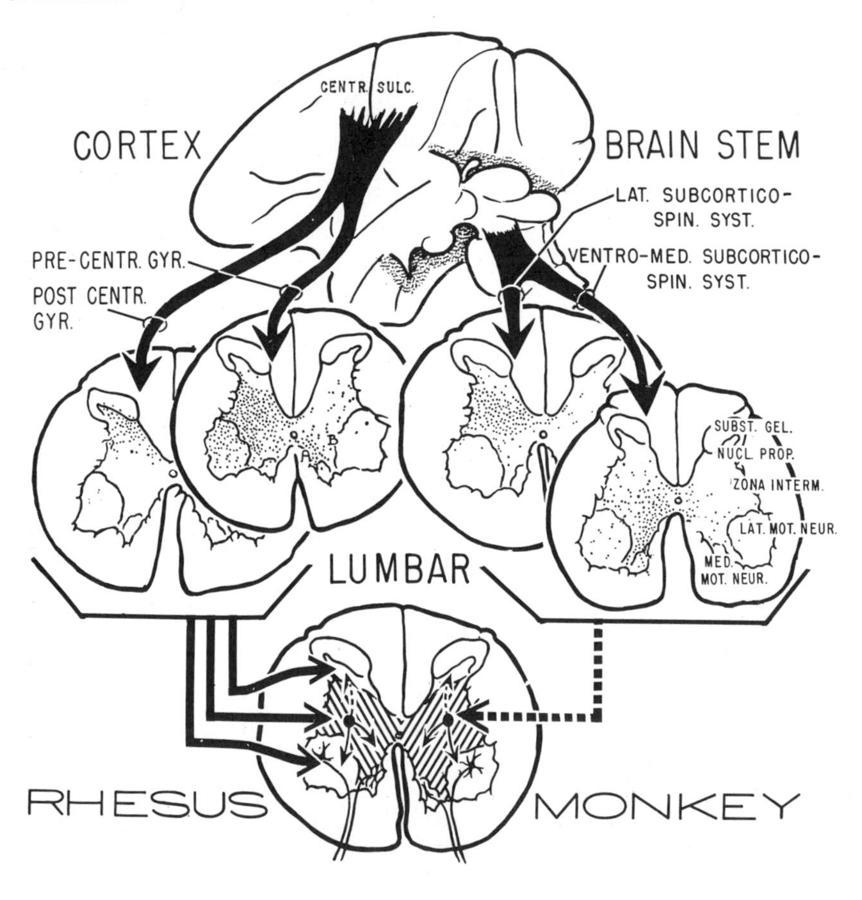

Fig. 3.

D.

WALLE J. H. NAUTA

Walter Reed Army Institute of Research, Washington, D. C.

I, TOO, should like to say first of all that I have found it a rare privilege to hear Dr. Young's paper. Few, indeed, of our contemporaries could have taken us on an intellectual expedition as exciting as the one from which we have just returned. What I have to say further must be interpreted, not as a criticism of Dr. Young's presentation, but rather as an elaboration upon some of the neurological principles which we heard him discuss.

With your permission, I shall invite attention to that part of the brain that apparently "might as well have been one and single." I am referring specifically, as you may have guessed, to the limbic system of the cerebral hemisphere and its associated subcortical structures. As we all know, the neural mechanisms in question are bilaterally represented in our brain; there is a hippocampal formation and an amygdaloid complex in each of our two hemispheres, and the hypothalamus, that prime affiliate of our limbic hemisphere, is found on both sides of the third ventricle. It has nevertheless been the experience of clinicians and physiologists alike, that destructive lesions of these structures, provided such lesions are nonirritative and do not interfere with major channels of blood supply or cerebrospinal fluid circulation, must be bilateral if they are to produce any identifiable functional deficit. For example, in the experience of Mason and his associates (1961), only bilateral removal of the amygdaloid complex causes marked changes in the monkey's ACTH response to stress. Scoville and Milner (1957) noted impairment of recent memory only in patients with bilateral hippocampal lesions and explicitly mention the absence of such symptoms in cases of unilateral surgical intervention. But the recent experiences with frontal lobotomy suggest that this principle of apparent bilateral equivalence is represented also in the neocortex. It would seem reasonable to ask, how it is that we have two brains of this kind when we could probably get along nicely with one?

The answer to this question, if one can be expected at all, will have to be based upon functional, as well as morphological, considerations. To begin with the latter, I should like to think that the bilateral symmetry of our brain results from the same morphogenetic forces that cause left-right symmetry in our skeletomuscular system. It appears certain that the notochord plays a major role among such forces, at least in the early stages of embryonic development. Once "induced" as a midline structure and sent on its way, the development of the neural tube was controlled by no other than bilaterally active mechanisms of organization. It seems likely that the cerebral hemispheres arose in response to a secondary inductive force, possibly emanating, again symmetrically, from a locally modified notochordal tissue.

From a functional point of view, we must ask which sensorimotor systems came to utilize the symmetry in the available neural lay-out in such manner that, for them, the two halves of the brain supplemented each other, and which systems did not do this. I believe that we can say that those systems that did capitalize on the bilateral symmetry of the brain have in common that they all have to do, in one way or another, with the stability of the organism in its spatial environment. Such stability necessitates the isomorphic neural maps which Dr. Young so beautifully analyzed for us, maps that become more elaborate in differentiation as the interaction of the organism with its spatial environment increases. As Dr. Scheibel pointed out, this greater differentiation of the map may well be achieved by a progressive numerical increase of Golgi type II cells in the sensory receiving areas, and these cells could possibly introduce different systems of decoding superimposed upon, and interacting with, the original map.

However, to return to the "single brain," it seems conceivable that some neural mechanisms, such as the limbic system and the frontal granular cortex, have a bilateral representation which is only incidental to the morphodynamically determined general symmetry of our organism. Such mechanisms, if one can be allowed at all to generalize their functional significance, appear to have to do less with the problem of spatial stability and much more with the requirements for stability in time. The mechanisms in question sustain the organism as it interacts with its spatial environment and drive it on to goals that promote its biological integrity, as well as the continuity of its species. These goals can range, in time and complexity, from the procurement of one's next meal to the hoarding of equipment—material or intellectual—to be used in distant exigencies. I strongly suspect that Dr. Young was thinking of, among others, such time-oriented mechanisms when he alluded to parts of the brain dealing with more abstract, nonisomorphically coded information.

E.

JAMES L. O'LEARY

Washington University School of Medicine, St. Louis, Missouri

THE MORNING started with Professor J. Z. Young's answers to his own two-dimensional question, "Why do we have two brains?"; his conclusion suggesting that we need but one. This led to my recall of a moment long ago when a nineteenth-century French pathologist discovered that the subject of an autopsy he was performing had been getting along with but one cerebral hemisphere. The pathologist, Piorry (La Lancette Fracoise, 1829), expressed his surprise in these words, "It was not a brain that I found but the half of one." The right hemisphere had been lost, and the loss had been incurred at an indeterminate period before death. The subject's intellect was said to have been unimpaired. Since then other such cases have been reported, and one other, at least, as the result of natural causes.

For 11 years, Dr. Levy and I followed a female patient who had suffered a massive cerebral hemorrhage at the age of forty. A neurosurgeon had clipped her right middle cerebral artery near the time of this hemorrhage, and upon re-exploration several years later, seeking the cause of intractable left-sided pain, he had noted that the right hemisphere was entirely missing. Post-mortem study of the brain proved that was the case, since all that remained of the right hemisphere was a nubbin containing fragments of the posterior medial group of thalamic nuclei. During life, the patient had been conscious, and she had lived a limited, although pain-wracked, existence. She continued to play bridge, however, with the aid of her nurse. There are now a number of instances in which hemispherectomies have been performed upon subjects of infantile hemiplegia, removing the "bad brain" of the affected hemisphere to ameliorate a severe behavior disorder. These patients have continued without unusual deficit. However, they do not belong with the cases representing losses from natural causes, for, in the infantile hemiplegics, we must presume that the affected hemisphere had never functioned properly. Thus, the conditional reply to Dr. Young's question is that a subject can sometimes get on with but one hemisphere, at least if it is the right member of the the pair, and if we do not attempt to establish too rigid criteria for the normality of behavior after the loss.

Dr. von Bonin's essay is admirable for the simple and direct approach he makes to the problem of weighing anatomical differences between right and left halves of the brain. If such differences were sufficient, they might establish the left hemisphere as anatomically the more complicated one, better suited to the control of speech and of the master hand. The anatomical differences, which point to the existence of a dominant hemisphere, are evidently minor and can be divided about equally between support for dominance of right and of left components. Minor volume differences appear to favor the right hemisphere, as compared with somewhat longer fissures (as the Sylvian), broader gyri, and deeper sulci for the left one.

An anatomical question remains concerning whether or not cyto- and myeloarchitectonic differences could exist, even though gross differences between the hemispheres are negligible. Dr. Bodian has noted the plethora of methods the student of cortical architecture now has at his disposal, and this has also been emphasized in the discussions of Scheibel, Kuypers, and Nauta. However, search for subtle differences, between hemispheres using histological criteria, could prove an endless task. Using only the Weigert and Nissl methods, Beck spent ten years at a comparative, architectonic study of the temporal gyri in primates and man. Today, the newer methods, made available by Nauta and his school, have introduced the possibility of meticulous analysis of the incoming fiber constituents of the cortex of the experimental animal. Scheibel has emphasized the wealth of synaptic connections made visible by the Golgi method and the diversity of types of short axon cells. The latter, since the time of Ramón y Cajal, are believed to increase in numbers and in complexity with ascent of the evolutionary scale. To my knowledge, no efforts have been made to compare homologous areas of the left and right sides of the brain by such advanced techniques. Nor has electron microscopy, with its immensely greater potentialities than the light microscopy methods, been employed for this purpose. In fact, past the differences sought by gross anatomists in the weight and configuration of the two sides of the brain, there has been little emphasis upon left/right comparisons. We, of the electrophysiological group, habitually set up our experiments to record from one cerebral cortex and presume that the data are equally applicable to the other. Everyone, I believe, does likewise.

A point deserving emphasis in this symposium is our ignorance of the size and complexity of the task that we could set ourselves in attempting to assay the cortices of the two hemispheres for their relative complexities. The size of the task would presumably relate to the order of complexity of the structural arrangements involved. In guessing as to order of complexity, only the fertility of our imaginations could serve us. However, in an analogous speculation involving the number of senses necessary to fully comprehend one's environment, Voltaire has this to say:

> "Tell me," says Micromegas, an inhabitant of one of the planets of the Dog Star, to the secretary of the Academy of Sciences in the planet Saturn, at which he had recently arrived in a journey through the heavens,—"Tell me, how many senses have the men on your globe?" . . . "We have seventy-two senses," answered the academician, "and we are every day complaining of the smallness of the number. . . . In spite of our curiosity, and in spite of as many passions as can result from six dozen of senses, we find our hours hang very heavily on our hands, and can always find time enough for yawning."—"I can very well believe it," says Micromegas, "for, in our globe, we have very near one thousand senses, and yet, with all these, we feel continually a sort of listless inquietude and vague desire, which are for ever telling us that we are nothing, and that there are beings infinitely nearer perfection." *Micromegas,* Voltaire.

In conclusion, I would put before you one of the key questions which this conference should set itself to answer. Blau, in a study called *The Master Hand,* reviewed a large literature, including twin studies, and concluded that handedness is not inherited. If not in the genetic code, in what other code could handedness be registered? Perhaps in the remaining sessions someone will attempt to solve this enigma.

■□ III

Some General Aspects of Interherhemispheric Integration*

by ROGER W. SPERRY

California Institute of Technology, Pasadena, California

THE TOPIC of this session leads us directly, of course, to the corpus callosum. Between 1900 and 1950, this structure had acquired a notable reputation for being, among all brain structures, the "largest, most useless." Many still remember Warren McCulloch's summary of the status of our knowledge, about 1940, with his jocular comment that the only demonstrated function for this structure seems to be that of aiding in the transmission of epileptic seizures from one to the other side of the body. More than 10 years later, Lashley still found ample justification to use his own facetious surmise that probably the principal function of this structure was not so much excitatory in nature as mechanical, i.e., to keep the two hemispheres from sagging.

The past ten years have changed the situation considerably. In a series of animal experiments, it has been possible to demonstrate, at last, definite and important functions for the corpus callosum. The first convincing evidence in this direction came from a series of investigations by Ronald Myers (1956, 1961), dealing with the function of the callosum in the interhemispheric transfer of visual discrimination learning in chiasma-sectioned cats. As illustrated in Figure 1, the mammal with crossed optic fibers sectioned in the chiasma retains the major part of its visual field, but stereoscopic overlap is eliminated and each eye feeds only to its homolateral hemisphere. What Myers found here, in brief, was that cats, trained with one eye masked, were unable to remember

* Chairman's informal introduction to the session on Interhemispheric Problems.

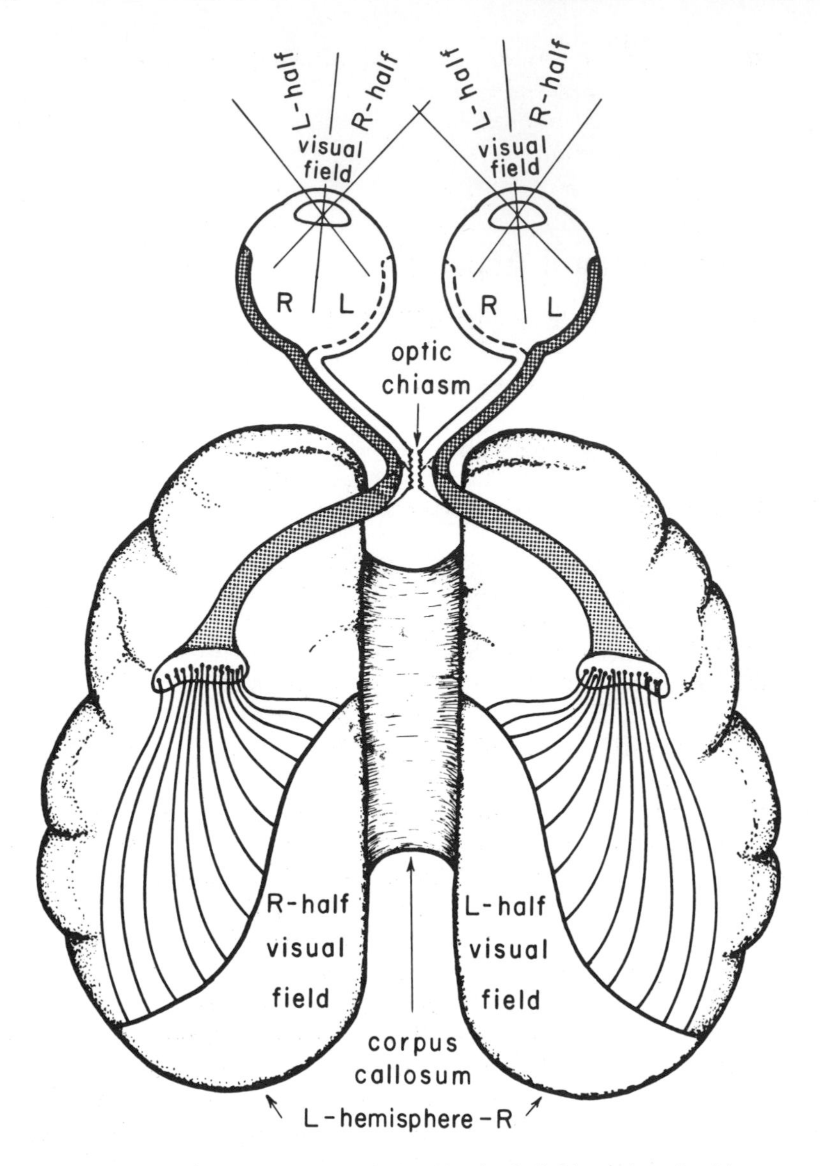

Fig. 1. Sketch indicating effects of midsagittal division of optic chiasma.

with the second eye what they had learned with the first eye, after both the optic chiasma and corpus callosum had been sectioned previously. In fact the second, or untrained eye, could be used to learn just the reverse of what the cat had been trained to do through the first, and apparently with no interference. This functional independence of the surgically separated hemispheres with respect to learning, memory, and other gnostic activity has since been amply substantiated, as will be evident in the discussion to follow.

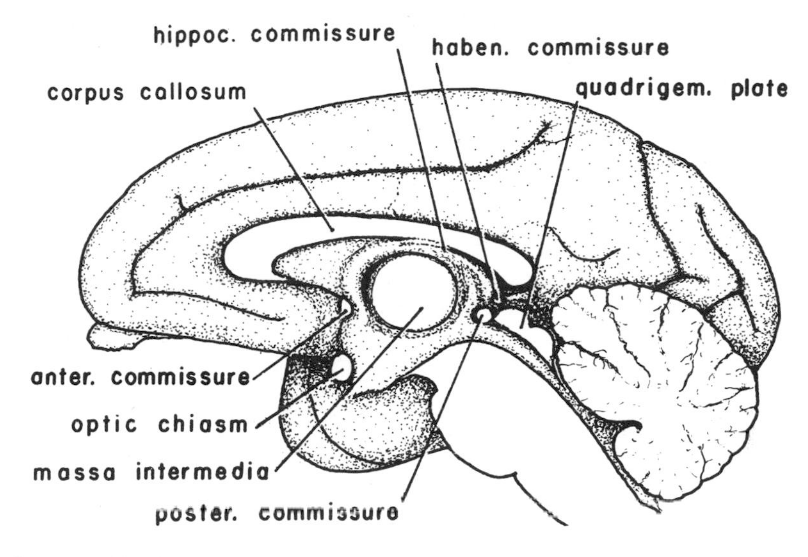

Fig. 2. Midsagittal aspect of monkey brain showing main structures involved in surgical bisection.

Figure 2 will recall the relations of some of the main mid-line structures involved in cross-integration in the mammalian brain. Our current mid-line surgery has been developed to the stage where we can now safely divide along with the optic chiasma, corpus callosum, and other forebrain commissures, the habenular and posterior commissures, the massa intermedia, the quadrigeminal plate, the rostral tegmentum, and the cerebellum in the monkey. This leaves undivided, at higher levels only, the remaining tegmentum and the pons. Dr. Voneida (1961) has succeeded in bringing cats through bisections that extend through the tegmentum to about midway through the pons. Cats with this extensive split, including the tegmentum, show marked cerebellar-like unsteadiness and an unexplained visual impairment immediately following the surgery. However, the animals recover and, in a month or so, their general behavior is much like normal to casual observation, excepting for some residual ataxia and visual weakness. Specific testing for perceptual, learning, memory, and emotional characteristics in these tegmental splits has only been started.

In any case, it is evident that this kind of mid-line surgery makes possible functional testing of the various brain commissures, as well as the anatomical and electrical tracing of their connections. One can section or leave intact specific segments of the callosum, or one or another of the lesser commissures in different combinations. The feasibility of thus splitting the brain into two rather independent halves also opens numerous analytic potentialities for attacking other physiological and behavioral problems. This becomes a rather lengthy subject in itself (Sperry, 1961) that we can hardly go into at this time. Suffice it to say for our present purposes, it has become increasingly important to learn more about the functions of the different commissures and also about the physiological properties of commissurotomized brains in their various forms, not only for the direct information obtained, but also with regard to the application of these preparations to other problems.

Although the old riddle of the corpus callosum, as such, has been largely resolved in recent years, the great cerebral commissure still presents something of a riddle with respect to the meaning of the prevailing symmetry of its fiber connections. Anatomical and physiological studies indicate that the majority of the callosal fibers tend to interconnect corresponding points in the two hemispheres (Bremer, Bridhaye, & Andre-Balisaux, 1956). More than that, it is suggested (Grafstein, 1959) that the fiber systems, arising from different layers within a given locus, tend to connect symmetrically with corresponding layers in the same locus on the opposite side.

What is accomplished by having this huge system of symmetrical cross connections in the highest control centers remains a puzzle. For example, what would be served by having the incoming information from one-half of the visual field interact symmetrically with that of the other half field? At first glance, the effect would seem to be about as helpful as a double exposure in photography. The same may be said for symmetrical cross-interaction of cutaneous information in stereognosis.

The simple principle of homotopic cross connection is illustrated on the left in Figure 3, for comparison with an alternative principle of possible interconnection on the right that I once favored, before the evidence for symmetrical, or homotopic, projection had become so strongly established. It may still be possible, despite the trend of the evidence, that something of the sort depicted on the right is really involved, i.e., that the callosum is not mainly or primarily so much a symmetrizing influence, as it is a means of supplementing the activity of each hemisphere with different and complementary information about what is happening on the other side. It appears there is something special and nonsymmetrical about the cross connections between the

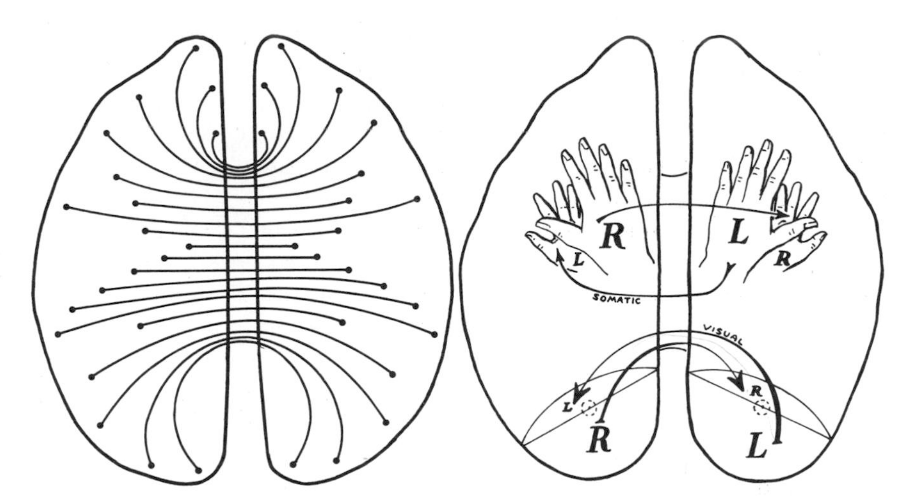

Fig. 3. Projection of corpus callosum: Simple homotopic projection principle on left compared with that of speculative "supplemental complementarity" on right.

visual areas (Bremer, Brihaye, & Andre-Balisaux, 1956; Myers, 1960). In the somatic cortex, where contralateral and ipsilateral points tend to be pretty much in register, the two alternatives shown here would be difficult to distinguish from the data now available. The scheme on the right accords better also with the development of lateral dominance in the human brain.

This leads to one more general point that boils down essentially to a note of caution. In earlier studies of interhemispheric transfer after callosum-section, including those of Myers (1956) and others (Sperry, Stamm, & Miner, 1956) on visual discrimination learning in the cat, those of Stamm and myself (1957) on somesthetic learning in the cat, and those on visual learning in the monkey (Downer, 1958; 1959; Sperry, 1958; 1959), it was found regularly that section of the cerebral commissures prevented the spread of learning and memory from one to the other hemisphere. It was as if each of the separated hemispheres had a complete amnesia for the experience of the other, as if each had its own independent perceiving, learning, and memory systems.

Upon extending our transfer studies in the monkey from visual to somesthetic and motor learning (Sperry 1958; 1959), the independence of the separated hemispheres was less clear-cut, in that some of the monkeys on some problems demonstrated rather strong transfer of learning from one to the other hand. Although such transfer was not seen in the later studies by Myers (1960) in the chimpanzee, or by Ebner and Myers (1960) in the monkey, its occurrence has been more intensively investigated and confirmed in the last few years by Glickstein (1960a; 1960b). The callosum was clearly playing an important transfer role when present, but even slight leakage of learning effects, across the mid-line following commissurotomy, had become critical with respect to certain uses of the split-brain preparation. That either forelimb can be governed from a single hemisphere, in both learned and unlearned activities in the split-brain cat and monkey, seems well established (Schrier & Sperry, 1959; Sperry, 1958; Trevarthen, 1961).

In other tests involving conditional sensory-sensory cross integration between the divided hemispheres (Sperry 1958; 1959), we found that visual information entering on one side can be cross-integrated with tactile information entering the other, even in deep-split cases with section of the midbrain as well as forebrain commissures. It has since been found by Meikle and Sechzer (1960), using cats, and by Trevarthen (1960, 1961), using monkeys, that easy brightness discriminations learned with one eye, transfer to the other in split-brain preparations. According to Trevarthen (1961), color discriminations similarly show some interocular transfer in the split-forebrain monkey. Bisection, through the habenular and posterior commissures and quadrigeminal plate in the monkey, seems to block the transfer of color, but not that for brightness discriminations. Simple visual pattern discriminations may show signs of interference (i.e., transfer effects) in the split-forebrain monkey, when tested by means of simultaneous reversal learning—i.e., under training and testing conditions that favor the detection, rather than occlusion, of the more subtle interactions between the divided hemispheres. Recently it has been shown that a visual brightness discrimination can be performed by split-brain cats (Robinson & Voneida, 1961) and monkeys (Trevarthen, 1961), when one brightness is projected through the left eye and the other through the right. Some of our split-brain monkeys are also performing size discriminations under these conditions as, for example, when one of four open circles of graded sizes is projected to one of the separated hemispheres and a second simultaneously to the other. Thus, cross comparisons for correct judgment of relative size are somehow achieved across the divided hemispheres, the surgical sections in this case extending through the anterior half of the quadrigeminal plate. Conditioned response studies, being carried out with conditioned tactile stimuli (Meikle, 1961) and with conditioned visual stimuli (Voneida and Sperry, 1961) in split-brain cats, are also revealing cross-integration effects.

In most of the above cases, the analysis has not been carried far enough so that one can say what phase of the neural process is involved in the cross-integration. However, it looks as if more is happening in some of these situations than a mere leakage of the sensory data. Possibly such cross-interactions are achieved by devious lower level devices that don't violate the notion of separate right and left mental systems. However, in view of evidence like the foregoing, it seems advisable to keep in mind the possibility that some of our earlier notions regarding the gnostic independence in the separated hemispheres may have to be qualified, as we learn more about the extent and nature of the potentialities for interhemispheric integration at lower levels.

■□ IV

Transmission of Visual Information Within and Between the Hemispheres: A Behavioral Study[1]

by RONALD E. MYERS

The Johns Hopkins University School of Medicine, Baltimore, Maryland

THE FOREBRAIN commissures are not necessary for across-the-midline exchange of information related to perception of more crude and undifferentiated forms of afferent stimulation. Learned responses, based upon discrimination of differences in luminous flux or frequencies of flickering lights acquired through the activation of one side of the brain, are available on testing through the opposite side of the brain, despite prior corpus callosum transection, in cats. In such instances, however, the capacity of subcortical mechanisms to effect information transfer breaks down early, as the differences in the stimuli to be discriminated are diminished (Meikle & Sechzer, 1960). Responses, conditioned to gross electrical stimulation of the cortex of one hemisphere, also may find expression on first stimulations of homologous cortex of the second hemisphere in cats with corpus callosum divided (Doty & Rutledge, 1959).

Brain stem mechanisms of cross communication have been found wanting when examined with reference to information transmission subserving more complex modes of stimulation. Evidence is accumulating, rather, that the forebrain commissures in higher mammals serve

[1] Supported in turn by the Abbott Memorial Fund of The University of Chicago, by the Hixon Fund of the California Institute of Technology, and by grants from the United States Public Health Service.

to interrelate the activities of the two hemispheres in the realm of more refined and differentiated engagements (Myers, 1961; Myers and Henson, 1960; Ebner and Myers, 1962). This is true not only for perceptual functions, but also for those, less well understood, related to perception and supported by the prefrontal cortex and by the cortex of the temporal lobes. (See chapters by Ettlinger, Downer, & Mishkin, this volume.)

The present discussion reviews data, collected over the last ten years, touching on corpus callosum function in vision. The primary concern will be to determine the capabilities and limitations of the great cerebral commissure in its task of information transmission. Beyond this, the forcefulness of direct sensory experiences will be compared with that of experiences achieved vicariously or indirectly through several types of association linkages.

Chiasma-sectioned cats were used throughout most of the experiments to be reported. As may be seen from Figure 1, section of the crossed retinal fibers at the optic chiasma restricts the patterns of excitation from the two separate eyes to the separate hemispheres through the

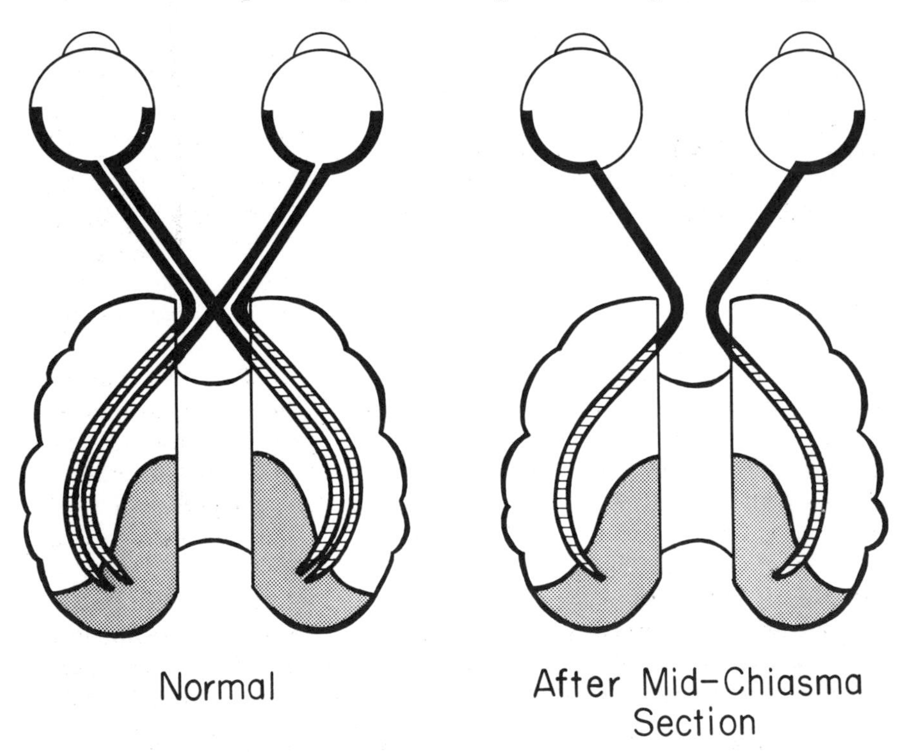

Fig. 1. After surgical transection of the crossing retinal fibers at the optic chiasma, each eye projects only to its ipsilateral half of the brain.

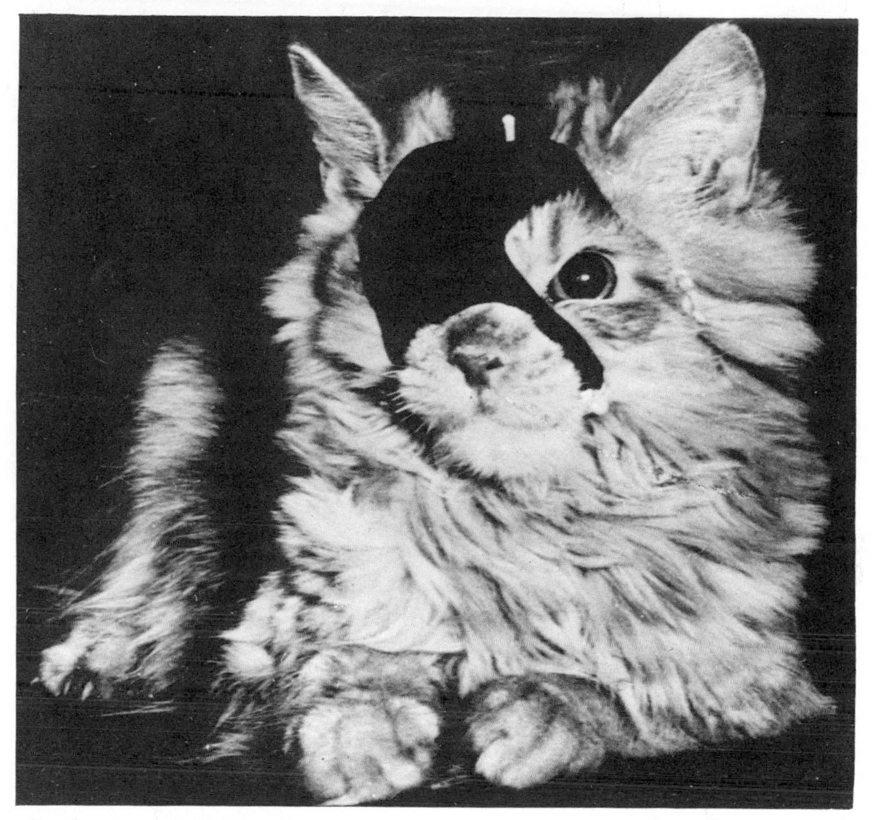

Fig. 2. The chiasma-sectioned cat, with one eye masked, receives afferent visual stimuli only through one half of his brain—that on the side of the seeing eye.

preserved, uncrossed afferent pathways. By occluding one eye, the retinal stimulation, during any given visual experience, may be limited entirely to one side of the brain (Figure 2). Under the circumstances, the deprived half of the brain may receive visual information only indirectly through the stimulated brain half.

The cats were taught visual pattern discrimination responses with one eye masked. Tests of transfer of training were then carried out through the untrained eye, to test for the cross-availability of information between the hemispheres under various circumstances. The problem box used for training and testing is illustrated in Figure 3. At one end of the box hung two transparent doors, each containing a translucent pattern. The animals learned to push on the door containing the "correct" pattern to obtain food reward. When they pushed on the door contain-

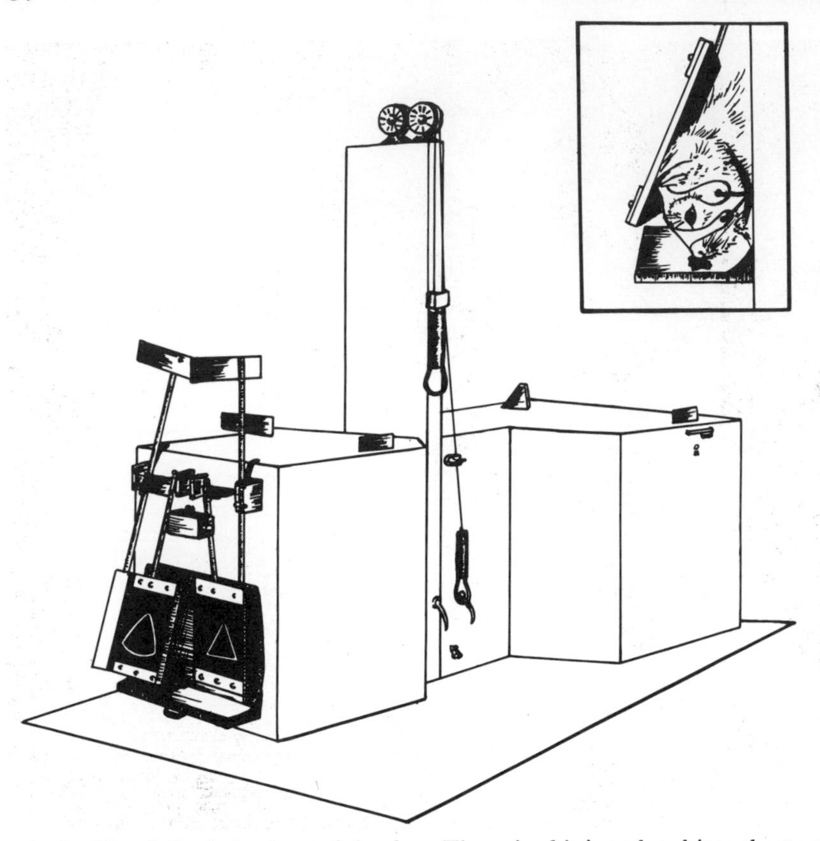

Fig. 3. Visual discrimination training box. The animal is introduced into the starting chamber to the right. The trial chamber to the left, containing the visual stimulus objects, is baited with food. An opaque and a transparent separator are raised in turn, admitting the cat to the trial chamber. He chooses one of the two patterns by pushing on one of the two swinging doors. The correct choice produces a food reward. The cat returns to the starting chamber between trials.

ing the "incorrect" pattern, they received mild punishment. Between responses, the two patterns were shifted between the doors according to a chance sequence. After the animals learned to choose regularly only the "correct" of the two patterns, performance was stabilized by long-term overtraining.

Completely normal cats, trained in such a problem box, exhibited a remarkably well-developed perceptual capacity, being able to distinguish and choose correctly between closely similar stimuli. Chiasma-sectioned cats, by contrast, were able to make only relatively simple discriminations. These animals exhibited, in addition to bitemporal field defects, a sharp decrease in visual acuity. The acuity loss and consequent decrease in ability to make discriminations seem likely to be due to the prominent crossing of central fibers in this species.

The chiasma-sectioned cats mastered monocularly discriminations II-ab and III-ab, the patterns of which are illustrated in Figure 4. However, the animals required many more trials to learn discrimination II-ab, as may be seen from Table I. Once the two responses were learned, the animals also performed at a lower level during overtraining on discrimination II-ab than on discrimination III-ab. From these facts, discrimination II-ab would seem the more difficult of the two responses for the chiasma-sectioned cats both to acquire and to sustain.

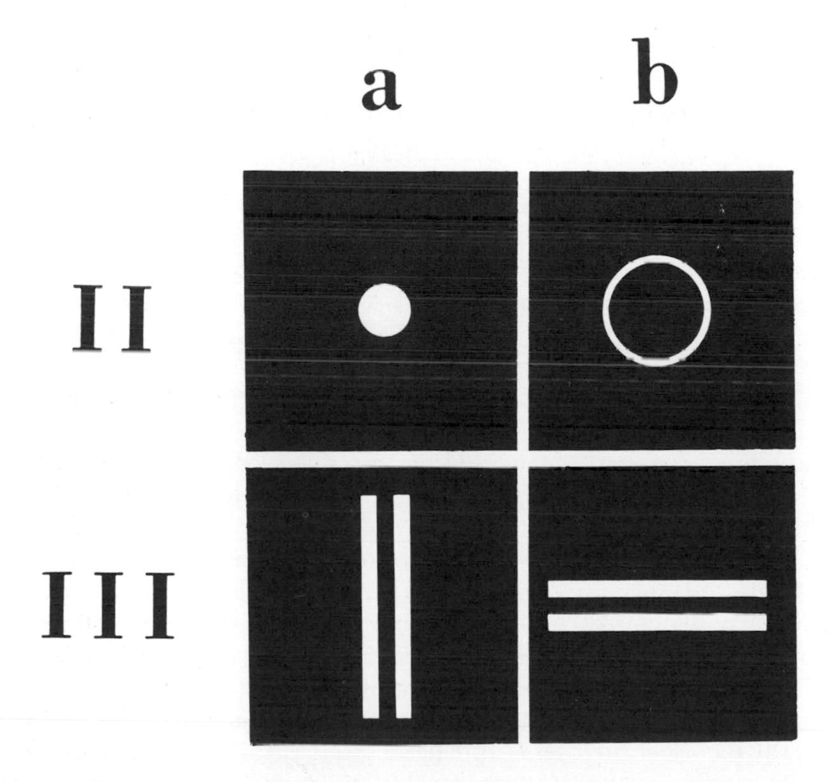

Fig. 4. Some patterns used to teach simple discriminations to the chiasma-sectioned cats. In describing a discrimination in the text, the positive rewarded pattern is listed first, as, in discrimination II-ab, the positive pattern is II-a, the small solid white dot.

Table I

Comparison of learning rates and of overtraining and transfer performances of nine cats on visual discrimination II-ab and III-ab.

	Discrimination II-ab	Discrimination III-ab
Mean number of trials to learn	850, $\gamma = 310$	320, $\gamma = 60$
Mean % correct on last 120 overtraining trials	95.2, $\gamma = 1.9$	99.6, $\gamma = .5$
Mean % correct on first 40 transfer test trials	86.0, $\gamma = 3.7$	94.8, $\gamma = 5.0$
Number of cases in population	4	5

All animals exhibited a performance decrement on tests of interocular transfer of training. Table I gives the average performances of two groups of cats run on the two discriminations. Whereas, on the average, four cats performed correctly on 95.2 percent of trials during final overtraining on discrimination II-ab, they performed correctly on only 86.0 percent of trials during transfer testing. Five cats, on the average, performed correctly on 99.6 percent of trials during final overtraining on discrimination III-ab and on 94.8 percent of trials during transfer testing. It may be noted that the performance decrement on transfer testing was disproportionately great for the more difficult discrimination II-ab. The mean depression of transfer test performance that might have been anticipated for this discrimination would have been only to 90.6 percent, rather than to the observed 86.4 percent, if it were calculated in direct proportion to the actual depression experienced on discrimination III-ab.

In these chiasma-sectioned cats, therefore, some imperfection exists in information exchange between the hemispheres to account for the regularly occurring performance decrement observed on transfer testing. Moreover, this imperfection is more readily revealed, the more difficult the differentiation tested.

The disproportionately poor transfer performance with the more difficult test suggests that some relationship may exist between the difficulty of differentiation which may be handled, and the degree of structural development required of the underlying signaling mechanism. That such a relationship does indeed exist may be seen from the following experiments, in which the system of intercommunication was surgically damaged. In a series of chiasma-sectioned cats, different anterior and posterior extents of the corpus callosum were transected. In animals with transections which began anteriorly, a definite decrement in interocular generalization of discrimination III-ab was observed only after destruction extended beyond 75 percent of the entire length of the commissure. On the other hand, in animals with transections beginning posteriorly, minor decrements in transfer performance occurred in all animals with sections which extended anteriorly beyond 25 percent of the length of the commissure, though major decrement occurred only after the transection extended beyond 40 percent. When the transection extended beyond 50 percent, there was complete or nearly complete interference with transfer. Importantly, some animals of both series, though able to transfer easier discrimination III-ab, failed with the more difficult discrimination II-ab.

From this partial sectioning experiment, it is clear that the transfer process does not depend upon a circumscribed and specific bundle of fibers within the posterior segment of the corpus callosum. Rather, both more anterior and more posterior bundles, within the posterior visual segment, may be equally effective in the generalization of the simple discrimination problem. However, as the number of corpus callosum fibers available for the transmission of visual gnosis is gradually decreased, there is a decrement, first, in the transfer of more difficult discrimination II-ab and then, in the transfer of the easier discrimination III-ab. There does exist, therefore, a relation between the number of fibers available for gnostic intercommunication and the difficulty of a differentiation which can be handled. Further, rather than being an "all or none" phenomenon, intercommunication between the hemispheres may best be characterized in statistical terms, with increasing damage to the mechanism resulting in decreasing degrees of information exchange.

Haggquist fiber-stained preparations of preserved segments of the posterior portion of corpus callosum, still successfully mediating transfer of discrimination III-ab, yielded fiber counts of between 2.5 to 3.5 million. The assumption may be made that a proportion of the fibers in such a segment may be involved in non-gnostic visual functions, such as mediating impulses influencing eye movement (Sherrington, 1894). Another group of fibers, in all likelihood, interconnects portions of the cortex which are not visual in function, such as the posterior ectosylvian gyrus. It therefore seems probable that somewhat less than 2.5 to 3.5 million fibers may be involved in the information exchange underlying interocular generalization of more simple discrimination III-ab.

Experiments have been carried out in which lesions were made of the "trained" hemisphere subsequent to training, but prior to transfer testing through the "untrained" hemisphere. The outcome of these experiments has given further indication of imperfections in the process of interhemispheric information transmission. In chiasma-sectioned cats, varying amounts of cerebral substance were removed from the hemisphere receiving the afferent visual inflow during the initial monocular training. It was hoped that the memory trace system, directly established in the "trained" hemisphere, might in this fashion be destroyed. The three types of lesions produced are illustrated in Figure 5. After postoperative recovery, performance was tested through the intact "untrained" hemisphere.

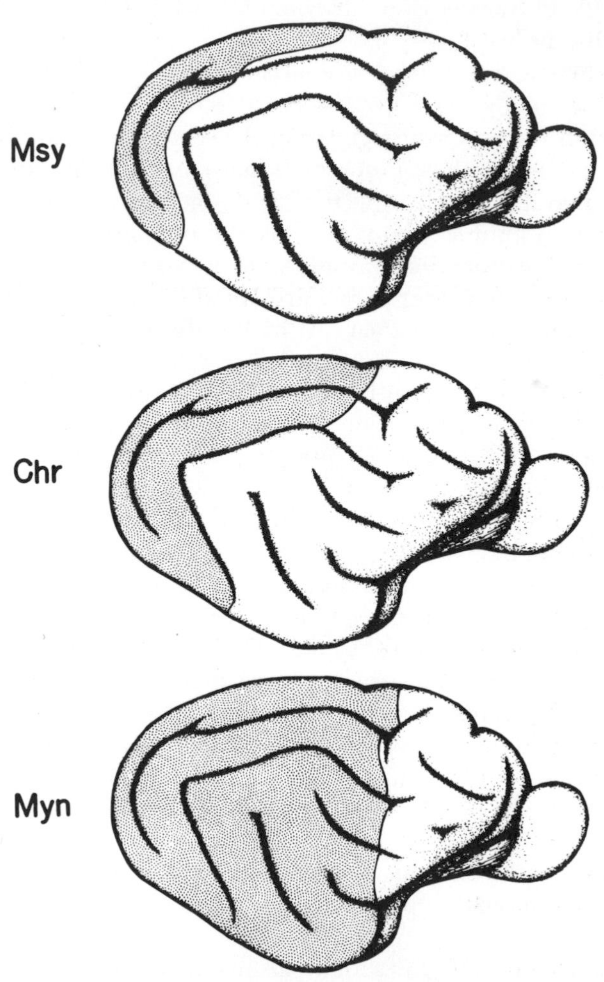

Fig. 5. Type-lesions made in the hemisphere receiving direct afferent visual stimulations during learning. It was hoped in this fashion to damage or destroy the directly established memory trace system of the "trained" hemisphere.

The majority of cats performed discrimination III-ab with a mild decrement on testing through the "untrained" hemisphere, whatever the extent of cortical removal from the "trained" hemisphere. About one cat out of three, however, showed a more extensive depression of performance which persisted through the first forty test trials. These animals, however, performed at a high level through the second forty test trials. Similar experiments, carried out using more difficult discrimination II-ab, gave a more extreme result. In all instances, regardless of the type of lesion of the "trained" hemisphere, performance was at or near a chance level and remained so for a number of testing sequences. There was, in fact, only slight savings in relearning on retraining through the second eye. A closely similar outcome was obtained in experiments with interocular generalization of training in cats with transection of the corpus callosum, subsequent to training but prior to testing.

These results give further indication of the limitation in information exchange between the hemispheres. The degree of development of the contralateral memory trace system, established by means of the corpus callosum, is shown to lack the definition of that established in the hemisphere which receives directly the afferent sensory stimulation during initial learning. Some degree of direct sensory experience seems to be required to fully consolidate the memory system of the "untrained" hemisphere when it is cut off from the memory system of the "trained" hemisphere. The drop in anticipated test performances, brought about by the cerebral lesions or by post training corpus callosum section, indicates that the "trained" hemisphere must normally contribute actively to performance through the "untrained" hemisphere at the time of transfer testing by means of transcallosal influences.

Still another line of evidence has clearly disclosed a relative ineffectiveness in information exchange between the hemsipheres, when this is compared to the competence of direct sensory influx. In the earliest experiments on interocular transfer in the chiasma-sectioned cat, it sometimes happened that animals were serially taught separate pattern discrimination responses, through the separate eyes, prior to transfer testing. Under these circumstances it was noted that a particular discrimination, discrimination IV-ab, was transferred at a level a great deal lower than anticipated, when tested through a second eye which had had prior experience with discrimination III-ab (Figure 6). When beginning the experiment, it had been anticipated that equivalence relationships or similarities, between the sets of patterns presented through the separate eyes during training, might affect performance levels on transfer testing. Patterns IV-a and IV-b had, therefore, been constructed so that

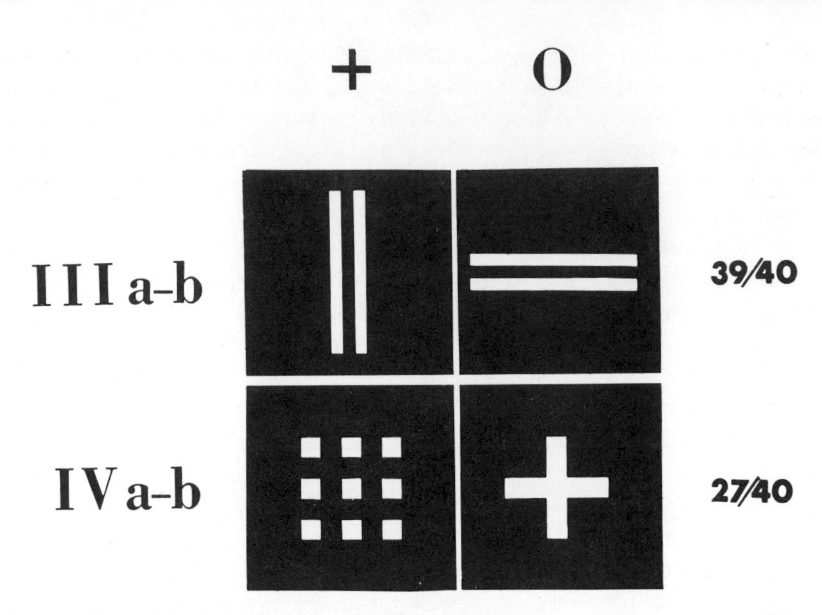

Fig. 6. Two discriminations taught through the two separate eyes of chiasma-sectioned cats. When the patterns of discrimination IV-ab were presented for transfer testing through the eye already trained on discrimination III-ab, a highly depressed performance was obtained (27 correct in 40 test trials). This was not so, however, when the patterns of discrimination III-ab were presented for testing through the eye trained on IV-ab, at which time high level performance was obtained (39 correct in 40 test trials). Note the closer similarity of the negative IV-b pattern to both patterns of discrimination III-ab.

each resembled equally, both the positive pattern III-a and the negative pattern III-b used in the response already established through one eye. It had been hoped that this equality of similarity would prevent equivalence effects from affecting transfer performances between the eyes. Subsequent re-examination of the patterns IV-a and IV-b in relation to patterns III-a and III-b made it clear that, though the two separate patterns of discrimination IV-ab, indeed did resemble equally the two patterns of discrimination III-ab; it was also true that the negative pattern IV-b resembled both patterns of discrimination III-ab much more than did positive pattern IV-a. The consequent tendency for the cat to choose frequently the negative pattern IV-b, on transfer testing, seemed understandable. In summary, this line of reasoning suggested the hypothesis that a degree of conflict in the conditioning achieved through the two separate eyes of chiasma-sectioned cats, may adversely affect the degree of transfer of training between the eyes.

This possibility seemed of more than passing interest, since it implied that information transmission between the hemispheres may, in part, depend upon the content of previous sensory stimulations and not merely upon the presence or absence of anatomical interconnections. The two eyes of chiasma-sectioned cats may be served by two separate, but interconnected, neuronal systems, each with properties of some lability. Overlapping influences through commissural pathways might be rendered to a degree ineffectual by virtue of conflict between the separate direct sensory inflows to the two separate systems.

Further experiments were carried out to test this hypothesis. In the example cited, the conflict between the discriminations taught through the two separate eyes was relatively slight. In the next experiment, conflict between the two discriminations was greatly sharpened by constructing patterns such that similarities between the individual stimuli

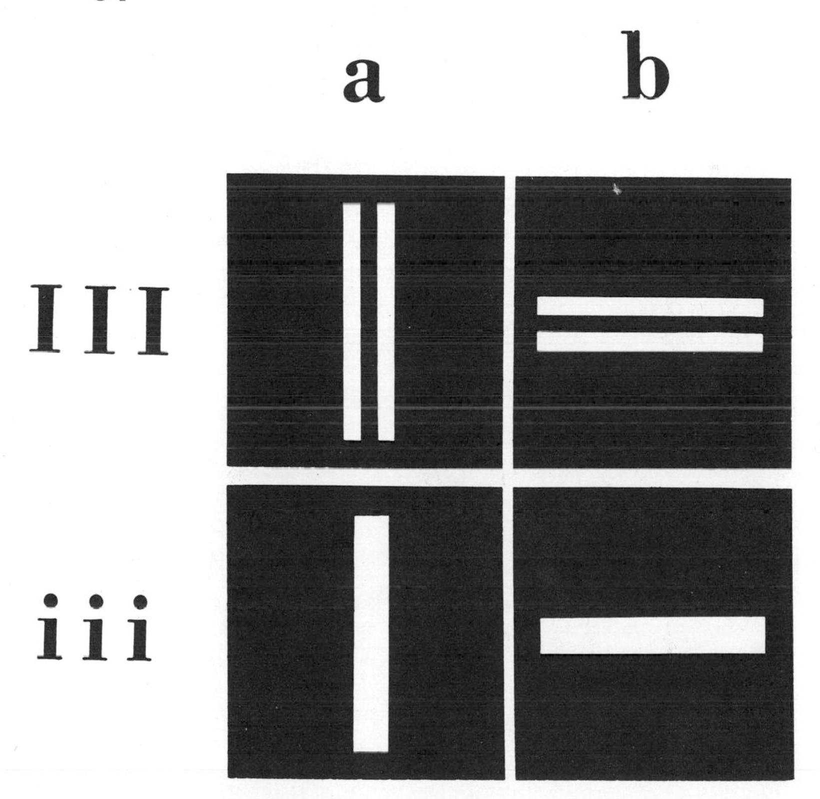

Fig. 7. Patterns constructed to accentuate similarities. Pattern III-a resembles iii-a; pattern III-b resembles iii-b. By rewarding choice of pattern III-a in training through one eye and pattern iii-b in training through the other eye, highly conflicting responses were taught through the separate eyes.

of the two sets were very much greater (Figure 7). Patterns iii-a and III-a resemble each other closely, as do patterns iii-b and III-b. That this resemblance was close for the cats was clear when normal cats, who had been taught discrimination III-ab, were found to choose regularly pattern iii-a and to avoid regularly pattern iii-b on tests of generalization.

Three chiasma-sectioned cats were taught discrimination III-ab through the right eye, pattern III-a being the positive or rewarded pattern. After this response had been established and stabilized through 120 overtraining trials, patterns iii-a and iii-b were presented through the left eye. The animals regularly chose pattern iii-a because, it is thought, of (1) transfer of training between the eyes due to transcallosal information transmission, and (2) generalization between the two sets of stimuli due to pattern similarities. Twenty such test trials were allowed through the left eye. Conflicting discrimination iii-ba was then established through this left eye, iii-b being the positive, rewarded pattern. After establishment, the response was overtrained a standard 120 trials. Discrimination III-ab was again re-established and overtrained through the right eye. This procedure was subsequently carried out through each eye in turn, until the cats performed correctly the separate conflicting discriminations through the separate eyes.

How do these animals perform on tests of interocular transfer of training under these conditions of marked conflict conditioning through the separate eyes? On presenting patterns III-a and III-b through the left eye, which had been trained on discrimination iii-ba, two processes will be interacting to influence the ultimate outcome on transfer testing. First, there will be the tendency for training transfer between the eyes, a process served by information exchange through the corpus callosum. Secondly, there will be the tendency for stimulus generalization between the response already established through the eye being tested, and the discrimination response undergoing transfer testing. The latter tendency toward generalization probably reflects properties inherent in the intrahemispheric visual interpretive mechanism itself. Consummation of across-the-midline information transmission would result in predominant choice of pattern III-a, the pattern rewarded on prior training through the opposite right eye. Alternatively, pre-eminence of intrahemispheric generalization effects would tend toward preference for pattern III-b through the left eye being tested, because of this pattern's resemblance to pattern iii-b, previously rewarded through this eye.

The animals regularly chose pattern III-b on transfer testing. Further, this mode of responding persisted for long periods of time, despite repeated punishment. The animals were thus seen to persist in performing in completely opposite ways through the two separate eyes. The animals preferred pattern III-a through the right eye and pattern III-b through the left eye. In this manner, it became clear that the visual interpretative mechanisms of the two hemispheres may indeed be induced, in a manner of speaking, to dissociate themselves one from the other through separate conflict conditioning, despite functional cross-relationships through the corpus callosum. This outcome gives further indication of some inperfection in the interhemispheric transmission of information and serves, at the same time, to emphasize the prepotency of direct sensory experience in establishing memory effects within a given interpretative system.

Reisen, Kurke, & Mellinger (1953) showed that general visual experiences of early life are important to the development of interocular equivalence in the cat. Conversely, conflict in experience through the two eyes should lead to some abnegation of ocular equivalence even in the normal adult animal. The difficulty encountered in breaking down interocular equivalence should be, in turn, related to the degree of development of associational relationships between the neuronal mechanisms related to the two eyes. By using cats with primary optic pathways destroyed in different combinations it should be possible to compare and to contrast in this manner the relative strengths of associational linkages between the several types of visual neuronal systems of the two hemispheres.

Accordingly, three groups of cats were prepared (Figure 8). Cats of group I underwent midsagittal chiasma section, which destroyed the crossing retinal fibers so that, as before, only the ipsilaterally projecting uncrossed fiber systems remained to transmit impulses from the two eyes to the separate brain halves. In cats of group II, the right optic tract was sectioned, so that only the crossed system from the right eye and the uncrossed system from the left eye remained, both to project their retinal impulses to the left brain half. Cats of group III, like those of group I, underwent midsagittal chiasma section.

Cats of group I were conditioned through the separate eyes on the conflicting discriminations III-ab and iii-ba. The characteristics of interocular differentiation among these cats were believed to indicate the strength of associative linkage between the "uncrossed" visual interpretive mechanisms of the two hemispheres through the corpus callosum. Cats of group II likewise were conditioned through the separate eyes on conflicting discriminations III-ab and iii-ba. The characteristics of interocular differentiation among these cats, however, were believed to indicate the strength of the associative linkage between the "crossed" and the "uncrossed" visual interpretive mechanisms within the left hemi-

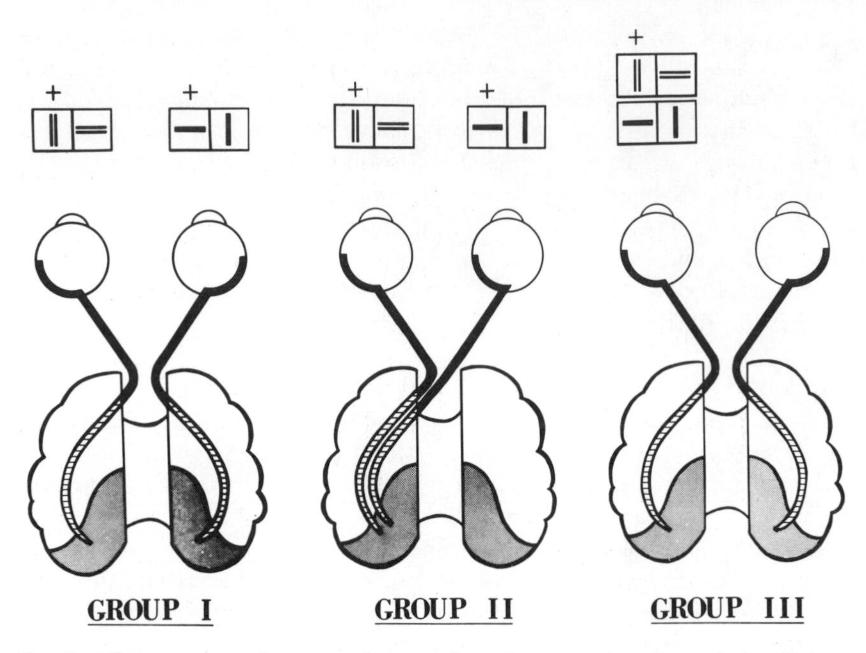

Fig. 8. Three groups of cats used to explore the strengths of associative linkage between the several visual interpretative mechanisms related to the several separable afferent projection pathways. With the Group I, chiasma-sectioned cats, the transcallosal associative binding between the "uncrossed" visual mechanisms of the two hemispheres is studied by determining the characteristics of interocular differentiation of the two conflicting responses. Similarly, with the Group II, tract-sectioned cats, the strength of associative binding between the "crossed" and "uncrossed" visual mechanisms within the left hemisphere is studied, again, by characterizing the course of interocular differentiation. The Group III cats serve as limiting controls in which the course of discrimination differentiation is studied through a unitary system consisting of the "uncrossed" visual mechanisms of the left hemisphere.

sphere. Cats of group III were conditioned alternately on the separate conflicting discriminations III-ab and iii-ba, always through the left eye. This group served as a limiting control, in which the conflicting conditionings were presented to the cats through identical, rather than separate, interpretive systems.

In establishing the conflicting responses, the following protocol was adhered to. Discrimination III-ab was established and subsequently overtrained 120 trials through the left eye. Conflicting discrimination iii-ab was then established through the right eye (or through the left eye in the instance of group III cats). Again, this second response was stabilized by the routine 120 overtraining trials. Discrimination III-ab was then re-established and re-overtrained through the left eye; to be followed by re-establishment and re-overtraining of discrimination iii-ba through the right eye of group I and II cats and through the left eye of group III cats. Separate re-conditionings in the separate circumstances proceeded in this alternate fashion until correct responses were regularly made immediately on renewed re-presentation of the separate pattern-sets through the separate mechanisms.

The course of conflict conditioning through the separate systems of the three groups has been characterized in several ways. The graphs of Figures 9, 10, and 11 represent the scores on discrimination iii-ba, achieved through the right eyes of the cats of groups I and II and the control left eyes of the cats of group III. On the ordinates is recorded the number of errors made in the first ten trials run through the particular eye on each *new* re-conditioning on the iii-ba response. On the abscissas is recorded the number of *cycles* of re-conditioning carried out.

Examination of the curves of Figure 9 shows that the chiasma-sectioned animals of group I made all or nearly all incorrect choices on

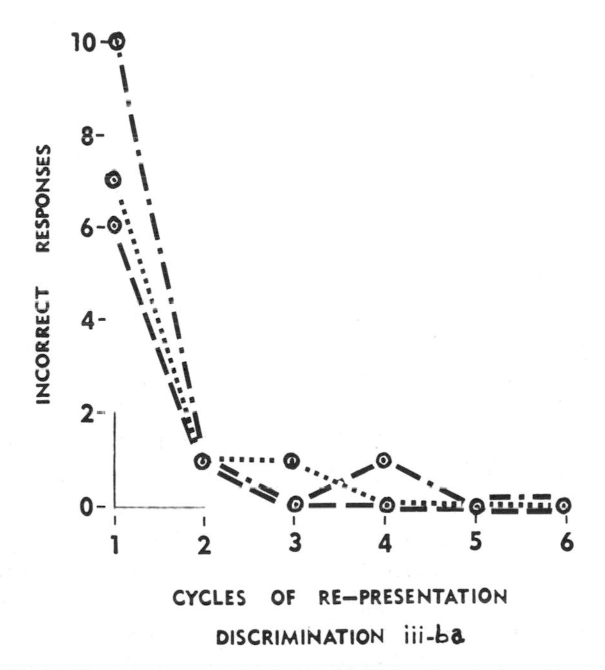

Fig. 9. Performances of Group I, chiasma-sectioned cats through the right eye on discrimination iii-ba. The number of errors made on the first ten trials run on each *new* cycle of re-conditioning through this eye is plotted on the ordinate. The number of such cycles of re-conditionings is plotted on the abscissa. Note the precipitous decline in number of errors made through the right eye on the second cycle of re-presentation of discrimination iii-ba.

the first ten trials run through the right eye on discrimination iii-ba. This outcome was to be anticipated because of the prior transcallosal transmission of the conflicting III-ab response tendency. By the second re-presentation of the patterns of discrimination iii-ba through the right eye, however, the number of incorrect responses on the initial ten test trials was decreased to either one or none at all. Furthermore, this performance level obtained despite the intervening re-conditioning on conflicting discrimination III-ab through the opposite, left eye. All subsequent cycles of re-presentations of the patterns of discrimination iii-ba through the right eye resulted in similar test performances with none or only one incorrect response in the first ten trials. Thus, it is seen that the initial transcallosal transmission of information between the uncrossed visual interpretive mechanisms of the two hemispheres supported the high level interocular transfer of discrimination III-ab. However, the subsequent learning of conflicting discrimination iii-ba through the second eye resulted in a lasting inversion of the response tendency. This rapid response inversion demonstrated through the second eye endured, despite repeated and long-term conflicting conditioning through the first eye. Further, when the cats were tested through each eye in turn with the patterns used for conditioning through the other eye, they exclusively chose the patterns which resembled the positive pattern of the discrimination originally established through the eye being tested. That is, they failed to demonstrate transfer of training between the eyes, and instead, showed a complete interocular response inversion. The cats responded through one eye in a fashion exactly opposite to that through the other eye. Thus, the rapid inversion of response tendency with conflict conditioning through the separate eyes did not represent differentiation of the two conflicting responses through the separate visual interpretive mechanisms, but rather a dissociation of the two mechanisms.

Reference to the group II curves of Figure 10 indicates that the optic tract-sectioned cats made *all* incorrect choices on the first ten test trials through the right eye, after prior conflict conditioning through the left eye. This outcome indicates the direct transmission of gnostic information between the uncrossed and crossed visual interpretive mechanisms within the left hemisphere. However, in contrast to the rapid inversion of response between the eyes exhibited by the chiasma-sectioned cats, the tract-sectioned cats demonstrated only a gradual interocular response differentiation. As many as six cycles of conflict re-conditionings through the separate eyes were required before immediate inversions of response began to occur on first shifting between the eyes. This outcome indicates a much closer functional linkage, between

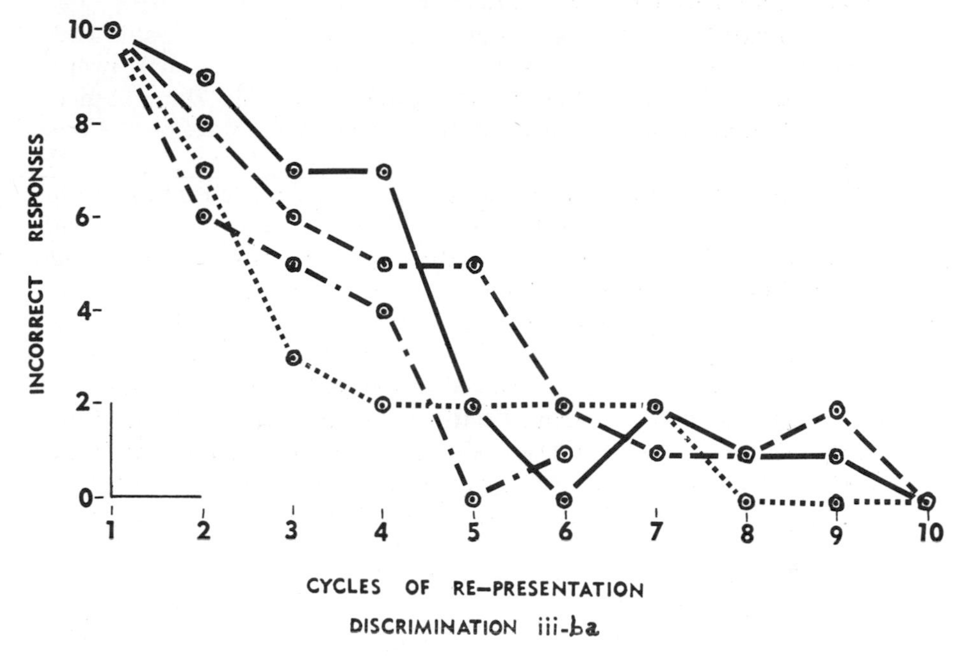

Fig. 10. Performances of Group II, right tract-sectioned cats through the right eye on discrimination iii-ba. The co-ordinates are the same as in Fig. 9. Note the gradual decline in number of errors made during the initial ten trials run on the successive cycles of re-conditioning. The solid line curve represents the results obtained with a single normal cat (see text).

the uncrossed and crossed visual interpretive systems within a hemisphere, than occurs transcallosally between the uncrossed visual systems of the two separate hemispheres.

The closer and more intimate associational relationships, between the crossed and uncrossed visual interpretive systems within a hemisphere, raises the question whether the final achievement of inversion of response between the eyes of the tract-sectioned cats represents a dissociative phenomenon, such as that which has been shown to obtain for the chiasma-sectioned cats; or whether instead, it represents a differentiation of conflicting responses presented through the separate eyes. The question has been answered in favor of dissociation of systems, since the tract-sectioned cats, like the chiasma-sectioned cats, failed to show transfer of training on tests of interocular transfer. Similar to the chiasma-sectioned cats, they performed through one eye in a fashion completely opposed to that performed through the other eye. Thus, the crossed and uncrossed visual neuronal mechanisms existing side by side, or intermingled within a single hemisphere, may endure in a dissociated state. It is significant, however, that the tract-sectioned animals broke down the reversal of response more quickly than did the chiasma-sectioned animals on continued transfer testing through the one or the other eye.

The group II cats sustained tract section in order to create for them limitations of visual field and visual acuity approaching that sustained by the group I and group III chiasma-sectioned cats. However, the results obtained using the tract-sectioned cats should, in theory, also obtain for entirely normal cats. In order to test this possibility, one completely normal cat was run in parallel with the group II animals. His curve of performance is included as the solid line in the graph of the group II animals of Figure 10. It may be seen that the shape of his curve falls clearly within the range of the curves of the tract-sectioned cats. Further, this normal cat, like the tract-sectioned cats, failed to show transfer of training on critical tests of interocular transfer, and,

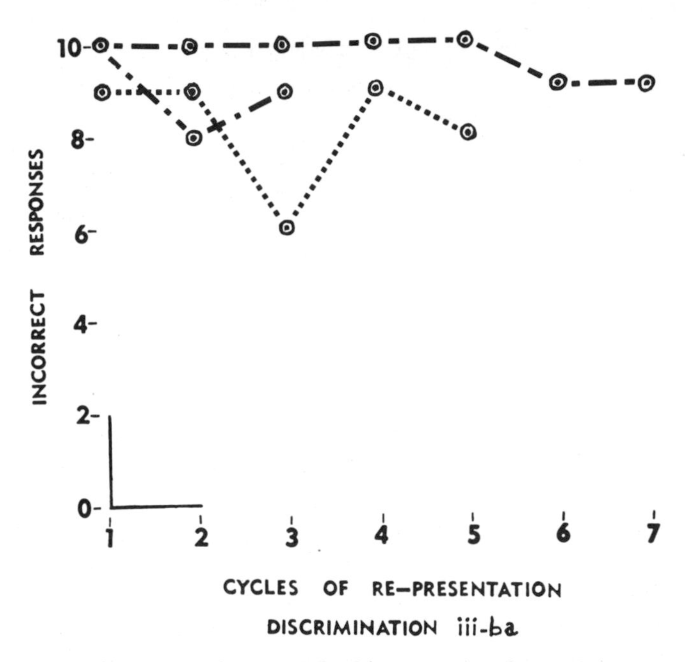

Fig. 11. Performances of group III, chiasma-sectioned cats through the left eye on discrimination iii-ba. Note that this represents presentation of the two conflicting responses always through the same eye. The animals revealed little indication of differentiation of the two responses through seven cycles of re-presentation. Large numbers of errors were regularly made during the early trials on each re-presentation cycle.

like the tract-sectioned cats, performed in completely opposite ways through the separate eyes.

The performance curves of the group III chiasma-sectioned control animals, shown in Figure 11, gave no indication of differentiation of the two moderately conflicting responses by the uncrossed visual interpretive mechanism of the left hemisphere, despite seven complete cycles of reconditioning. Functional dissociation, which obtained in the interocular circumstance of the group I and II animals, could not occur in the instance of the intraocular training and testing of the group III animals. The separate conditionings and reconditionings on the two conflicting responses all took place through the same neuronal system. A mere oscillation of response tendency was seen in these control cases, instead of a functional dissociation *or* a differentiation of response. Differentiation of these selfsame conflicting responses has been observed, however, through the uncrossed visual mechanism, under the circumstance of prior vicarious experience with one of the involved responses through associative channels.[2]

Another manner of expressing the relative degree of development of associative interrelationships between the several neuronal mechanisms is illustrated by the bar graphs of Figure 12. This figure gives the number of trials required to invert the response on the separate cycles of re-conditioning of conflicting discrimination iii-ba through its test systems. The portions of the bars with right oblique shading represent the standard 120 trials of overtraining run after criterion of learning has been achieved or re-achieved with each such re-presentation. It may be seen again that the group I cats (chiasma-sectioned, tested interocularly), once having achieved inversion of the response by prolonged conflict conditioning through the second (right) eye, no longer required re-conditioning but only overtraining on subsequent re-presentations through this eye. This remained true despite repeated intervening re-conditionings with conflicting discrimination III-ab through the first (left) eye. From this it would seem that once a chiasma-sectioned cat has developed a mode of responding through one eye in relation to direct afferent sensory experience, it appears to be affected minimally by conflicting conditioning subsequently acquired through the other eye.

[2] Consider the earlier statement that the tract-sectioned cats break down the inverted response on continued transfer testing more quickly than the chiasma-sectioned cats. It would seem that the closer the associative relationships between two test systems, the greater the effectiveness of the transmitted associative experience in facilitating differentiation of the conflicting responses within a system. Paradoxically, when the conflicting situations are experienced entirely through the direct input pathway, differentiation either fails to be achieved or is achieved only with great difficulty.

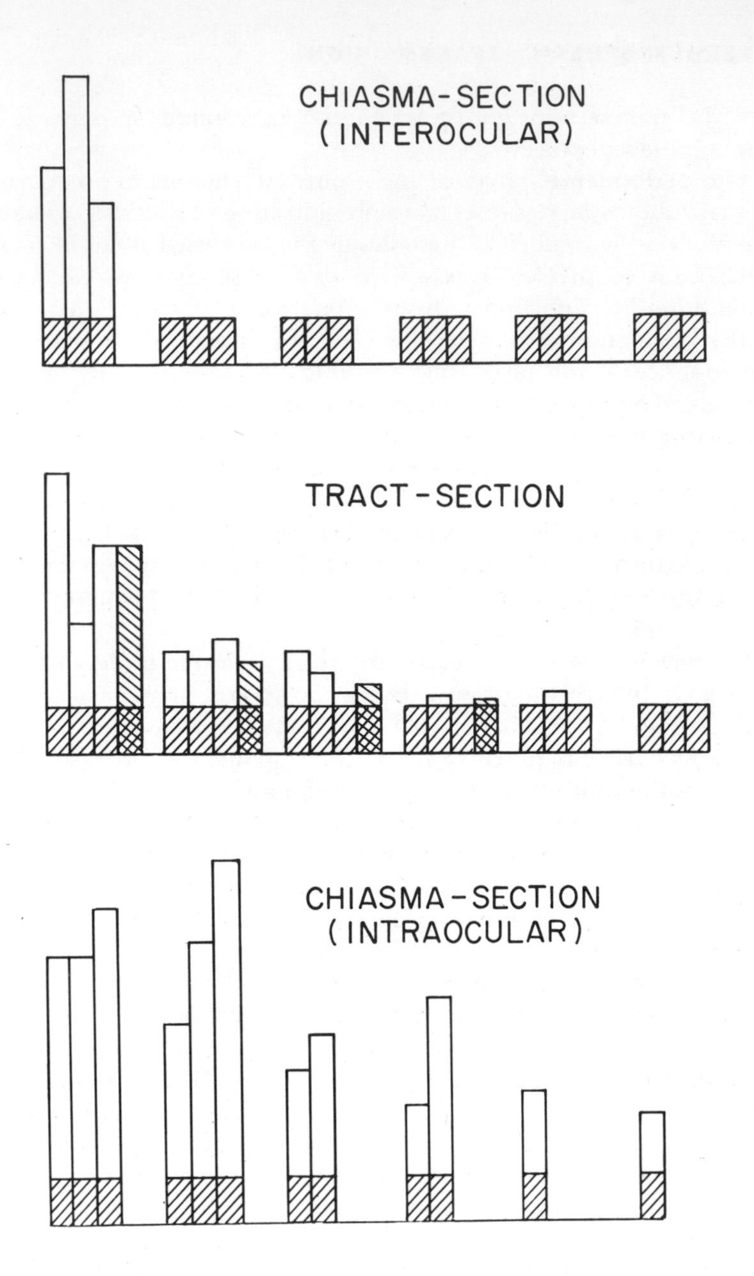

Fig. 12. Bar graphs illustrating the total numbers of trials required to achieve response reversal through succeeding cycles of re-presentations of discrimination iii-ba through its test system in the several circumstances. The right oblique shading denotes the standard 120 overtraining trials run in each cycle by all animals. The bars with left oblique shading, in the tract-sectioned series, denote the performances of the normal animal. Each of the separate groupings of bars along a line represents a separate cycle of re-presentation. The performances of individual animals are represented by the individual bars of each grouping to be followed through the separate cycles.

This is not so for group II cats with tract-section tested interocularly. Examination of the middle bar graphs, related to these cats, shows that they require repeated re-conditionings on discrimination iii-ba through the right eye, after each cycle of discrimination III-ab conditioning through the left eye. However, the number of trials required to invert the response tendency on each subsequent re-presentation through the right eye decreased, so that by the fourth to sixth test cycle, no further re-conditioning was necessary. Tract-sectioned cats that have acquired a mode of responding to direct sensory experience through one eye still may be influenced by conflicting conditionings through the other eye, but in a decremental sense on repeated re-conditionings. The normal animal performed in a closely similar fashion.

The group III control cats did not monocularly resolve the conflict between discrimination III-ab and iii-ba. Instead, they exhibited mere oscillations between the two modes of responding, with a gradual decrease in the number of trials required for inversion (see the lower bar graphs, Figure 12). As may be seen, one cat completed only two cycles, while a second completed only four during the course of the experiment.

Another measure of the strengths of associational linkages between the several systems was thought to be the number of trials required for the first inversion, within the secondary system relative to the number of trials required to establish the initial response through the primary system. The bar graphs of Figure 13 depict these results. The 100 percent level on the bars represents the number of trials required for the initial learning of discrimination III-ab through the left eye. The overall height of the bars, with corresponding percentage figures, expresses the comparative number of trials required to establish discrimination iii-ba through the right eye (or left eye in the case of group III cats). It is seen that the group I, chiasma-sectioned animals, as a whole, required 40 percent more trials to learn conflicting discrimination iii-ba through the right eye than they did initially to acquire discrimination III-ab through the left eye. Surprisingly, the group II, right-tract sectioned animals required fewer trials to learn discrimination iii-ba through the right eye than they did to learn discrimination III-ab through the left eye. This unexpected result may be a reflection of the greater visual acuity available through the right eye of these animals, giving an important advantage during the learning of the conflict discrimination through this system. In contrast to this, the entirely normal cat required 50 percent more trials for inversion of response through the right eye than for the initial learning through the left eye. The group III, chiasma-sectioned cats required 80 percent more trials to acquire discrimination iii-ba, after initial learning of discrimination III-ab, both through the left eye.

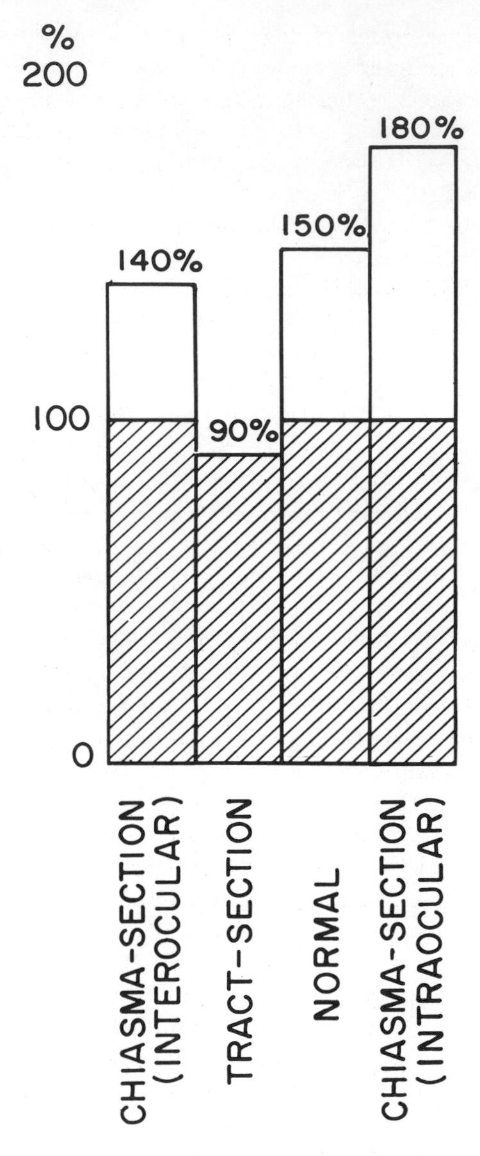

Fig. 13. Relative numbers of trials required for first learning of discrimination iii-ba through the secondary test system, compared to the numbers required for the prior learning of discrimination III-ab through the primary system. The 100 percent level represented on the bars, by the right oblique shading, represents the total trials required for discrimination III-ab learning through the primary system.

The differences in the relative numbers of trials required to invert the responses through the different test systems are surprisingly slight, when the great differences in degrees of functional interrelationship in the several circumstances are considered. It must be concluded that the channels of intercommunication extending between the various visual interpretive mechanisms are all sufficiently well developed to cross-induce nearly fully developed mnemonics, whichever associated mechanisms are tested. It is only by repetitive counterposing of direct sensory experiences, with those vicariously achieved through associative systems, that differences in development of the several types of cross linkages may be more fully revealed.

In summary, lines of evidence have been reviewed which reveal definite limitations in the corpus callosum transmission of information between the hemispheres in the cat. It has been found that: a) performance on transfer testing through the untrained eye is always somewhat depressed when compared to final performance through the trained eye, b) destructions within the "trained" hemisphere or dissociation of the two hemispheres by corpus callosum section after training results in an additional decrement in performance level through the "untrained" hemisphere, c) interocular equivalence is put in abeyance by conflict conditioning through the two eyes. Further, data have been presented which demonstrate a much closer association linkage between the "crossed" and "uncrossed" visual interpretative mechanisms located within a hemisphere than between the "uncrossed" mechanisms of the two hemispheres connected through corpus callosum.

Acknowledgments:

The author extends his gratitude to Roger W. Sperry for his support and his many suggestions which made the present studies possible.

■□ V

Interhemispheric Integration In the Somatic Sensory System

by GEORGE ETTLINGER

The Institute of Neurology, The National Hospital, Queen Square, London, England

PSYCHOLOGISTS HAVE investigated the integration between the cerebral hemispheres in somatosensory function in two distinct and yet complementary ways. With the one method, that of transfer testing between the hands, the subject is taught to perform a given somatosensory task first with the one hand and is subsequently tested with the other. As performance with the second hand is generally superior (at a comparable stage of testing), the training given to the first hand is said to have transferred to the second. A number of investigators have identified the corpus callosum as the major one of the brain structures concerned in such transfer between the hands, and thereby implicated it in the integration between the hemispheres.

The second method has involved study of somatosensory defect, associated with either unilateral or bilateral cerebral lesions in man or animals. In the case of unilateral lesions, this might be contralateral, bilateral, or even ipsilateral. In animal experiments, the results of successive left and then right ablations have been observed and compared with those of one-stage bilateral removals of the same parietal areas. With such brain injured subjects, full integration between the hemispheres is reflected by one of two results: either if a defect occurs only with bilaterally symmetrical lesions; or if a defect in one hand results equally from left and right unilateral lesions.

I intend to review briefly certain of the previous works in each of these two fields of study and, in addition, to present some recent observations on transfer between the hands and the effect of successive, posterior parietal ablations in the monkey.

Evidence for extensive integration between the hemispheres in somatosensory function is derived from the accepted finding that there is a considerable degree of transfer between the hands in healthy human subjects and other primates. Thus, Smith (1951) has shown that learning a stylus-maze with one hand greatly improves learning of the same task with the other. Ebner & Myers (1960) have stated that "normal monkeys recognize immediately with one hand, discriminations learned with the other." A similar, though somewhat less certain, transfer of tactile learning between the paws has been reported by Stamm & Sperry (1957) in cats. It is of interest that the degree of transfer between the feet is less complete than that between the hands in monkeys, according to Ebner & Myers (1960).

The detailed neurophysiological basis for such transfer between the hands in tactile performance is not yet understood. However, at least one of the structures that may be critically concerned has been identified. Section of the corpus callosum has been shown to abolish such transfer between the hands in chimpanzees (Myers & Henson, 1960), in monkeys (Ebner & Myers, 1960), and in cats (Stamm & Sperry, 1957). Admittedly, further evidence of a similar effect of destruction or absence of the callosum in man is needed, particularly in view of the differing information at present available (Russell & Reitan, 1955; Smith, 1951). Moreover in animal experiments, the corpus callosum has yet to be sectioned (according to the method of Myers, 1957) *after* training with one hand and *before* testing with the other. This would establish whether integration between the hemispheres takes place predominantly at the time of learning, at the time of testing for transfer, or at both of these times, depending perhaps on the nature of the tactile task. Nor have partial sections of the callosum yet been made, with a view to identifying which regions within the commissure are specifically concerned with somatosensory integration.

Additional extracallosal structures may be involved in transfer between the hands under certain special conditions, which perhaps may depend upon the amount of training given to the animal. Glickstein & Sperry (1960) failed to demonstrate total absence of transfer after section of the callosum in monkeys. The existence in animals of a cutaneous representation (through the lemniscal system) of the ipsilateral body surface in the first somatic projection area has been fully discussed and denied by Rose & Mountcastle (1959, pp. 400, 424). Moreover Orbach & Chow (1959), using the ablation technique, failed to establish that the second somatic area (with its bilateral representation) plays an important part in the somatosensory discrimination behavior of the monkey. It seems, therefore, unlikely that a direct ipsilateral somatosensory afferent projection is concerned in transfer between the hands.

However, there exists evidence, dating from 1950, that the posterior cortical areas may be of importance for transfer between the hands. For of the six monkeys trained by Blum, Chow, & Pribram (1950) on somatosensory tests of size, form, roughness, and weight discrimination, four animals were retrained after surgery, separately with each hand. Three of these animals received bilateral ablations of parieto-temporo-occipital (P.T.O.) cortex; the fourth animal sustained a bilateral temporal lobe removal. Following these cortical removals, the animals were initially retrained with the preferred hand. As soon as they had relearned each problem with this hand, they were tested with the other (postoperatively nonpreferred) hand on the same problems. The one animal with temporal ablations was tested for transfer between the hands on only three out of four problems. Combining all results, only four of a total of fifteen postoperative tests for the four animals showed evidence of transfer between the hands, as indicated by quicker relearning with the second than with the first hand. The temporal animal showed transfer on only one of the three problems; one P.T.O. animal, on two out of four; another, on one of four; and the remaining animal showed no transfer. In evaluating these results, it must be recalled that there was no overtraining with the first hand before transfer testing with the second. Moreover in all animals, the direction of transfer testing was from preferred to nonpreferred hand.

As part of a more extensive investigation, Dr. J. E. Kalsbeck and I have looked for immediate transfer between the hands in 12 rhesus monkeys with posterior cortical removals. All animals were initially taught to perform a tactile shape discrimination test (L vs. T) with the left hand. Training was always continued until animals reached a standard level of performance of 10 or less errors in 100 trials. Following a period of 14 days' rest, the animals were retrained and then received their first ablation. In Table I are shown details for 6 animals that received successive right and then left, or left and then right, posterior parietal removals. These operations were separated by periods of 3–6 weeks, and the animals were retrained with the left hand after the first, and again after the second, operation. Whenever an animal showed an impaired performance postoperatively, it was allowed 14 days' rest after first achieving the standard level of performance and was then retrained once again before the second operation or before transfer testing. As soon as each animal was finally retrained with the left hand after the second operation, it was given 40 further trials on the same tactile test,

Table I

The effect of successive right and left posterior parietal ablations on the transfer between the left and right hands of a tactile shape discrimination habit.

Animal	**1**	**2**	**3**	**5**	**6**	**7**
Sequence of ablations		Right:Left			Left:Right	
Interval between operations (weeks)	6	3	6	3	3	3
Impairment from 1st or 2nd operation (left hand)	1st	0	1st	0	2nd	2nd
Total of criterion trials on test (left hand)	500	400	500	400	500	500
Total of criterion trials after impairment	300	400	300	400	200	200
Hand preference at time of transfer testing	L	R=L	R	R	R	R
Double (D) or Single (S) reward with right hand	D	D	S	D	S	S
No. of correct choices in 40 trials with right hand	23	29 $p = 0.003$	22	22	20	21

Criterion trials in this and the next table comprise those during which the animal was performing at a level of 90% correct responses or better. They do not include the number of trials required to reach the criterion. Hand preference was determined when neither hand was restrained.

but with the right hand. For certain animals, rewards were placed under both cues, to eliminate correct responses due to rapid learning; for the remainder, only choice of the correct cue was rewarded. Only one animal, No. 2, gave evidence of significant immediate transfer between the left and right hands.

Similar details are shown for six other monkeys in Table II. Two animals were tested for transfer after either right- or left-sided posterior parietal removals; three animals after one-stage bilateral removals of the same areas; and one animal after a right-sided parietal ablation sparing only part of the postcentral gyrus. The training histories (also with the left hand) are very like those of the animals whose performances are indicated in Table I, except that there was no interoperative training. Only two animals, Nos. 11 and 14, gave evidence of significant immediate transfer between the left and right hands. The occurrence of transfer does not seem to be related to the amount of overtraining, to hand preference, or to postoperative impairment.

Table II

The effect of other parietal ablations on the transfer between the left and right hands of a tactile shape discrimination habit.

Animal	**4**	**8**	**9**	**10**	**11**	**14**
Nature of lesion	Posterior Right	Parietal Left	Simultaneous Bilateral Posterior Parietal			Right Parietal
Impairment from operation (left hand)	Yes	0	Yes	0	Yes	Yes
Total of criterion trials on test (left hand)	400	300	400	300	400	200
Total of criterion trials after impairment	200	300	200	300	200	0
Hand preference at time of transfer testing	R	R=L	R	L	L	R
Double (D) or Single (S) reward with right hand	S	D	S	D	D	D
No. of correct choices in 40 trials with right hand	21	20	22	24 p = 0.001	32	39 p = 0.001

It must be stressed that, although these 12 animals performed at the standard level (90 percent or better correct) for between 200–500 trials (mean of 400) with the left hand before transfer testing, this overtraining was not massed. Moreover, there were on the average only 250 trials of overtraining after any impairment to performance with the left hand, resulting from a contralateral or bilateral ablation. In addition, there are no results for unoperated control animals with comparable training histories. Nevertheless these findings, taken in conjunction with the earlier work of Blum, Chow, & Pribram, suggest that a systematic study is required, with adequate controls, of the effect of posterior cortical removals on transfer between the hands in monkeys.

In connection with transfer testing between the hands, it is appropriate to consider briefly the importance of the preferential use by man and many animals of the one hand for skilled activities. It seems that lateral preferences during skilled movements are not associated with comparable lateral differences in somatosensory thresholds. For instance, significant differences between the left and right hands of 33 human control subjects were found on only one test, namely pressure sensitivity, by Semmes, *et al.* (1960). On this test, lower thresholds were recorded for the left side in both right- and left-handed subjects. Moreover, the strength of lateral preferences is reduced when movements are guided by nonvisual cues, according to a recent report on intact monkeys

(Ettlinger, 1961). This finding is in agreement with the proposal of Parson (1924) that hand preference in man is more intimately related to visual than nonvisual control. Evidence for this is needed from a study of laterality in blind children. Nevertheless, we can not entirely set aside questions of lateral preference when considering the integration of the two hemispheres in somatosensory function; for important differential effects related to laterality are found in studies of neurological patients.

Perhaps outstanding, among all the relevant work for its quality and importance, is the recent systematic investigation by Semmes, *et al.* (1960) of somatosensory changes in 124 brain-injured patients. In the present context we can only discuss one of their findings: "that sensation of the left hand is frequently affected by lesions of the ipsilateral sensorimotor region," as well as by lesions of the contralateral hemisphere. Thus 10 of the 41 subjects, with unilateral left hemispheric lesions that were tested for point localization, were impaired in the left hand (with or without defect in the right hand) (*loc. cit.,* p. 25). Impairment in the left hand for point localization was associated with a right hemispheric lesion in only a slightly greater number of subjects (*loc. cit.,* p. 33). Therefore, both hemispheres appear to be concerned with point localization in the left hand, suggesting a measure of interhemispheric integration. However, only 2 of the 40 subjects, with unilateral right hemispheric lesions that were tested for point localization, showed a defect in the right hand (alone or with defect also in the left hand) (*loc. cit.,* p. 25). Impairment in the right hand for point localization was associated with a left hemispheric lesion in a far greater number of subjects (*loc. cit.,* p. 33). There is then little evidence from this study of integration between the hemispheres for point localization with the right hand.

Similar results are to be found in the earlier report of these workers (Weinstein, *et al.,* 1958). Eleven of 43 subjects with unilateral penetrating cerebral lesions gave evidence of significant defect when they were tested for roughness discrimination with one hand at a time. Five of these 11 subjects had right- and 6 had left-sided unilateral lesions. Nevertheless, all 11 were defective when tested for roughness discrimination with the left hand, whereas only one subject was also defective with the right hand. The same asymmetry of defect, namely impairment with the left but not right hand, was found on this test in a further group of subjects with bilateral lesions. These results again imply that there is integration between the hemispheres during roughness discrimination with the left hand. For the right hand, the data are inconclusive.

Comparable results of systematic ablation experiments are not to be found in the animal literature. Certainly both Blum, *et al.* (1950) and Kruger & Porter (1958) each describe single animals in which the (respectively left- and right-sided) disabilities, resulting in the arm from a first contralateral parietal removal, recurred after a second symmetrical ipsilateral ablation. In addition, there is the earlier report of Ruch, Fulton, & German (1938). Their results on weight and roughness discrimination tests are given separately for the two hands, after successive left and right parietal ablations in a small number of monkeys and chimpanzees. However, in the majority of recent investigations of somatosensory discrimination behavior, symmetrical removals have been made from both the left and right posterior parietal areas, either at one operation or with no interoperative testing. A number of such experiments have been reviewed by Bates & Ettlinger (1960). The assumption is then frequently made that little if any disorder would result from comparable unilateral ablations. If valid, this would imply a greater degree of integration between the posterior than anterior left and right parietal sectors. An experiment, involving successive left and right posterior parietal ablations in the monkey, has recently been completed in co-operation with Dr. J. E. Kalsbeck. In the present context, I shall make detailed reference to only one kind of effect of these lesions, namely upon performance of a tactile shape discrimination test with one hand.

Thirteen rhesus monkeys were given preliminary training on a simple visual and a tactile discrimination test. The right hand was restrained during the training, so that the animals learned to perform all the necessary movements with the left hand. They were then taught to discriminate again with the left hand between two shapes, an "L" and a "T," by touch in the dark. These shapes were both made of ½ inch by ½ inch wood and measured approximately 1½ inches by 1¼ inches. The animals' performance in the dark was observed through an infrared telescope. Training of 40 trials a day, using standard procedure, was continued until animals reached a level of performance of 10 or less errors in 100 successive trials.

After each animal reached this level, it was allowed 14 days' rest and was then retrained on the same tactile shape discrimination test. A measure of performance decrement over a period of 14 days' rest was thus obtained. The animal then received its first ablation, followed again by 14 days' rest, and then by further retraining on the same tactile shape discrimination test to the standard level of performance.

Eight animals underwent successive posterior parietal ablations, three animals were given one-stage bilateral posterior parietal removals, and

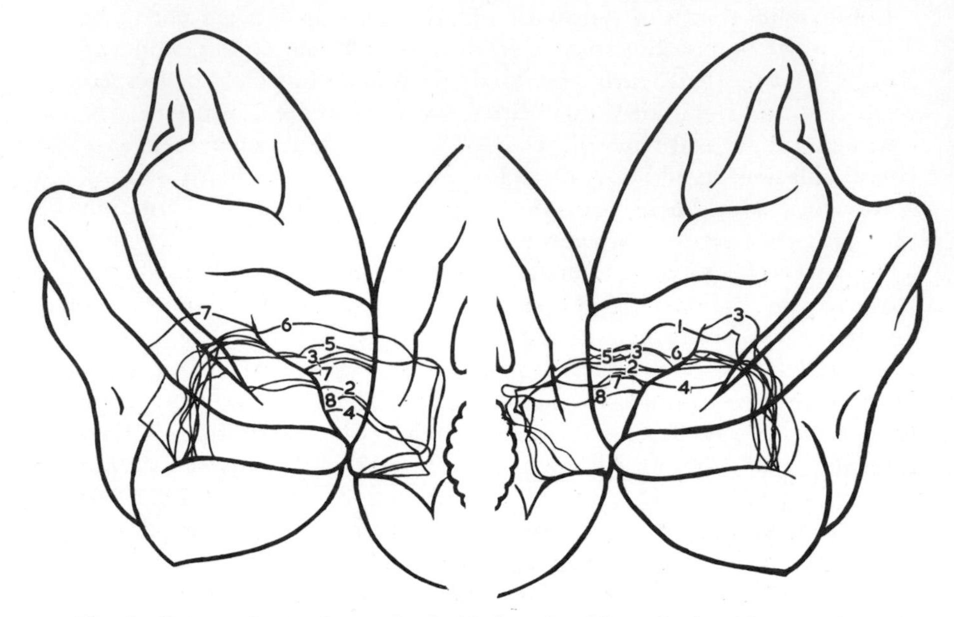

Fig. 1. Extent of posterior parietal ablations in eight animals with successive unilateral removals.

two received control anterior parietal ablations. As histological reconstructions of the lesions are not available, I shall present in Figure 1 diagrammatic outlines, prepared after death, of the posterior parietal ablations in eight animals with successive ablations. It should be noted that the "posterior parietal" ablation includes a small part of the temporal cortex on the lateral surface, a portion of preoccipital cortex on both lateral and medial surfaces, and a large section of the posterior parietal cortex on the medial surface.

Table III

The effect of left posterior parietal ablation (first operation) on the performance with the left hand of a tactile shape discrimination test.

Animal	**5**	**6**	**7**	**8**
After 14 days' rest	0	0	0	0
After first operation (ipsilateral)	10	0	10	0

In this and subsequent Tables, the figures refer to the number of trials (in excess of 100) required to achieve the standard level of performance (10 or less errors in 100 consecutive trials).

In Table III are shown the performance scores of four animals (5–8) taken on the tactile shape discrimination test, before and after receiving a left posterior parietal ablation as their first lesion. In this and subsequent tables, the figures refer to the number of trials in excess of 100 required to achieve the standard level of performance (10 or less errors in 100 trials). Thus, according to convention, the final 100 trials of training have been excluded. Therefore, a score of zero indicates that the animal made 10 or less errors in the first 100 trials of retraining; a score of 10 that it made more than 10 errors in the first 100 trials, but 10 or less in the 100 trials preceding the 110th trial. It is seen that the scores are little if at all raised (reflecting little or no impairment) after a single ipsilateral ablation.

Table IV

The effect of right posterior parietal ablation (first operation) on the performance with the left hand of a tactile shape discrimination test.

Animal	**1**	**2**	**3**	**4**
After 14 days' rest	0	10	0	0
After first operation (contralateral)	210	0	110	60

In Table IV can be seen the performance scores of four other animals (1–4) taken on the same tactile shape discrimination test, before and after a right posterior parietal ablation as the first lesion. Three animals are moderately impaired after a contralateral ablation. If the postoperative scores of these four animals (1–4) are compared with those of animals (5–8) of Table III, a single contralateral ablation is found to give rise to more impairment than a single ipsilateral ablation at the $p = 0.057$ level of confidence (Mann–Whitney Test).

Table V

The effect of left posterior parietal ablation (second operation) on the performance with the left hand of a tactile shape discrimination test.

Animal	**1**	**2**	**3**	**4**
After first operation (contralateral)	210	0	110	60
After 14 days' additional rest	0	—	0	0
After second operation (ipsilateral)	10	0	10	0

The scores of the four animals (1–4) of Table IV taken on the same tactile test, but before and after a left posterior parietal ablation as the second lesion, are presented in Table V. Three of these animals were retrained twice, with an interval of 14 days' rest, after their first operation. It is evident that the scores are little if at all raised after an ipsilateral ablation, even when the symmetrical contralateral area has been previously removed.

Table VI

The effect of right posterior parietal ablation (second operation) on the performance with the left hand of a tactile shape discrimination test.

Animal	**5**	**6**	**7**	**8**
After first operation (ipsilateral)	10	0	10	0
After second operation (contralateral)	0	280	310	50

In Table VI, the scores of the other four animals (5–8) can be seen, reflecting performance before and after receiving a right posterior parietal ablation as the second lesion. The performance of three animals is moderately impaired after this contralateral ablation. When the postoperative scores of these four animals (5–8) are compared with those of the animals (1–4) shown in Table IV, a contralateral ablation is found not to give rise to any significantly greater impairment, when performed after removal of the ipsilateral area than without such a pre-existing ipsilateral removal ($p = 0.44$).

Table VII

The effect of one-stage bilateral posterior parietal ablation on the performance with the left hand of a tactile shape discrimination test.

Animal	**9**	**10**	**11**
After 14 days' rest	0	0	0
After simultaneous bilateral operation	160	0	40

Finally, in Table VII can be seen the performance scores, on the same tactile shape discrimination test, of 3 animals (9–11) before and after one-stage bilateral posterior parietal removals. Only 2 animals are impaired, and then moderately. The mean postoperative score for these 3 animals is 67 trials, compared with the higher mean of 95 trials for the 4 animals (1–4, of Table IV) having only a contralateral ablation. This difference is not significant ($p = 0.37$).

Taken together, the results of this experiment indicate that there exists, in the monkey, a predominantly crossed relationship between each posterior parietal area and the performance with the opposite hand of a tactile shape discrimination. This finding is in agreement with our qualitative and quantitative observations of purely contralateral defects in the accuracy of visual reaching, and in the visual and tactile placing reactions of the same animals.

Such findings are not really in conflict with the evidence gained from transfer tests between the hands of a large measure of integration between the hemispheres in somatosensory function. They merely suggest that, in the intact monkey, the somatosensory functions of the posterior parietal regions are predominantly located in the contralateral hemisphere for each hand; and also that, when such a contralateral cortical region has been removed, the corresponding ipsilateral region does not readily assume the functions of the contralateral area. Naturally this implies a lesser degree of interhemispheric integration than would have been inferred if defect had resulted from only bilaterally symmetrical removals, or if additional defect had resulted from either a first or second ipsilateral ablation. However, we are not at present able to define what the somatosensory functions of the posterior parietal areas may be; nor yet do we know what alternative structures are involved in relearning the tactile shape discrimination test when there was impairment after posterior parietal removals. Finally, as has been already suggested, the posterior parietal areas may be concerned in transfer between the hands. Then such ablation experiments as ours might give a peculiarly misleading picture, minimizing the degree of integration between the hemispheres in somatosensory function.

This work has received financial support from the Research Fund of the Institute of Neurology, and from the Medical Research Council. It is respectfully dedicated to Dr. E. A. Carmichael, on the occasion of his retirement from Queen Square, in gratitude for his interest and help in securing primate behavior research facilities at the National Hospital. Its presentation owes much to the help given me with early drafts by Dr. A. M. Halliday, Dr. J. Wegener, and Dr. M. Cole.

VI

Interhemispheric Integration In the Visual System

by JOHN L. deC. DOWNER

University College, London, England

IN A CONFERENCE on cerebral dominance, it may seem perhaps somewhat out of place that the studies in this report were undertaken because of the apparent absence of cerebral dominance in infrahuman animals. It seems to be well established, in experimental animals, that bilateral brain lesions must be produced in order to bring about defects in those functions broadly grouped under the term "cognition." This stands in marked contrast to the data on man, in which damage to one (the dominant) hemisphere may result in drastic impairment of these functions.

Since, in experimental animals, each cerebral hemisphere appears to be equal to the other, with respect to cognitive functions, it seemed that advantage could be taken of this to overcome two problems frequently encountered in research concerned with the behavioral correlates of central nervous system lesions.

In this type of research, one is often confronted by the difficulty of producing brain lesions that are consistently, bilaterally symmetrical. This may be due, in part, to slight morphological differences between the two halves of the brain, but more probably to the lack of reliable surgical controls.

Most troublesome, however, is the problem of establishing behavioral controls that would isolate the effects due to repeated exposure to the experimental situation. It is, of course, possible to use the control group method, but apart from its other limitations, this procedure becomes quite unsatisfactory when using large animals such as monkeys; since with so few animals in any one sample and the considerable individual differences among them, reliable norms of behavior are difficult to establish with any high degree of confidence. Furthermore, the bilaterally brain-damaged animal cannot always be used as its own control in the strict sense, since its performance in each new learning situation improves so much and in a nonlinear fashion that it is difficult to estimate how a particular animal would have performed at a particular time on a particular problem had the brain lesions not been made. Especially with the development of learning sets, the magnitude of change between the preoperative and the postoperative behavior of a single animal may not be due solely to the brain lesions (Harlow, 1949; Riopelle & Ades, 1953).

The possibility of splitting the brain through the mid-sagittal plane seemed to offer a potential solution to these problems. It was reasoned that by severing the commissural fibers between the two halves of the brain and dividing the optic chiasma in the mid-sagittal plane, the visual input from each eye would be restricted to its ipsilateral half of the brain. If one eye is now closed by suturing the eyelids together, only one-half of the brain will receive visual information. Any lesion, placed in the cerebral hemisphere receiving the visual input, should be functionally comparable, with respect to vision, to symmetrical bilateral lesions in the otherwise normal animal. Furthermore, it was thought that this procedure would have the advantage of permitting *repeated* control and experimental observations to be carried out in the same animal. For example, in each new learning situation, the animal could be trained using its intact cerebral hemisphere (by closing the eye projecting to the damaged side), then trained on the same problem when using the damaged side (by opening the eye projecting to the damaged side and closing the other eye). This procedure could be carried out for a considerable number of times, and valid comparisons made between the normal and brain-damaged sides of the same animal in visual learning, without the results being complicated by learning sets and interpretation from control groups.

These ideas were prompted by the interesting observations of Myers & Sperry (1953) on the "split-brain" preparation. They reported that following mid-sagittal division of optic chiasma and corpus callosum in cats, interocular transfer no longer occurred. Each animal had been trained, with one of its eyes covered, on a simple visual discrimination problem. Upon reaching criterion, the cover was placed over the opposite eye, and the animal was tested for its ability to continue choosing the correct stimulus-object. It was concluded that as the animals performed at the chance level with the "untrained" eye, visual learning had been restricted to the "trained" half of the brain.

Before testing the previously mentioned hypotheses, it was decided to extend Myers & Sperry's (1953) observations to monkeys. The monkey was thought to be the preferred experimental animal in this type of investigation, since dividing the optic chiasma in the mid-sagittal plane would restrict the visual fields to a lesser extent than would be the case in other laboratory animals.

Transfer of visual learning was examined in two groups of monkeys *(Macaca mulatta)*. One group was tested before and after mid-sagittal division of the corpus callosum. The other group was tested before and after mid-sagittal division of the optic chiasma; then tested again following mid-sagittal division of the corpus callosum. The surgical techniques

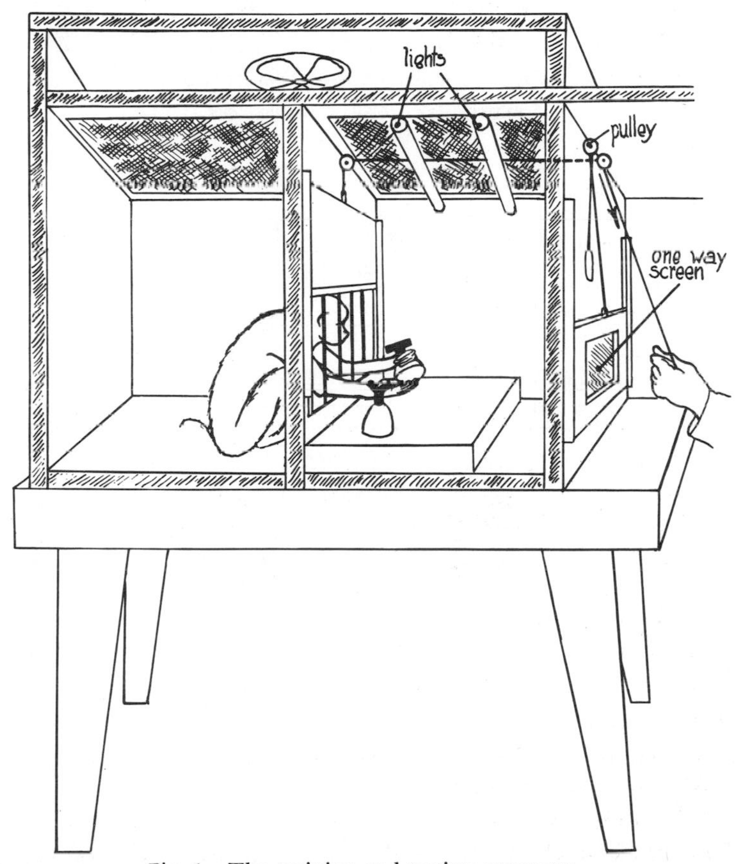

Fig. 1. The training and testing apparatus.

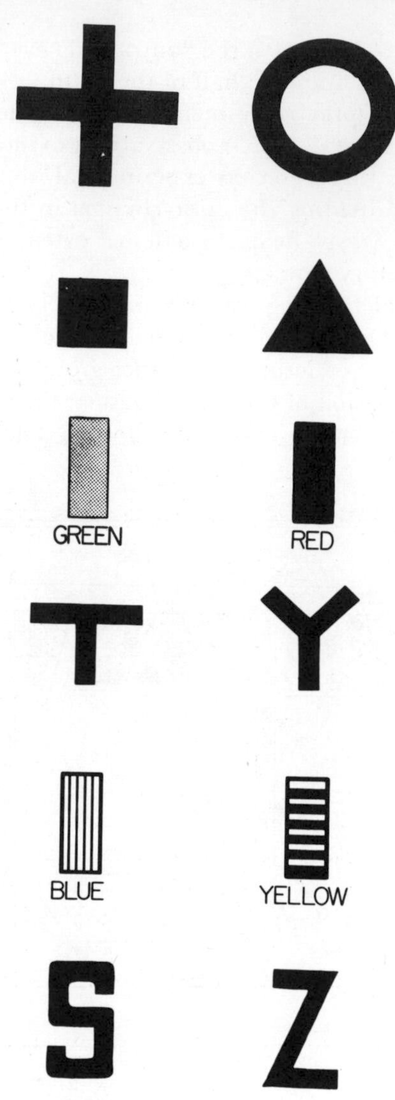

Fig. 2. Visual stimuli used in these studies. With the exception of patterns "S" and "Z," each pair is equated for total surface area. The color stimuli are of the Munsell Series and are equal in terms of saturation and reflectance.

used for sectioning the optic chiasma and the corpus callosum have been described previously (Downer 1959).

Prior to training, each animal had one eye closed by approximating the trimmed margins of the eyelids and suturing them together. Each animal was placed, in turn, in the training apparatus (Figure 1). This consisted of two compartments, separated by a sliding door. The animal was placed in one compartment, the stimulus-objects in the other. When the door was raised, the animal was confronted by two different visual stimulus-objects (Figure 2). Each of these was mounted upon a cup. A reward (raisin) was placed under the cup of the positive (correct) stimulus-object. No punishment was introduced for choosing the negative (incorrect) stimulus-object. The stimulus-objects were varied randomly from side to side at each presentation to prevent positioning cues. Thirty trials a day were given until the animal reached an arbitrarily set criterion of 90 percent correct responses on two successive days. Upon reaching criterion, the closed eye was opened, the open eye closed, and the animal reintroduced to the apparatus and tested on its ability to continue choosing the correct stimulus-object. If the animal maintained criterion, transfer was assumed to have taken place. If the animal did not show immediate transfer, it was kept in the apparatus and trained to criterion.

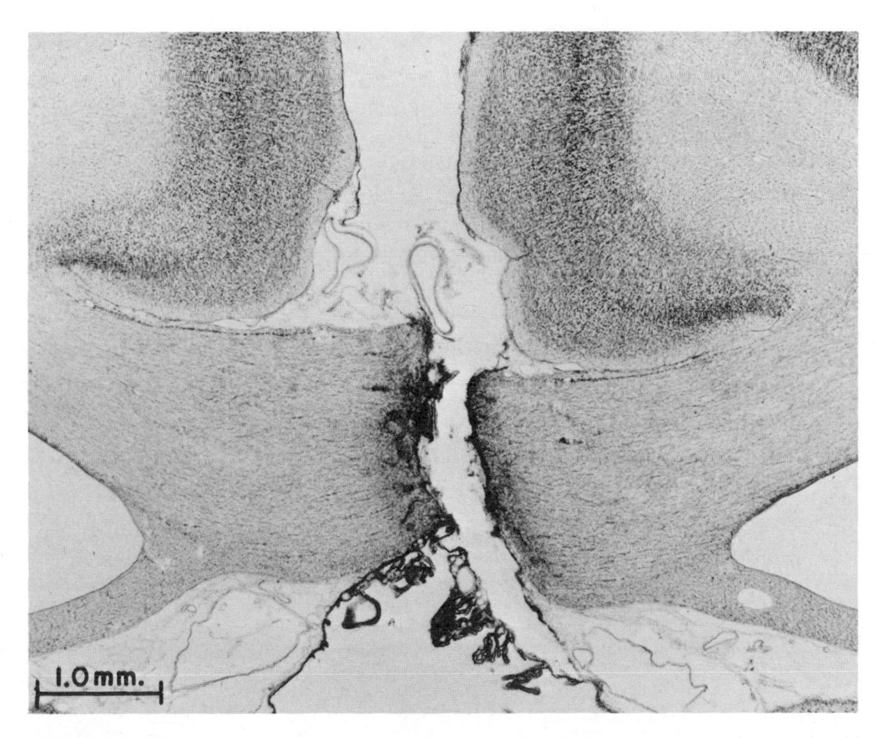

Fig. 3. Animal D-16. Coronal section through corpus callosum, cut at 28 micra and stained with cresyl violet.

Figure 3 is a typical illustration of the sectioned corpus callosum. It should be pointed out that, in all instances, the hippocampal commissure has been sectioned where it lies subjacent to the corpus callosum. From Table I, it can be seen that transfer readily occurred following mid-sagittal division of the corpus callosum.

Table I

The total number of errors made in reaching criterion, excluding criterial trials.

	PREOPERATIVE		CORPUS CALLOSUM SECTIONED	
	+ vs. O		T vs. Y	
	Right eye	Left eye	Left eye	Right eye
D-2	25	0	72	0
D-4	43	0	88	0
D-5	44	0	74	0
D-6	37	0	26	0
D-7	77	0	66	0

A second group of animals was then trained and tested before and after mid-sagittal division of the optic chiasma. Figure 4 is a typical illustration of the split optic chiasma. Transfer of pattern and color discrimination habits readily occurred (Table II).

Table II

The total number of errors made in reaching criterion, excluding criterial trials.

	PREOPERATIVE		OPTIC CHIASM SECTIONED			
	+ vs. O		Red vs. Green		■ vs. ▲	
	Left eye	Right eye	Right eye	Left eye	Left eye	Right eye
D-16	71	0	85	0	206	0
D-17	35	0	129	0	35	6
D-22	51	0	65	7	36	0
D-24	60	0	78	0	55	0

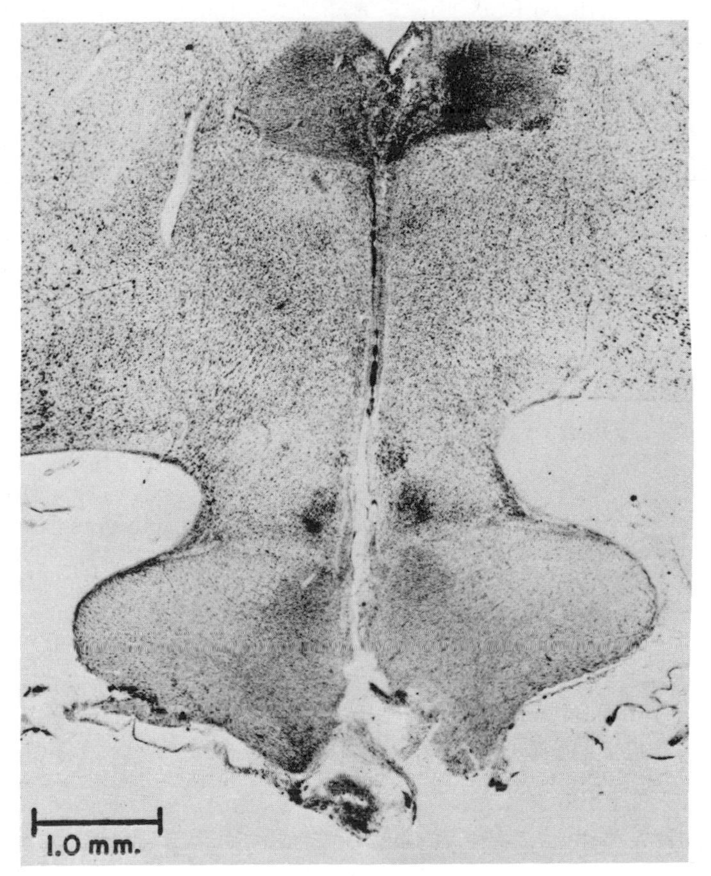

Fig. 4. Animal D–16. Coronal section through optic chiasma, cut at 28 micra and stained with cresyl violet.

From these data, it can be seen that transfer of monocularly learned visual discrimination habits occurs if either the optic chiasma or the corpus callosum is sectioned in the mid-sagittal plane. With the testing technique used in this study, nothing was found to indicate that transfer via one route was different from the other. This is not to suggest that there are no differences, nor that with finer testing techniques they could not be detected. It is logical to think that some differences may, in fact, exist. In one instance, the phenomenon of transfer is the result of direct sensory input to both cerebral hemispheres, leading, presumably, to the development of similar memory traces in each. Transfer of this type does not depend upon information passing from one cerebral hemisphere to the other. This is called "peripheral" transfer. On the other hand, transfer that occurs following mid-sagittal division of the optic chiasma must depend upon information passing from one cerebral hemisphere to the other. This is called "central" transfer.

While peripheral transfer is understandable in principle, central transfer is rather puzzling, since it seems, in primates, that fibers of the corpus callosum do not originate or terminate within the striate areas (Brodmann's A. 17) (Valkenburg, 1913; Myers, 1960; Powell & Cowan, Curtis & Bard, 1939; Curtis, 1940; McCulloch & Garol, 1941). In peripheral transfer, sensory input via the geniculocalcarine bundle discharges into both striate areas primarily and involves extrastriate areas secondarily; with central transfer, the striate area of the "untrained" side is not stimulated either directly via the geniculocalcarine bundle nor from the "trained" side via the corpus callosum. It would seem that central transfer occurs between extrastriate areas. This suggests that the visual memory trace is laid down in the "untrained" cerebral hemisphere, without the visual primary projection area of that side being involved. What little evidence is available suggests that there is no back discharge from Brodmann's Areas 19 and 18 to Area 17 (Bonin, Garol & McCulloch, 1942; McCulloch, personal communication) ; yet, when the visual primary projection area of this side is used for the first time, there is immediate recognition of the correct stimulus-object. If sensation depends upon the primary projection areas, this raises the anomalous situation that the animal recognizes something that it has never "seen." This is like saying perception occurs in the absence of sensation!

Table III

The total number of errors made in reaching criterion, excluding criterial trials.

OPTIC CHIASM AND CORPUS CALLOSUM SECTIONED				
	S vs. **Z**		Blue vs. Yellow	
	Left eye	Right eye	Right eye	Left eye
D-16	41	62	24	41
D-17	48	0	6	0
D-22	27	34	6	0
D-24	47	48	14	29

The animals that had previously undergone mid-sagittal division of the optic chiasma were then subjected to an operation designed to section the corpus callosum in the mid-sagittal plane. From Table III, it can be seen that under these circumstances all animals but one (D–17) failed to transfer both pattern and color discriminations. It was concluded that in animal D–17 either or both the optic chiasma and corpus callosum had not been completely sectioned. One animal (D–22) appeared to transfer the color problem but, owing to the rapid initial learning on this problem (only six errors made in reaching criterion), it is difficult to state unequivocally that what appeared to be transfer was not, in fact, very rapid learning. These data indicated that there are no significant differences in the learning capacity of each half of the brain. Again, it should be emphasized that with more refined testing techniques possibly some differences might be found.

Table IV

The total number of errors made in reaching criterion, excluding criterial trials. "T" indicates the "trained" eye, "U" indicates the "untrained" eye.

	PREOPERATIVE		OPTIC CHIASM SECTIONED IN MIDSAGITTAL PLANE									
							CORPUS CALLOSUM SECTIONED					
	+ vs. ○		Red vs. Green		■ vs. ▲		+ vs. ○		Red vs. Green		■ vs. ▲	
	Left eye	Right eye	Right eye	Left eye	Left eye	Right eye	Left eye	Right eye	Right eye	Left eye	Left eye	Right eye
D-16	71	0	85	0	206	0	0	0	8	0	5	39
D-17	35	0	129	0	35	6	0	0	0	0	0	0
D-22	51	0	65	7	36	0	0	0	0	0	0	13
D-24	60	0	78	0	55	0	0	0	0	0	6	22
	T	U	T	U	T	U	T	U	T	U	T	U

All animals in this group were then retested on all previously learned and successfully transferred visual discrimination problems. These test scores are shown in Table IV. The scores, obtained preoperatively and following mid-sagittal division of the optic chiasma, are recapitulated for easier comparison. From these data it can be seen that the preoperatively learned discrimination, cross-circle, was retained perfectly when either eye was used. The red-green discrimination, learned following mid-sagittal division of the optic chiasma, was also retained when either eye was used. Retesting with the pattern discrimination problem, square-triangle, produced rather ambiguous results. The discrimination was retained when the animal used the eye with which it had originally learned the problem but appeared not to be retained when the animal used the other eye. This occurred in all animals with the exception of D–17. These results are in marked contrast to the animals' performance before the corpus callosum was sectioned; at that time they all exhibited retention of this discrimination when using the "untrained" eye. This raises the following question: when the sensory input is restricted to one cerebral hemisphere is the memory trace formed in that hemisphere alone, or is it formed in both cerebral hemispheres simultaneously? From the animals' performance on the problem, square-triangle, it might be assumed that the memory trace was established in the "trained" cerebral hemisphere alone. Transfer might have taken place when the commissural fibers were intact, not because of the establishment of a second memory trace in the "untrained" cerebral hemisphere via the commissures, but because the "untrained" side was able to utilize the trace of the "trained" side via the commissures. When these structures were destroyed, the trace was no longer available to the "untrained" side, and the animals performed as if confronted by a new problem. This did not seem to be the case with the color problem (red-green); the results clearly indicate that the memory trace was formed in both cerebral hemispheres during the original learning procedure.

The conditions under which the memory trace may be formed in one or both cerebral hemispheres is by no means clear. So many possibilities may be considered to account for these findings that it would be futile to speculate with so little information available at this time. Current investigations in this laboratory are concerned with analyzing the properties of the stimuli to see if this analysis can throw some light on the problem.

Upon completion of these studies the animals were sacrificed, and their brains prepared for histological examination. The entire length of the optic chiasma and the corpus callosum was found to be completely sectioned in the median plane in all animals. There were no signs of damage to the medial walls of the cerebral hemispheres, nor were there any signs of intracranial infection. Laminae I, IV, and VI of the lateral geniculate bodies had undergone extensive cellular atrophy (Figure 5). A few large cells were present in Lamina I, but those lacked well-defined nuclei. In three animals (D–16, D–22, and D–24), the anterior commissure was either completely sectioned or greatly damaged. In a fourth animal (D–17), which had transferred both pattern and color discrimination habits, the anterior commissure was intact (Figure 6). As mentioned earlier, that part of the hippocampal commissure, lying subjacent to the corpus callosum, was sectioned.

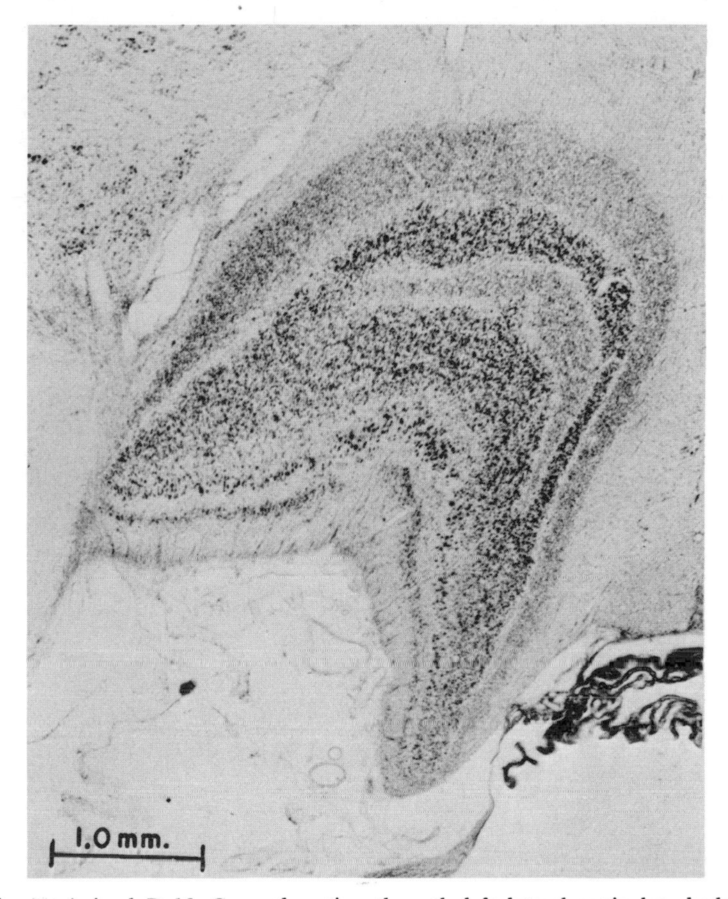

Fig. 5. Animal D–16. Coronal section through left lateral geniculate body, cut at 28 micra and stained with cresyl violet.

The rather surprising finding that transfer occurred in an animal (D–17) in which the anterior commissure was intact, although the optic chiasma, corpus callosum, and part of the hippocampal commissure had been sectioned, suggested that the temporal poles might play some role in transfer of visual discrimination habits, since the anterior commissure is the major commissure between the temporal poles (Fox, Fisher, & Desalva, 1948; Problate, Ruben, & Walker, 1959). In order to test this, a unilateral temporal pole resection was carried out in an animal that had previously completed a visual discrimination training sequence, following mid-sagittal division of the optic chiasma, corpus callosum, and part of the hippocampal commissure. Upon recovery, the eye projecting to

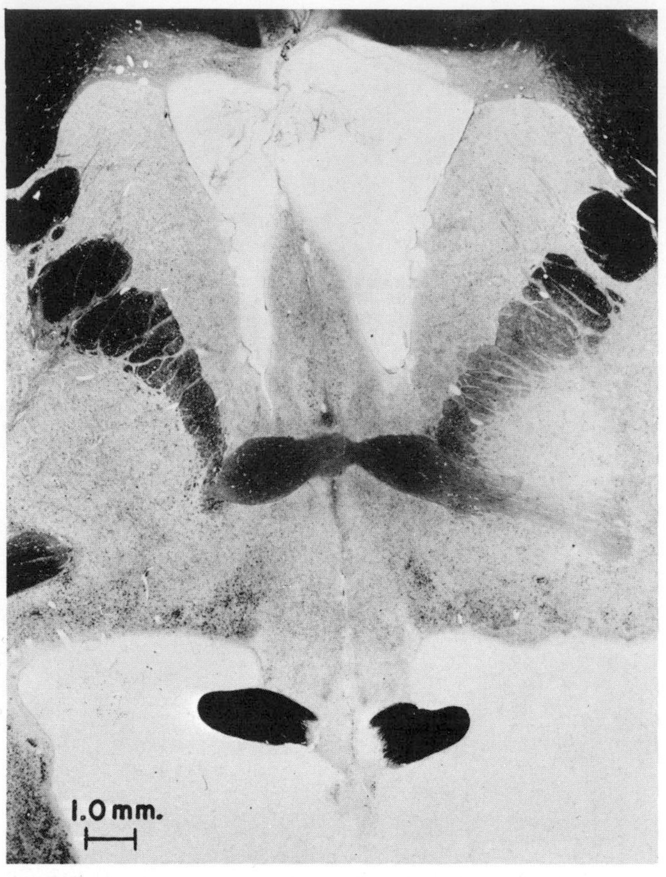

Fig. 6. Animal D–17. Coronal section, cut at 28 micra, stained with **Luxol** Fast Blue MBS, and counterstained with cresyl violet.

the side of the temporal pole lesion was left open, and the opposite eyelids sutured shut. This produced a rather remarkable change in the animal's behavior which had many of the characteristics of the Klüver–Bucy Syndrome (Klüver & Bucy, 1937; Bucy & Klüver, 1940). That is to say, the animal seemed unable to distinguish between edible and non-edible objects, by visual cues alone, but would spend considerable time sniffing and biting before either eating or rejecting them. Even more remarkable were the changes in emotional behavior. Prior to the temporal pole removal, this animal exhibited the typically wild and aggressive behavior of the rhesus monkey in the presence of onlookers. Following the temporal pole removal, the animal responded quite placidly to the appearance of laboratory personnel. It is important to note that this placid behavior occurred only in response to visual stimuli, for attempts to touch the animal or grasp its limbs produced a full aggressive reaction. Closing the eye projecting to the side of the temporal pole removal and opening the other eye resulted in an abrupt change in behavior back to the aggressive, immediate preoperative level.

The question then arose as to whether or not the change in emotional behavior to visual stimulation was merely a reflection of the visual agnosia or due to damage to the amygdaloid complex, which had occurred during the unilateral temporal pole ablation. In an attempt to answer this, another, especially aggressive, animal that had previously undergone mid-sagittal division of the optic chiasma, corpus callosum, and part of the hippocampal commissure was subjected to a unilateral amygdalectomy. To avoid damaging the temporal neocortex, the amygdaloid area was approached from beneath the right frontal pole. It was necessary to section the right olfactory tract in order to obtain adequate exposure.

This animal showed no signs of visual agnosia, irrespective of which eye was open. Similarly, there did not appear to be much change in emotional behavior although, superficially, it seemed as if the animal was a little more placid when the eye projecting to the side of the amygdalectomy alone was open. Another craniotomy was then performed in this animal, and an attempt made to sever all commissural fibers. This animal's brain has not been examined as yet, so the full extent of these transections is not known with certainty. However, the incision along the corpus callosum was reopened, the entire length of the hippocampal commissure was divided in the mid-sagittal plane, and the anterior and posterior commissures were sectioned. The incision extended through the massa intermedia. The supraoptic recess was entered, and the tip of the knife passed between the walls of the hypothalamus until the sphenoid bone was reached. Postoperative recovery revealed a transient left abducens nerve palsy and a mild, but persistent, right hemiparesis.

Following this operation, the animal appeared to be as wild and intractable as in its preoperative state when observed with both of its eyes open. At the sight of an observer, it would grimace, bare its teeth, and jump to the front of the cage, attempting to bite and claw. Closing the eye projecting to the side of the amygdalectomy did not produce any observable change. However, opening the eye projecting to the side of the amygdalectomy and closing the other eye produced a dramatic change in behavior. The animal then showed no signs of aggression or fear at the sight of human observers and would approach the front of the cage and take proferred raisins quite peacefully.

As in the instance of the animal with the temporal pole removal, this placidity occurred only in response to visual stimuli; touching or prodding the animal's arm would produce a momentary aggressive reaction. The placid response to visual stimuli promptly disappeared when the eye projecting to the side of the amygdalectomy was shut and the other eye opened. These alternations in emotional behavior were observed over a period of three months and appeared to persist without abatement. In effect, it seemed that one could "remove" and "replace" the amygdala, merely by opening and closing the appropriate eyes.

In summary, the data presented from these studies provide corroborative evidence to support Myers & Sperry's (1953) observations that, in the "split-brain" preparation, each half of the brain reacts to visual pattern and color stimuli as if completely independent. Professor Sperry (1958) has discussed previously many uses for this preparation. In addition to his comments, it should be pointed out that the "split-brain" preparation provides a means for achieving many of the surgical and behavioral controls that are troublesome in neuropsychological investigations. Splitting the brain in the mid-sagittal plane produces an animal with two apparently independently functioning cerebral hemispheres, with respect to visual stimuli, thus permitting *repeated* control and experimental observations to be carried out, in the same animal, by opening and closing each of its eyes in turn. Furthermore, in this preparation, a unilateral cerebral lesion appears to be functionally comparable to symmetrical bilateral lesions, again with respect to visual stimuli. Comparisons can be made between damaged and intact sides of the brain merely by opening and closing the appropriate eye.

Discussion Second Session

A.

A Possible Link Between Interhemispheric Integration in Monkeys and Cerebral Dominance in Man

MORTIMER MISHKIN

Section on Neuropsychology, National Institute of Mental Health, Bethesda, Maryland

We have heard a lot this afternoon on the topic of the session, which was to deal with integration between the hemispheres; but we have heard nothing yet on the topic of the conference, which was to deal with cerebral dominance. What I would like to do is take this leap and try to link the evidence on interhemispheric integration in animals to the phenomenon of hemispheric dominance in man. Whether or not my attempt succeeds, it may at least help to provoke some discussion of this intriguing phylogenetic puzzle.

All three of our speakers (and our Chairman as well) became involved in interhemispheric problems initially, I believe, through their experiments on the visual system. It may not be inappropriate, therefore, to restrict my discussion to the visual system, drawing upon their earlier work, bringing in the new work we have heard about today, and adding some unpublished studies from the National Institutes of Health. The task of summarizing all these studies on vision in animals is not as formidable as it sounds, since for once, all the data are delightfully consistent. And they lead to a simple principle: Visual mechanisms in the two hemispheres *are* integrated, but not nearly so well as the visual mechanisms within a hemisphere.

We might have guessed this principle earlier, from the initial experiments of Drs. Sperry and Myers. They found that when they sectioned only the chiasma, leaving the corpus callosum intact, simple discrimination habits would transfer perfectly from a trained to an untrained eye, but more difficult discrimination habits might not. Dr. Myers has now taken all the guess work out of this seeming imperfection of the callosal system with his direct comparison between the effects of tract and chiasma cuts. His new results on interocular transfer demonstrate clearly that there is more effective integration of visual processes within a hemisphere (i.e., when the two eyes project only to the same side, as after one tract has been cut) than between hemispheres (i.e., when the two eyes project only to different sides after a chiasma cut).

Dr. Downer also has presented evidence supporting the principle of strong intrahemispheric integration; but here we must consider visual mechanisms beyond the primary projection system. I am referring to the dramatic experiment Dr. Downer reported, in which he combined a split-brain preparation with a unilateral temporal lobectomy. The monkey operated on in this way exhibited the classical Klüver-Bucy syndrome, but only if it viewed the world through the eye on the same side as the lesion. The inference from this finding, that there is an intimate relationship between the primary visual system and the temporal lobe of the same hemisphere, is even more directly supported by some findings of Dr. Ettlinger. In monkeys in which he had already severed one optic tract, Dr. Ettlinger compared the effects on visual discrimination of adding an ipsilateral, versus adding a contralateral, ablation of temporal isocortex. The results demonstrated that animals that had both their tract and temporal lesions on the same side, and thus had the other homolateral system completely intact, were consistently superior in visual learning to the animals that were forced to use a transcallosal system.

Finally, let me add the results of an experiment from our laboratory at NIH. This one differed slightly from Dr. Ettlinger's in that it involved unilateral occipital lobectomies, rather than unilateral sections of the optic tract. But the area in the temporal lobe with which the two studies was concerned is the same: von Bonin and Bailey's cytoarchitectural area TE, located on the inferior convexity of the lobe. Bilateral removal of this region in monkeys is known to produce severe impairment on visual discrimination tasks. In this instance, however, (as in Dr. Ettlinger's study) the inferotemporal area was removed only unilaterally, and later, either an ipsilateral or a contralateral occipital lobectomy was added. The animals that had their second lesion on the same side as the first relearned a difficult pattern discrimination almost immediately. But the animals that had "crossed" lesions, and thus had only a transcallosal pathway remaining (between the intact striate cortex of one hemisphere and the intact temporal cortex of the other), required an average of nearly 500 trials to relearn the discrimination. That the relearning of this group did depend on the functioning, albeit inefficient functioning, of a transcallosal pathway became clear later when the corpus callosum was sectioned; for then these animals had even greater difficulty in relearning the discrimination, if, indeed, they were able to relearn it at all.

The results of numerous studies then, each using a somewhat different technique, lead to the same conclusion: Interconnections of visual mechanisms within a hemisphere are more potent or more efficient than are the connections between the hemispheres.

I believe that an explanation for this inequality between homolateral and transcallosal connections may be found in the data provided by physiological and anatomical studies. The early neuronographic work of Professor von Bonin and his associates indicated that strychinization of the striate cortex evokes activity only as far forward as the prestriate cortex of the same hemisphere. Strychninization of the prestriate cortex, on the other hand, fires:

a. directly into the ipsilateral inferotemporal area (the area that has since been implicated in visual discrimination functions); and
b. across the callosum, not into the opposite temporal lobe, but only into the opposite prestriate area.

The striate-inferotemporal pathway within a hemisphere is thus seen to be relatively more direct than the crossed pathway, the latter involving a minimum of one additional synapse.

This picture, derived from the early strychninization studies, has been neatly corroborated recently by Dr. Kuypers and Dr. Maria Szwarcbart, using the Nauta-Gygax silver technique for the study of degenerating fibers. If a lesion is confined to the striate cortex, degenerated fibers can be traced forward mainly into the ipsilateral prestriate area; and after a prestriate lesion, heavy degeneration can be traced into the ipsilateral inferotemporal region. Relatively few degenerated fibers, however, are seen to enter the opposite temporal lobe, the vast majority ending symmetrically in the opposite prestriate cortex. As with the neuronographic results, the neuroanatomical evidence indicates that for activities in striate and inferotemporal areas to interact, at least one additional synapse must be traversed if there is only a transcallosal pathway between them.

Combining the data from the behavioral studies, the physiological studies, and the anatomical studies, we are in a position, I believe, to begin diagramming some connections, such as those shown at the top of Figure 1. For simplicity, the prestriate relay is excluded from this diagram, and differences in the directness or effectiveness of the crossed

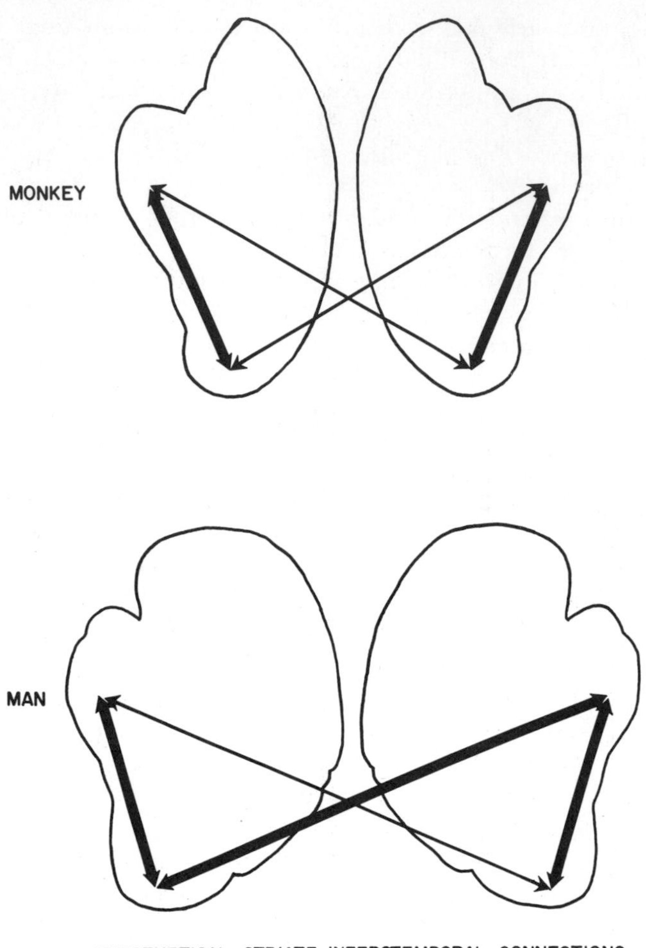

Fig. 1.

and uncrossed pathways are portrayed by differences in the width of the connecting arrows. The arrows are shown double-headed, since the anatomical and physiological evidence suggests that neural activity may proceed in both directions (though there are undoubtedly important functional differences between rostrally and caudally directed activity). It should be noted, finally, that the connections of the two hemispheres are drawn symmetrically, for although the data are admittedly slim, no evidence has been obtained as yet of any inequality or asymmetry between the two hemispheres of the monkey's brain. In short, this neural model of the cortical visual system in the monkey shows strong homolateral connections between striate and inferotemporal cortex, somewhat weaker transcallosal connections, and probably no functional asymmetry between the hemispheres.

Now how can we modify this model, derived from animal data, to account for the definite asymmetry known to exist in the cortical visual mechanisms of man? We have known for a number of years from the investigations of Dr. Brenda Milner, and more recently from the work of Dr. Lansdell, that visual perception in man is impaired by a right temporal lobectomy. In fact, the impairment can be detected in patients with right temporal epilepsy even before a removal is made; the surgery simply exacerbates the impairment. But curiously, this deficit in response to complex visual material is not found in patients with left temporal epilepsy, not even after the left temporal lobe has been removed. Clearly, the right temporal lobe in man is dominant for visual functions.

Faced with this phenomenon, yet recognizing from the animal data that there must be a strong preferential relationship between each temporal lobe and its ipsilateral striate area, it seemed a reasonable supposition that left temporal removals in man *could* be shown to impair visual perception, if the material were restricted to the part of the visual field served by the left striate cortex. The converse defect would of course be expected after right temporal removals. Two experiments have recently been conducted which provide a test of this hypothesis—one by Drs. Mirsky and Dorff at NIH, the other by Dr. Doreen Kimura at McGill. The results bear out the prediction. After left temporal removals, tachistoscopic recognition of a row of letters is poorer in the right visual field than in the left, just as, after right temporal removals, tachistoscopic recognition is poorer in the left visual field than in the right. It might be thought that these deficits in the visual field, contralateral to the damaged hemisphere, could have resulted simply from a direct invasion during surgery of the ventral portion of the visual radiations. This type of damage frequently occurs; but its relationship to the deficit is questionable, since analysis showed that the amount of recognition loss in the field opposite the temporal lesion was entirely unrelated to the presence or absence there of an upper quadrantic field defect. Rather, the recognition loss would seem to imply that in man, as in the monkey, there is a functional interdependence between the visual system and the temporal cortex, and that this interdependence is greater within than between the hemispheres.

But here we must introduce an important qualification. This stems from another finding in Mirsky and Dorff's experiment. A group of normal control subjects were run under the same conditions as the patients, and, in line with a good deal of earlier work on normal subjects, their recognition was found to be better in the right visual field than in the left. Since the left temporal cases showed just the reverse effect, i.e., *poorer* recognition in the right visual field than in the left, their impairment relative to the controls turned out to be very severe in the right field, but only minimal in the left. The right temporal cases, on the other hand, were impaired equally severely in both visual fields. That is, while they resembled the controls in scoring higher on the right, they were nevertheless depressed, compared with the controls just as much in the right, or "ipsilateral," field as in the left.

Assuming that this "ipsilateral" deficit in the right temporal group, like the "contralateral" deficits discussed earlier, also reflects the nature of striate-temporal interaction, it might be explained by positing an asymmetrical development in man of the transcallosal connections. Such a possibility is diagrammed in Figure 1. Thus, a selective strengthening of the transcallosal pathway from left striate to right temporal cortex, combined with the strong homolateral pathway already existing on the right, would permit the right temporal cortex to integrate activity from both striate areas (i.e., both visual fields). This would lead, in man, to the development of right temporal-lobe dominance for visual functions, and would account, simultaneously, for the tachistoscopic data and for the data on complex perceptual tasks presented in the central visual field.

There are a few additional facts which this model might help to explain. In the normal subjects tested by Drs. Mirsky and Dorff, recognition scores in the left and right visual fields were found to be positively correlated. In the left temporal group, also, there was a significant positive correlation. In the right temporal group, on the other hand, this positive correlation disappeared. These findings would seem to fit the view that, normally, stimuli in both visual fields initiate well organized activity within a *single* neural substrate, i.e., the right temporal cortex. It may not be irrelevant that this greater degree of cortical specialization in man than in monkey would provide an especially efficient system of visual integration.

It may be worth noting one final point that is suggested by the hypothetical model. Any dominance relationship that may exist between the striate areas should be just the reverse of the dominance relationship between the temporal lobes. That is, the left striate area should be functionally superior to the right. There is, perhaps, just a little evidence to support this idea. One such finding, already referred to, indicates that tachistoscopic recognition of words and letters in the right visual field is superior to recognition in the left, at least in the majority of testing situations. A second possible line of support stems from some data on the effects of occipital injuries. Only infrequently do unilateral occipital injuries in man produce so severe a symptom as agnosia, but in the cases in which it has been reported (e.g., by Nielsen, and Goldstein), *left* occipital injuries seem to have been responsible more than 75 percent of the time.

B.

KARL H. PRIBRAM

Stanford University School of Medicine, Stanford, California

We've come a long and very profitable way from this morning. We were initially asked a question by Professor Young: Why do we have *two* brains?; we have ended with a lovely demonstration by Dr. Mishkin that we may, after all, have just one brain. But my approach to the problem of "dominance" will be the reverse of Dr. Mishkin's. I will try to answer the "why do we have two brains?" question in two parts: (a) I will maintain that in order to get dominance à la J. Z. Young, we must have *at least four* brains; (b) the evidence suggests that even four brains are not enough; we are dealing in fact with *more* than four brains.

Let us begin by thinking in twos. The first dichotomy is that characterized by Professor Young as a difference between analogue and digital. May I try to define this difference for you in behavioral terms (Pribram, 1954)? When we make removals of the inferotemporal cortex, the lesion with which you have become thoroughly acquainted during the last hour, we produce a monkey who cannot choose between a plus and a square (or, for that matter, between other patterns, objects, colors, or brightnesses). However, such a monkey, on the way to the testing situation, will reach out of its cage and catch a flying gnat out of the air and put it in its mouth. In the testing situation, the monkey acts to all intents and purposes as if it were practically blind; it makes random choices among visually presented objects. Yet outside the test situation, he catches gnats. Visual *tracking* obviously is unimpaired. This observation can be translated into an experiment. Dr. Ettlinger (1959), whose excellent presentation on somesthetic transfer you have heard this afternoon, devised the following demonstration: What he did was to train monkeys to press a lever in response to a given brightness of light; then he varied the brightness of the light; and he measured the changes in the monkeys' lever-pressing rate as a function of the varying brightness. He also trained the same monkeys to choose between a plus sign and a square. After inferotemporal lesions, these monkeys performed exactly as they had performed preoperatively in the brightness situation but failed miserably on the choice problem. In other words, when a particular behavior is contingent on only one environmental event, the monkey shows no change after such a cortical removal. When, however, alternatives are involved, the inferotemporal lesion makes a difference. William James (1950) distinguished these types of behavior: he called the one an "existential discrimination"; the other, involving choice, he called a "differential discrimination." Differential discriminations are made among alternatives, and alternatives are digital; they are "either-or." Thus the first of our dichotomies is between existential discrimination, served by the classical projection systems, and differential discriminations, served by the related "association" cortex.

The other dichotomy is an entirely different one. We can use Professor Young's lizard to make the point; the lizard who suns himself in order to warm sufficiently to be able to move about properly. Professor Young suggested that this lizard may be operating on a digital basis. I don't agree. The lizard is also tracking. He is tracking his internal environment over time, instead of the location of events external to him. The mechanism of homeostasis was proposed by Cannon to account for just this kind of behavior. Our second dichotomy, therefore, can be stated, as did Dr. Nauta this morning, as the difference between mechanisms that provide stability (invariance, constancy) in space, *vs.* those that provide organisms with stability in time—more of this in a moment.

The difference in function between *these* two brains is clearly demonstrated by the use of Professor Klüver's stimulus equivalence problem, the technique which Dr. Myers has used so ingeniously to study the split-brain preparation. In my own work with Drs. Schwartzbaum and Bagshaw, similar techniques are applied to analyze the components of the Klüver-Bucy syndrome—to fractionate the effects of temporal lobectomy (Pribram & Bagshaw, 1955; Schwartzbaum & Pribram, 1960). We have made a comparison between the already noted results of lesions of the inferotemporal isocortex and those of the more medially placed structures of the temporal lobe: amygdala, entorhinal cortex, and

Ammon's formation. When these medially located structures are removed, the monkeys' visual choices are *un*impaired. They learn to choose as readily as do controls; they perform without deficit when the problem was learned prior to the brain lesion. When, however, one tests their ability to transfer their training to a *new* problem, their performance is very different from that of controls. Problems that are responded to as *equivalent* by the normal monkey are treated as *novel* by these monkeys with medial temporal lesions. (A momentary digression: Dr. Sperry has already mentioned that Western monkeys are not like Eastern monkeys. Our Western monkeys seem to *learn* their equivalences, they don't come equipped with them as did Professor Klüver's animals.)

The results of the experiments suggest that these medial forebrain structures deal not only with the organism's stability with respect to his internal milieu, but also to his performance, over time, with regard to his external environment. Dramatic support of this hypothesis has come this afternoon from Dr. Downer's superb demonstration of the effect of unilateral amygdalectomy with split–brain monkeys.

Dr. Jasper's electrophysiological work (Sharpless & Jasper, 1956) has done a great deal to clarify for us the mechanisms involved in the production of equivalence and, therefore, of novelty. In his hands, about the only lesion which interferes with habituation of the electrocortical activity, manifest when the organism alerts to a novel stimulus, is in and around the medial part of the temporal lobe. There is now a large body of information about habituation (Brazier, 1960): Habituation of orientation appears as a critical, initial step in the memory process (Pribram, 1961). Only by remembering, in some form or other, can organisms maintain their stability in time.

We are thus faced with a double division: according to space *vs.* time and according to analogue *vs.* digital. This quadruple must therefore include a mechanism that codes behavior over time; in other words, a digital memory mechanism. In a sense, homeostats are rudimentary "memory" devices; they "remember" the setting around which they control their environment. Coded memory devices that control behavior, we might call Plans (Miller, Galanter, & Pribram, 1960). And though the afternoon is too short to permit this to be done here, review of the evidence suggests that the frontal "association" cortex is critically involved when such Plans are to be executed.

To review briefly: The evidence is that we are possessed not of two, but of four, brains. One brain, our "perceptual" brain we might call it, maps the everchanging *spatial* array of our external environment from some of its constant features. A *second* brain is involved in managing our behavioral economy in the face of changes that take place over time. This is our "homeostatic" brain. Each of these brains, the "perceptual" and the "homeostatic," has, in primates, an associated brain. These associated brains, classically called the "association areas," serve to code the neural events involved in perception and homeostasis: Alternatives and Plans thus become possible.

My amendment to Professor Young's proposal is that before dominance can develop, these associated brains must become preponderant. In other words, only when the coded, digital functions, supplied by the associated brains, become fully developed is there sufficient freedom from isomorphic mapping to allow hemispheric dominance. Still more simply put, selective hemispheric function in man is a result of the relative growth of his associated brains.

Now for part two: We have seen that in order to provide for the kind of selective hemispheric action to which we refer as cerebral dominance, we need four brains, not two. We have also heard an afternoon of papers based on animal experiments. Does dominance exist in subhuman mammals? I believe it does, but in a rudimentary form. For, what do we mean by dominance? We mean that if we test the function of a neurobehavioral system, the results of the test do not fit the anatomical facts. We find that each cerebral hemisphere in man subserves unique functions but, as Professor von Bonin told us this morning, anatomically, the hemispheres appear simply to be mirror images. (This situation is not peculiar to neurology; Louis Pasteur found a similar problem when he investigated chemical substances that are optical isomers.) Are there any instances in subhuman mammals where functional and anatomical facts are disparate? There are. For instance, the basis for some of the discrepancies in the somatic mode that Dr. Ettlinger brought forward. (By the way, did you all catch that spirited recantation by Dr. Ettlinger of his earlier notions that the posterior part of the parietal lobe has no function?) An electrical stimulus to the sciatic nerve of a deeply anesthetized monkey will yield a wide distribution of potentials, evoked around the rolandic region of his cerebral cortex. On the other hand, when one is more delicate in approach, as Professor Mountcastle has been, and gently displaces a hair, one finds a much more restricted distribution of potentials produced by such a "physiological stimulus." Anatomically, there must be pathways that correspond to the maximal distribution; when distribution is restricted, some parts that could function, do not. On this phenomenon, dominance must be based. This is the type of evidence that leads me to believe that in the monkey, and perhaps in the cat and rat, there is already an emergence of some rudimentary mechanism that allows dominance to take place.

Such a mechanism might even result in Dr. Downer's "perception without sensation." One of the ways in which the inferotemporal mechanisms could work is by means of an efferent tract to a subcortical locus where input events are controlled (Pribram, 1958). Dr. Kuypers, this morning, referred to the evidence that such a tract may terminate somewhere around the deeper portions of the superior colliculus. Lesions made here give rise to a syndrome that looks a lot like the one that follows lesions of the inferotemporal cortex. Could this be the tract that allows coding of the events in the visual system? These events might be partitioned into sets and subsets, thus digitizing them into alternatives. The anatomical evidence would thus lead us to believe that such a partitioning could take place as far downstream as the collicular level, *before* the events reach the cortical surface. Could this be the root of the "perception without sensation" problem?

In conclusion, the point I want to make is that often the available neuroanatomical substrate is only partially activated in a situation that determines a specific physiological or behavioral response. Further, because of overlap of anatomical systems, a portion of the neuraxis may participate as part of one functional system at one time in one situation, and as part of another functional system at another time in another situation. When, phylogenetically, these anatomically multidetermined locations come to predominate, freedom is enhanced—possibly to the point that portions of the neuraxis may participate at any one time as part of two (or more) functional systems, each related to a different aspect of the situation. "Dominance" under these conditions refers to the observation that we consider *one* function the most obvious for consideration; "equipotentiality" refers to the converse observation that, under other circumstances, we can demonstrate those other functions that are ordinarily dominated.

In this sense we really may have many brains; i.e., multiple possible cerebral organizations, each of which is activated in its own special circumstance, dominant for the moment, only to be dominated in turn by others more appropriate to now changed conditions. The four brains thus give way to four categories of many brains, actively mapping and controlling, partitioning and planning, to assure the organism some stability in the face of ever-shifting events.

C.

JOHN C. LILLY

Communication Research Institute, Miami, Florida

The problem of cerebral dominance in the human is best exemplified by the tendency for a lateralization of the speech areas and of handedness as is presented in other papers in this symposium. In the case of another species, the bottlenose dolphin (Tursiops truncatus Montagu), some unexpected additional evidence of another type of cerebral dominance is beginning to appear in our current research program (Lilly, 1961a), alternation of dominance. Here I will present a short summary of our findings. Since the dolphin properly has no hands, one might look for a question of lateral dominance of one flipper or the other. None such has been found. The animals can use each flipper independently or co-ordinated with the other.

Some swimming patterns show a preference for one side. In the case of Elvar, a swimming pattern has appeared in which he swims in very tight circles, touching his flukes to his rostrum as he swims: his preference is to swim to the left. He does this so frequently that wrinkles have appeared in his skin on the left side; no similar wrinkles have appeared on the right. The animal most closely associated with Elvar, Chee Chee, also tends to swim in tight circles to the left, similar wrinkles are appearing on her skin on the left side.

In regard to lateralization of the sleep pattern, these animals sleep with one eye closed at a time. The eye closures are 180 degrees out of phase; it is rare to have both eyes closed at once. The accumulated sleep for each eye runs from 120 to 140 minutes per day. The sleep occurs in brief periods between each respiration running from 20 to 40 seconds per eye closure. A dolphin wakes up in order to take each breath. Alternate sides are rested alternately.

Their phonation mechanisms are bilateral though unsymmetrical. We have demonstrated (Lilly & Miller, 1961b; 1961c) that a dolphin can whistle and click or whistle and buzz simultaneously under water. Recently we have had opportunities to observe animals in air with open blowholes, using the right and left phonation mechanisms separately and/or simultaneously for different kinds of emissions (Lilly & Miller, 1962a). A small female, Sissy, recently has been clicking with her left side and whistling with her right side simultaneously in air. Elvar has been producing humanoid sounds simultaneously with his left side and with his right side, or with his left side alone, or with his right side alone. In several emissions we have detected very large frequency differences, and quite different patternings between what he says with his left side versus what he says with his right side simultaneously. He can produce humanoid sounds at a low frequency on one side and at a very much higher frequency on the other.

Eye movements can be quite independent of one another. An animal can scan a whole 180 degrees of solid visual angle on each side of its body quite independently of the eye movements of the other side. The dolphins have a stereoscopic binocular visual field, forward and downward, which they apparently use at the last instant before grabbing their prey. In mapping the motor cortex of these animals in the unanesthetized state, we found that the monocular eye movements are represented contralaterally and that binocular eye movements are represented homolaterally and contralaterally.

There are no obvious gross neuroanatomical findings which can adequately account for the above behavioral and physiological findings (Lilly & Miller, 1962b; Langworthy, 1932). To gross inspection the two halves of the brain look equal; the corpus collosum in the adult is well developed, as are all the subcortical cross-connections.

The phonation sacs just below the blowhole are paired, and usually the right side is larger than the left. This may be merely a matter of the lowest pitch which the animal can produce by each of the right and the left sides. Questions as to whether all animals prefer the right side for whistling and the left side for clicking are yet to be answered. Other kinds of preferences establishing laterality of action are yet to be explored. The one generalization that we can make about this species is that they are able to control quite independently, and yet simultaneously, with different patternings the two sides of their body in regard to vision and in regard to phonation and swimming. They are able to control quite independently the motions of the right and the left flippers and have control of symmetrical movements of the tongue.

Motions such as those of swallowing, of high speed swimming straight ahead, and of slow speed swimming backwards are done with great exactness and presumably require symmetrical use of the nervous system on both sides equally.

Problems such as the dominance of one hemisphere over the other hemisphere during these extremely complex vocalizations are yet to be explored. Central representation of the phonation mechanism (afferent and efferent) is yet to be determined. It may turn out that like the eye movements, the phonation mechanisms have a contralateral and a homolateral representation. It would be expected that the phonation mechanism, for example, during respiration would be a bilateral representation. During respiratory movements the two sides of the phonation mechanism each open very widely, allowing the passage of air quite symmetrically on the two sides.

Problems such as the localization of their whistling language on one side and their click language on the other, or each of them bilaterally, in the cerebral cortex are yet to be answered. From our results with the humanoid sounds, it looks as though each cortex will turn out to be functionally able to carry on quite independently of the other side. However, during emotional states, i.e., when the dolphin is irritated or sexually aroused, the phonation mechanism on each side says the same thing and is operated simultaneously with great vigor and intensity. The dolphin's bark or angry buzz is a highly symmetrical and single minded operation. The independence of the two sides is seen best with a relaxed dolphin who can concentrate on the problems in hand without emotional involvement.

D.

HENRICUS G. J. M. KUYPERS

University of Maryland School of Medicine, Baltimore, Maryland
(present address: University of Western Reserve School of Medicine, Cleveland, Ohio.)

In his most interesting presentation, Dr. Pribram touched upon the possible functional importance of the fiber connections from the temporal lobe to the superior colliculus (among other, Nauta & Withlock,

J. Comp. Neurol., 1956). These temporal fibers terminate in the stratum opticum and the stratum griseum medium of the superior colliculus, a termination area which seems to be identical with layer V of Olszewski and Baxter's description (Olszewski & Baxter, *Cytoarchitecture of the Human Brain Stem,* J. B. Lippincott Co., Philadelphia, 1954).

During the last few years, Dr. Swarcbart (NIMH, Bethesda, Md.) and I have been studying experimentally the intracortical connections in the Rhesus monkey, using the Nauta-Gygax silver impregnation technique. Once in awhile we have allowed ourselves a glance at the superior colliculus, in spite of the fact that the orientation of our transverse sections is not too well suited for an extensive study of this structure.

In the few sections studied, the distribution of the degenerating cortical fibers appeared to vary according to the location of the cortical lesion. Following lesions of the striate, pre-, and peristriate areas in our sections, the degenerating cortical fibers were found primarily in the superficial gray layers of the superior colliculus (layer I–IV). Some fibers were distributed also to layer V. Following lesions of the ventral aspect of the temporal lobe on the other hand, the great majority of the degenerating fibers were found one layer deeper (layer V). In this case, only a few fibers were present in the superficial layers (I–IV). Finally, following a lesion primarily of the ventral bank of the intraparietal sulcus, the great majority of the degenerating fibers in the superior colliculus were found still one layer deeper (layer VI). A few fibers additionally spilled over into layer VII.

In regard to these preliminary findings, it seems important to note that, e.g., in the cat and the rat, the optic fibers from the eye terminate in layers II–IV (Cajal, 1911 and among others, Nauta & Van Straaten, *J. Anat.,* 1946). In other words, the striate areas and the superficial layers of the superior colliculus represent cortical and subcortical primary optic receiving stations (disregarding for a moment the synapse in the lateral geniculate body). Therefore, the striate- and peristriate-collicular fibers seem to connect cortical with homologous subcortical cell groups. The other corticocollicular connections might follow the same pattern. If this be correct, the present findings would suggest that the functional interrelation between the striate, temporal, and parietal cortical areas resembles the functional interrelations between the corresponding layers of the superior colliculus.

It is clear that further speculations regarding functions are rather hazardous at the moment, especially in view of the limited material studied. Therefore, I would prefer to limit myself to presenting a semi-diagrammatic representation of the fiber distribution, as found in the present material (Figure 1).

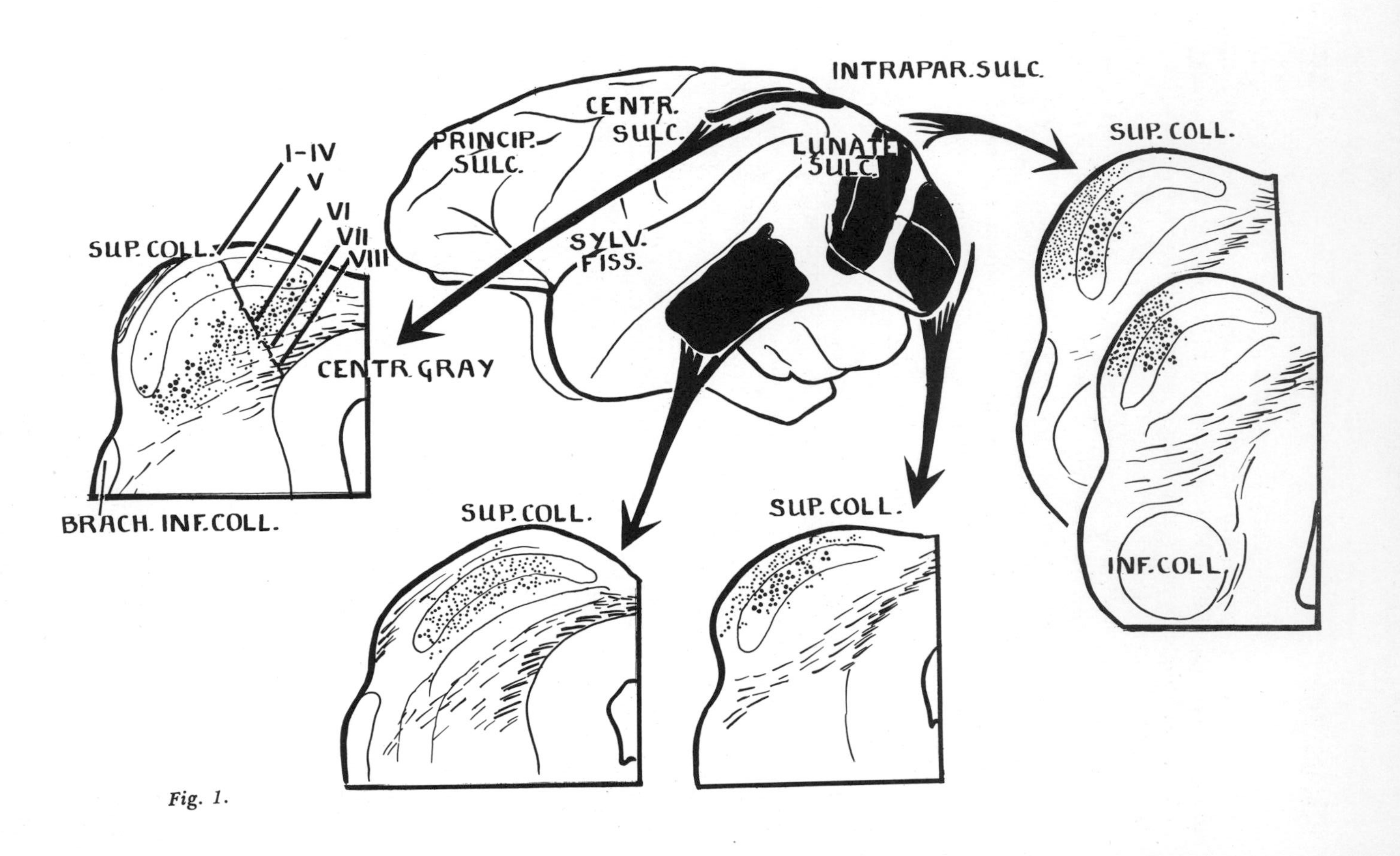
INTRAPAR. SULC.
CENTR. SULC.
PRINCIP. SULC.
LUNATE SULC.
SYLV. FISS.
I-IV
V
VI
VII
VIII
SUP. COLL.
CENTR. GRAY
BRACH. INF. COLL.
SUP. COLL.
SUP. COLL.
SUP. COLL.
INF. COLL.

Fig. 1.

E.

RONALD E. MYERS

The Johns Hopkins University School of Medicine, Baltimore, Maryland

It may be of interest to discuss here findings, obtained in the last two years, with two patients having lesions of the corpus callosum. The first patient, N. B., presented with a lipoma of the corpus callosum.* Clinically, the patient had been an acute and chronic behavior problem, having been hospitalized because of apparent demonstrations of suicidal tendencies. He had no neurological complaints, and his neurological examination on admission was within normal limits. On routine skull films, a mid-line mass with a calcified capsule was noted in the region of the genu of the corpus callosum. This measured close to two inches across on anteroposterior view and revealed only indistinct borders on lateral view. Left carotid angiogram demonstrated anterior and superior displacement of the anterior cerebral artery (Figure 1.).

Transfer of training studies were carried out in collaboration with Dr. Allan Mirsky of the National Institutes of Health, using the Seguin-Goddard formboard. In these tests, the times required for blindfolded solution of the formboard, first through one hand and then through the other hand, were compared. N. B. achieved problem solution through the right hand in 3 minutes and 24 seconds, and subsequent solution through the left hand in 1 minute and 14 seconds. During initial solving of the formboard through the right hand, N. B. exhibited repeated tactile exploration of the form patterns and the recipient slots in the formboard. In contrast, solving through the left hand was direct and deliberate, and appeared clearly guided by the prior experience through the right hand. The time required for initial solving and the amount of saving exhibited on transfer testing both fell well within the range exhibited by normal controls. Also on visual tests, requiring *same-*

* The author would like to express appreciation to Lt. Col. Hayes of the Walter Reed Army Medical Center for permission to study this patient.

different comparisons of visual patterns presented tachistoscopically in the two half fields, N. B. performed as well as normal subjects.

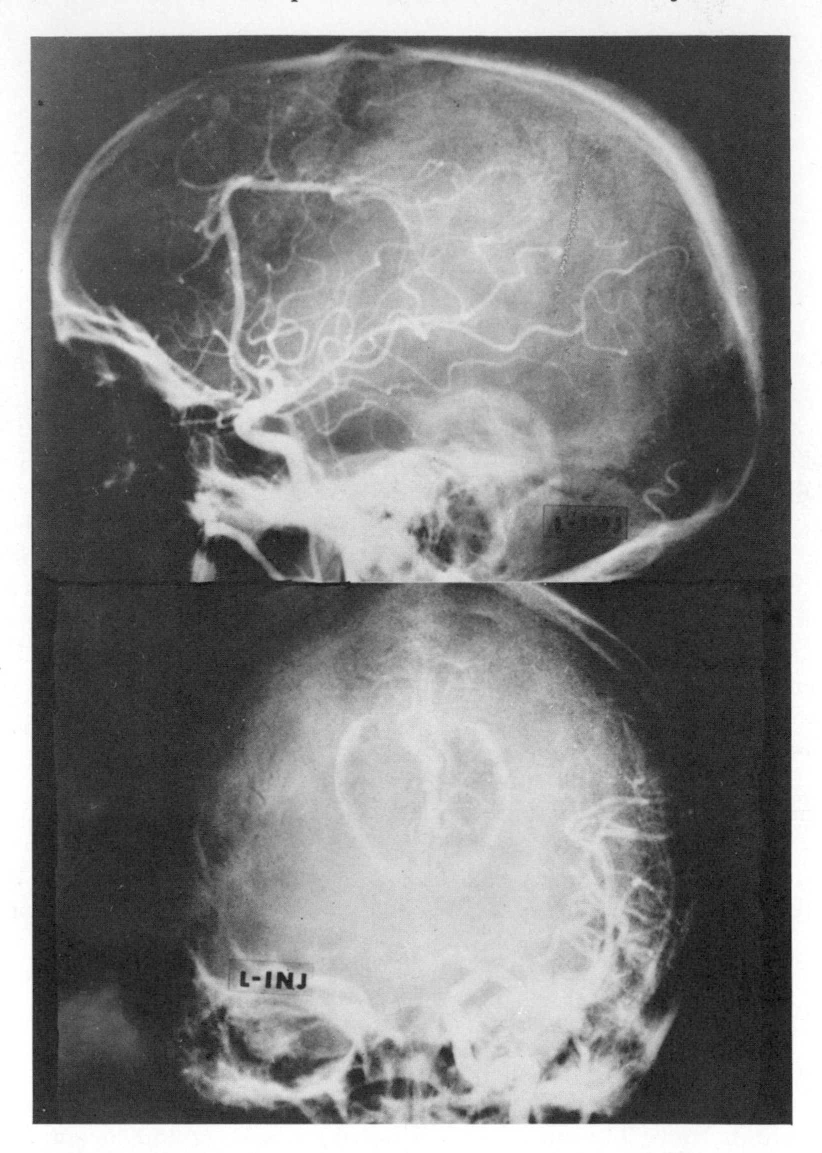

Fig. 1. Left carotid angiogram of patient N. B., showing characteristic radiological appearance of lipoma of the corpus callosum. The mid-line lesion is in the region of the genu of the corpus callosum and exhibits calcification in its capsule. The anterior cerebral arteries are displaced superiorly and anteriorly by the mass.

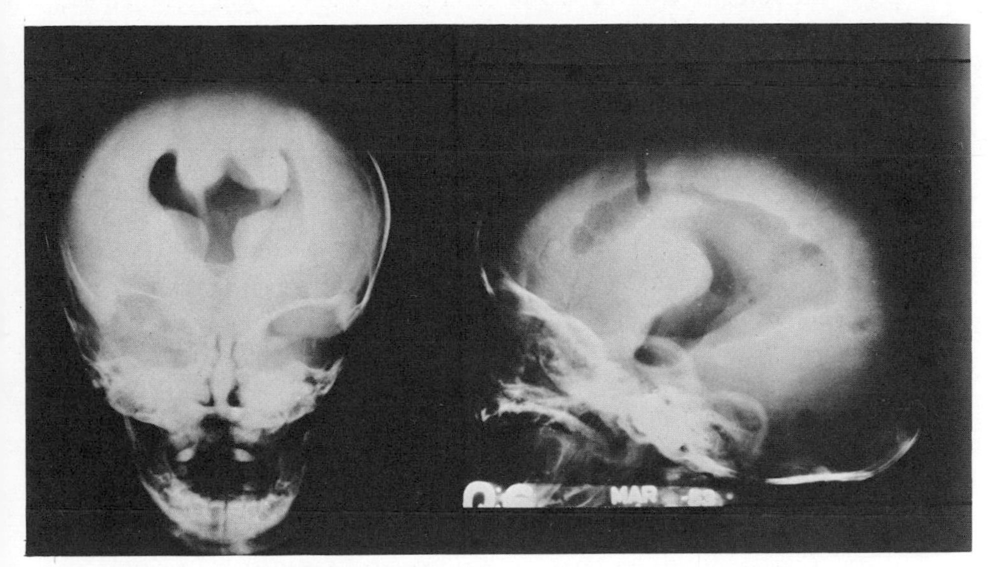

Fig. 2. Ventriculogram on R. C., at the age of one and a half months, revealed characteristic pattern of agenesis of corpus callosum coupled with mild ventricular enlargement.

The second patient, R. C., was brought by his mother to the Baltimore City Hospitals at the age of 1½ months, with the complaint that his head was growing too large.** A ventriculographic study, carried out during this admission, indicated an agenesis of the corpus callosum (Figure 2). In addition to agenesis of the corpus callosum, a diagnosis of communicating hydrocephalus was made, and a Nichols–Crosby subarachnoid–iliac crest shunt was performed. No localizing or lateralizing neurological signs were found on examination at that time.

Other than generalized seizures, controlled with anticonvulsants, the patient did well until readmission at age 8 years, with the complaint of vomiting and drawing back of the head of 4 days' duration. Examination during the second admission revealed a slight ataxia of gait and very slight increase in reflexes on the left side, but bilaterally negative Babinski responses. Air studies and studies of cerebrospinal fluid dynamics led to diagnosis of atresia of the foramina of Luschka and Magendie, in addition to diffuse ventricular enlargement and agenesis of the corpus callosum. Psychological studies carried out by Dr. Robert

** This patient was studied with the cooperation of Drs. J. Donald McQueen and Perry Black of the Division of Neurosurgery, Baltimore City Hospitals.

R. White revealed a verbal IQ of 62, a performance IQ of less than 44, and a full scale IQ of 45, using the Wechsler Intelligence Scale for children. R. C. showed an elementary grasp of simple logic and was able to do simple counting. His speech was mutilated in pattern, so that it was unintelligible at times. He could retain 5 digits forward but could not grasp the idea of repeating them backwards. R. C. was presented with a simplified form of the Seguin formboard. Without the aid of vision, he required 4 minutes and 32 seconds to first solve through the right hand, and 2 minutes and 10 seconds to subsequently solve through the left hand. This represented a saving of more than 50 per cent on testing through the untrained hand. It was not possible to obtain co-operation for visual testing.

Agenesis of the corpus callosum occurs as a frequent malformation of the nervous system. Very often it is associated with other malformations, both of the brain and of other parts of the body. Only infrequently does it occur as the only abnormality. When agenesis does occur, either alone or with other malformations, it usually is incomplete with sizable bundles of fibers still remaining more anteriorly in the anterior body, genu, and rostral regions. Only very rarely are cases of total agenesis described, and particularly rare are cases of total agenesis unassociated with other cerebral malformations.

Lipoma of the corpus callosum has generally been interpreted as another type of brain malformation rather than as a neoplasm. Lipomas are associated with maldevelopment or agenesis of the corpus callosum in up to 50 percent of cases. Once again, total agenesis associated with lipoma is a rarity.

From these pathoanatomical facts alone, it is probable that the subjects studied in the present investigation still retained portions of the corpus callosum intact. Air studies which might have clarified this issue were never carried out on subject N. B. Also, though he underwent exploratory craniotomy, no attempt was made to determine the state of development of the underlying corpus callosum. The ventriculograms of the second patient, R. C., suggested preservation of more anterior portions of the corpus callosum. The lack of definite knowledge, as to the state of preservation of contingents of the corpus callosum in these subjects, renders uncertain the real meaning of the results found in the present study. These cases have been presented primarily to urge the need for careful and complete *post-mortem* anatomical check of the brains of human clinical material before results are closely interpreted.

Dr. Ettlinger, in his presentation, has described the need for studies on localization of the touch-training transfer functions of the corpus callosum. Drs. Ebner, Niemann, and Black are in the midst of such an analysis, and some of their results may be described here.

A series of monkeys of the *Macaca mulatta* species were used. Varying portions of the corpus callosum were sectioned in different locations. Afterwards, these animals were unimanually taught a roughness discrimination task. Following stabilization of the responses through the first hand by overtraining, tests of transfer of training were carried out through the inexperienced hand. Figures 3–7 illustrate the outcome of the separate training and testing through the two separate hands of several of these animals.

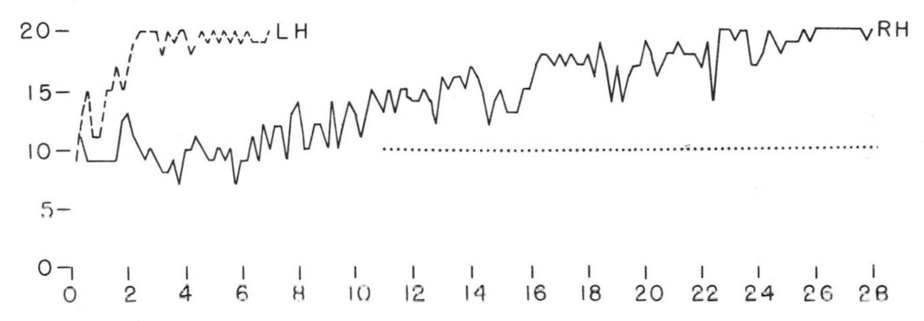

Fig. 3. Learning curves on a roughness discrimination, achieved through the two separate hands of Monkey No. 10. This animal had undergone transection of all the corpus callosum except the *body,* prior to training. The solid line relates to initial learning through the right hand, the dashed line to subsequent learning through the left hand.

Monkey No. 10 sustained section of the *splenium,* the *rostrum,* and the *genu,* leaving intact the major part of the *body* of the corpus callosum. This intact part included segments grossly related to posterior portions of the frontal lobe and to major anterior portions of the parietal and temporal lobes. As may be seen from Figure 3, this animal required 2,300 trials through the right hand to acquire and sustain a high level performance on the discrimination. On subsequent transfer of training tests through the left hand, the monkey reached a sustained high level performance during the third 100 trials. The degree of transfer of training exhibited by this animal falls within the range demonstrated by normal animals on transfer testing with this particular discrimination. Excellent transmission of tactual learning may be mediated through the *body* of the corpus callosum.

Monkey No. 76 sustained section of the entire corpus callosum except for the *splenium*. Thus, connections between the hemispheres were disrupted except for those interconnecting the occipital lobes and possibly a few interconnecting the most posterior portions of the parietal lobes. This animal required 1,000 trials through the right hand and subsequently 800 trials through the left hand to first reach criterion of learned performance as illustrated in Figure 4. The course of learning through the two hands of this animal as expressed by the learning curves failed to give evidence for any transfer of training between the hands. Thus, *splenium* seems to support no transmission of tactual information between the hemispheres in the monkey.

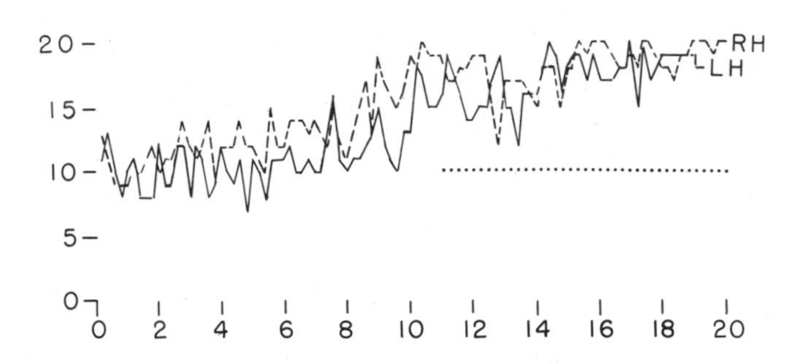

Fig. 4. Roughness discrimination learning through the two hands of Monkey No. 76 who has had transection of the entire corpus callosum except the posterior *splenium*. The discrimination and sequence of testing are as in Figure 3.

Monkey No. 75 received section of the entire corpus callosum except for the posterior *body* which lies grossly in relation to portions of the parietal and temporal lobes. Figure 5 shows the results of this animal's performances in initial learning through the right hand and in subsequent test learning through the left hand. He achieved sustained high level performances with the right hand after 1,200 trials and with the left hand after 200 trials. A second animal with a similar lesion showed an even greater amount of transfer of training between the hands. Thus, a high degree of training transfer may be sustained through the posterior *body* of the corpus callosum alone.

All portions of the corpus callosum were sectioned in Monkey No. 21 except for the anterior *body*. This portion of the corpus callosum is grossly related to the posterior portions of the frontal lobe. Monkey No. 21 re-

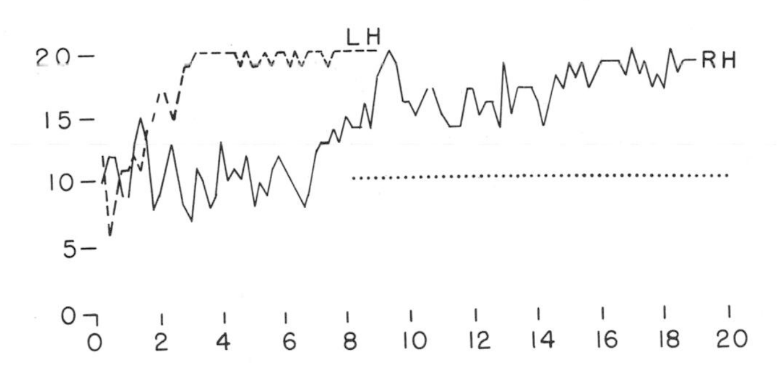

Fig. 5. Roughness discrimination learning through the two hands of Monkey No. 4. This animal sustained transection of all the corpus callosum except the posterior *body*. Initial learning through its right hand is figured in the solid line and subsequent learning through the left hand in the dashed line.

quired 400 trials to initially acquire the roughness discrimination through the right hand, and 300 trials to reacquire the response through the left hand (Figure 6). This monkey, with the anterior body of the corpus callosum preserved, gave evidence for only very slight, if any, transfer of training between the hands. Another animal with a similar lesion, Monkey No. 33 (Figure 7), gave no evidence of training transfer between the hands, having achieved high level performance through both hands only after 400 trials through each. The more anterior portions of the *body* of the corpus callosum seem, therefore, more or less incapable of tactual information transmission between the hemispheres. These cases, taken as a whole, indicate that only the posterior body regions of the corpus callosum, related to the parietal lobes, function in the intermanual transfer of tactual learning in the monkey.

Similar studies are in progress with a series of chimpanzees having partial commissure sections. These animals have been trained and tested with latch box problems through the two separate hands. The results obtained with a simple cabinet ring problem are schematically described in Figure 8. After normal animals were taught the simple latch box problem through one hand, they showed immediate solving through the other hand. Animals with the total corpus callosum sectioned, by contrast, required entirely separate training on the problem through the two separate hands. The animal with posterior *splenium, genu,* and *rostrum* sectioned was indistinguishable from the normal

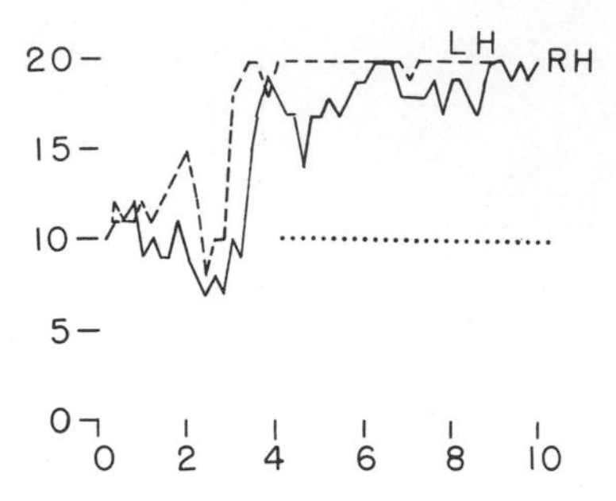

Fig. 6. Learning of the roughness discrimination through the two hands of Monkey No. 21 with only the anterior portion of the *body* of the corpus callosum preserved. Solid line shows learning through the first hand and dashed line, learning through the second hand.

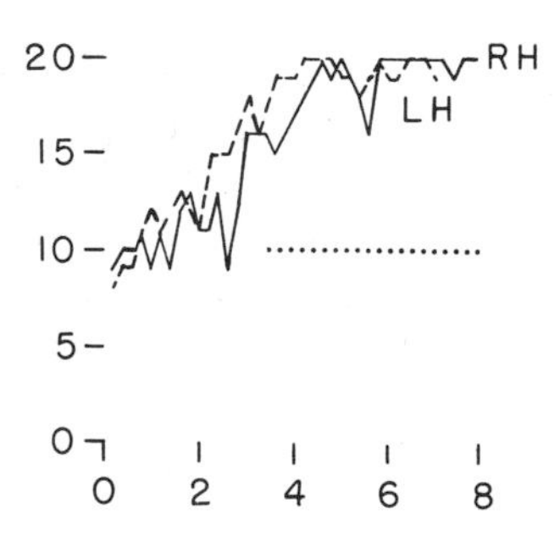

Fig. 7. Graphs of learning through the two hands on another monkey with only the anterior *body* of the corpus callosum intact. Monkey No. 33 learned first through the right hand (solid line) and then, through the left hand (dashed line).

animals on transfer testing. The animal with the entire corpus callosum sectioned but for the anterior *body* exhibited only slight hesitation before solving through the untrained hand. Greater fumbling, but still quick solution, characterized the animal with all portions sectioned but

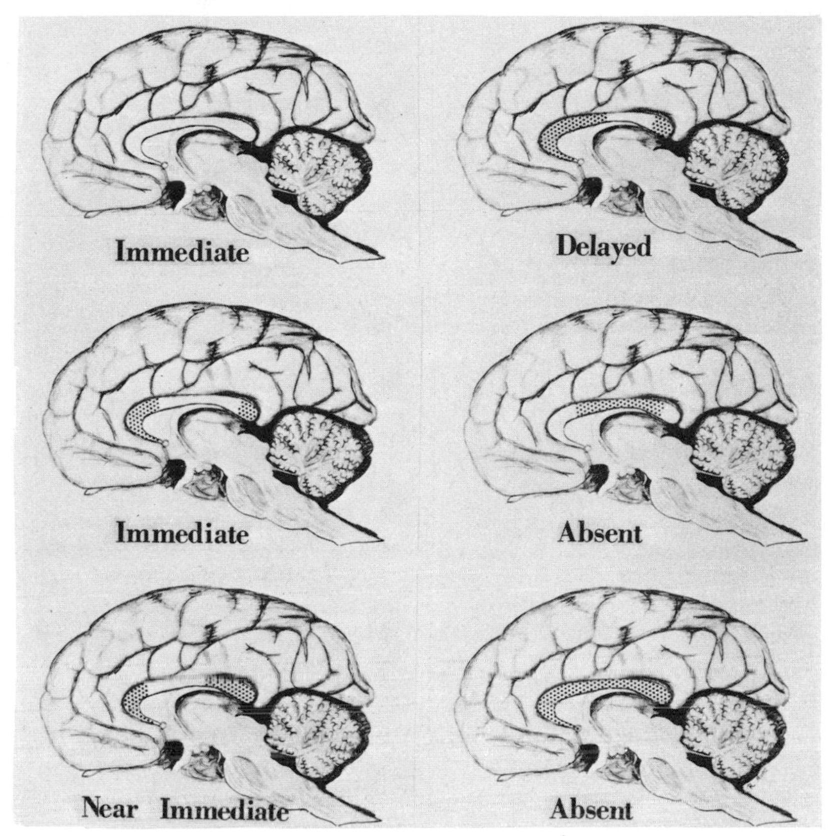

Fig. 8. Schemas demonstrating the extent of commissural section in a series of chimpanzees as determined by measurements made at the time of surgery. The degree of transfer of training between the hands, in these animals, is expressed as the rapidity of solving on problem presentation through the second untrained hand. The task utilized was a simple latch box problem.

the posterior *body*. The animal with the entire *body* of the corpus callosum severed, leaving the posterior *splenium,* the *genu,* and the *rostrum,* performed in a manner similar to the animals with total section.

Definite conclusions again must await further progress of the investigation. Yet the results to date suggest that intermanual transfer of latch box solving may be supported both by more anterior and by more posterior portions of the *body* of the corpus callosum in the chimpanzee.

Transfer of training in the normal animal is of relatively high order. Figure 9 records the learning curves acquired through the two hands of three normal monkeys studied earlier on a grooved-smooth tactual discrimination. Considerable variation was noted in the trials required

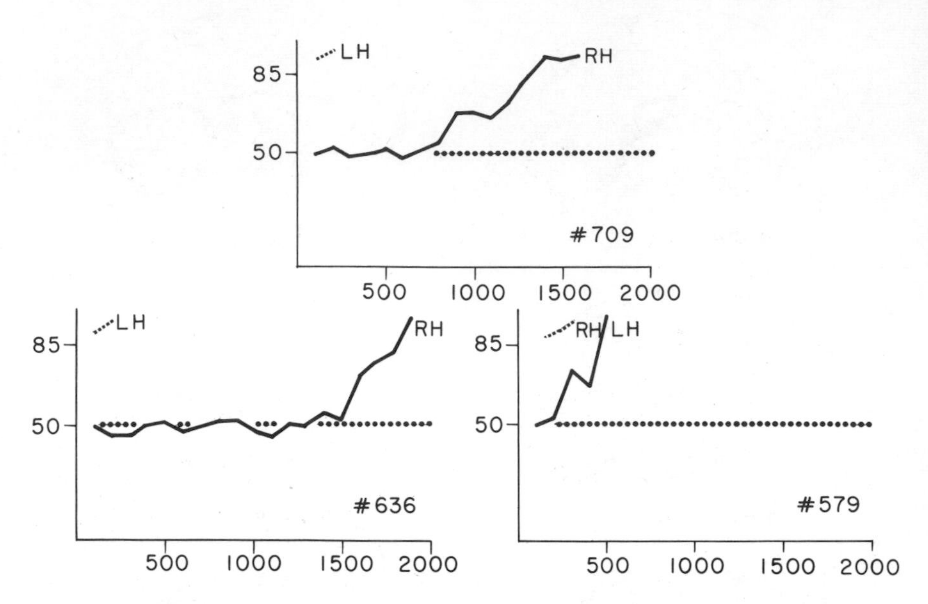

Fig. 9. Learning through the two hands of a group of normal monkeys, using a grooved-smooth discrimination. The solid lines denote first learning through the one hand and the dotted lines subsequent test performances through the second hand. Overtraining is not depicted in these curves. Note the variability in rapidity of initial learning from animal to animal. Performances on this discrimination were always at a high level on transfer testing.

for initial learning through the first hand. Nevertheless, performance through the untrained hands on transfer testing was at a high level in all instances.

The effects of total corpus callosum section on transfer of training between the hands may be seen from Figure 10. With severance of this massive connecting link between the hemispheres, learning through the second hand seemed not at all aided by the prior learning through the first hand. In fact, the learning curves achieved through the two hands tended to mirror one another almost exactly.

The great variability in rates of first hand learning observed among the normal monkeys also was noted among those with commissure section. However, it is of interest to note that the mean number of trials required to learn through the first hands of the two groups was about the same. The three normal animals required on the average 1,300, and the commissure-sectioned animals 1,200, trials for first hand solving. Similar results were obtained in discrimination learning through the feet. From this outcome, it seems clear that commissure section, in and

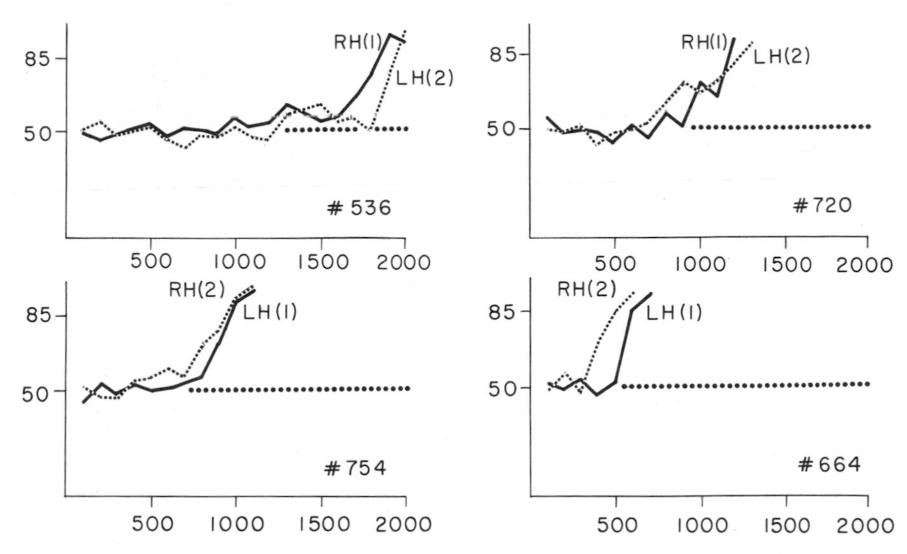

Fig. 10. Learning through the two hands of a group of corpus callosum-sectioned monkeys, using the same grooved–smooth discrimination as for Figure 9. Note the closely similar course of learning through the two hands. The callosum-sectioned animals exhibited a similar variability in rate of learning and, as a whole, learned about as rapidly as the normal animals.

of itself, does not affect the learning capacity of the animals through either hand or foot separately.

It is not known whether memories develop bilaterally or only in one hemisphere when the learning experience is restricted through one hand. This question may be answered by functionally dissociating the two hemispheres through corpus callosum transection *after completion* of one-hand training. On later testing through the second hand, full recognition would indicate bilateral development of memory trace systems, while failure to recall would portend a restriction of mnemonic systems to the hemisphere receiving the afferent sensory stimulation during learning.

When put to the test, monkeys with *posttraining* section of the corpus callosum perform about as well as normal monkeys on trials run through the inexperienced second hand. Table I illustrates these results, using a tactual pattern and three roughness discrimination tasks of graded difficulty. Each subject learned a specific discrimination response through its right hand, in the number of trials indicated in the column labelled *right hand.* This learning represented the first formal training each of these animals had experienced in the laboratory setting. Follow-

Table I

Discrimination Task	*Normal* Right Hand	*Normal* Left Hand	*Operated* Right Hand	*Operated* Left Hand
Tactual Pattern				
Groove-smooth	1400	80	500	120
Roughness				
Easy	400	20	400	60
Moderate	500	40	600	60
Difficult	1600	140	1500	140

Transfer of training from right to left hand in normal monkeys and in monkeys with *post-training* corpus callosum transection. The numbers in the *right hand* columns represent trials to achieve learned performance through first trained right hands. The numbers in the *left hand* columns represent trials to reachieve learned performance through previously inexperienced left hands. Data under the *normal* columns represent results with four normal animals each performing a different one of four tasks studied. Data under the *operated* columns represent results with four matched, operated animals.

ing establishment of response, four animals were set aside as controls, while four sustained total commissure transection. After two weeks the animals of the two matched groups were again tested with the discrimination tasks, but through their inexperienced left hands. As may be seen, solution of the problems was achieved equally rapidly by the two groups. However, minimal amounts of retraining were often required through the left hands of both groups, in order to consolidate learning. Performances through the initially trained right hands were later tested and found unaffected by the transection of corpus callosum.

It is concluded that sensory experiences, transmitted to one hemisphere through the afferent touch pathways, result in the establishment of memory trace systems in both hemispheres. These trace systems of the two hemispheres thereafter enjoy the potential of separate existence apart from one another, as witnessed by their continued expression subsequent to total commissure section. The memories induced vicariously, through corpus callosum in the hemisphere not receiving the afferent stimulation, seem less well defined than those induced directly in the receptive hemisphere. Yet, it may be noted that the vicariously induced memory systems suffer little apparent decrement on being split off from the directly induced systems by severance of corpus callosum.

As a final point, we should like to record an agreement of our findings with those of Dr. Ettlinger on the effects of unilateral parietal lesion on transfer of tactual training in animals with corpus callosum sectioned. The learning curves of Monkey No. 2 will serve to illustrate the tenor of our results on this question. Monkey No. 2 sustained total section of the corpus callosum and anterior commissure, prior to any training. He was then taught an easy warm–cold discrimination through the two separate hands. Comparison of the shapes of the derived curves indicated no transfer of training, even for this simple task. The areas 3, 1, and 2 of the right parietal lobe were then surgically aspirated, without affecting performances on the already learned warm–cold response. The animal was then taught a roughness discrimination response, first, through the right hand and then, through the left hand. As may be

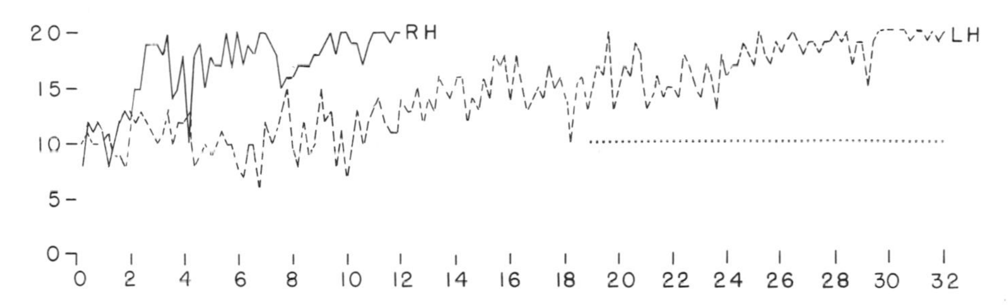

Fig. 11. **Learning through the two hands of Monkey No. 2 who had prior section of the corpus callosum and extirpation of areas 3, 1, and 2 of the right hemisphere. The solid line represents first learning through the right hand and the dashed, subsequent learning through the left hand. Learning through the left hand was much impeded by the ablation of areas 3, 1, and 2 of the right hemisphere.**

seen from Figure 11, he required 500 trials through the right hand and later, 2,500 trials through the left hand to achieve sustained high level performance. If transfer of training has occurred in this animal, it is hidden in the crippling effects of the parietal extirpation. This result does not support the thesis that damage to one parietal lobe forces transfer of training between the hands by virtue of presumed ensuing utilization of the undamaged parietal lobe by both hands (as suggested by Glickstein and Sperry, 1960). Rather, it has been our experience that the shapes of the learning curves through the two hands, after commissure section and parietal lobe lesion, are determined by relation to the cortical lesion rather than to sequence of training and transfer testing.

■□ VII

Effects of Brain Wounds Implicating Right or Left Hemisphere in Man:

Hemisphere Differences and Hemisphere Interaction in Vision, Audition, and Somesthesis

by HANS-LUKAS TEUBER

Psychophysiological Laboratory,[1] Massachusetts Institute of Technology, Cambridge, Massachusetts

AS A PAIRED ORGAN, the vertebrate forebrain with its conspicuous cerebral hemispheres poses questions of origin and present function. The evolution of this twin structure is undoubtedly related to the bilateral symmetry of the body itself; the widespread decussation of neural pathways, connecting one half-brain with the opposite half of the body, reflects the need for contraversive movements in any bilaterally symmetrical organism as it strives to maintain its course and posture in water, air, or on the ground.

Given this duality of cerebral hemispheres, we have the question of how these paired structures normally interact. By concentrating on animals below man, much can be learned from studies involving the experimental disconnection of one lateral half of the forebrain from the other. By interrupting major interhemispheric commissures, as has been done by Sperry and his co-workers (this volume), we can attempt to define the relative interdependence or independence of the hemispheres in learning and perception.

[1] Work supported by program grant M-5673 from the National Institute of Mental Health, USPHS, to the Psychophysiological Laboratory, M.I.T.

The same problem of hemispheric interaction can be studied in man, but here the problem appears with a crucial difference: As far as is known, all infrahuman forms have cerebral hemispheres that are mirror images of each other—both in structure and function. It is only in man that we have to face the additional problem of hemispheric differentiation. For a century and more, the prominent sign of such hemispheric differentiation has been the greater dependence of speech in adult man on the integrity of his left cerebral hemisphere. More recently, other differences in function have been noted: it becomes increasingly probable that right hemispheric lesions in man may alter perception in ways rather different from corresponding lesions on the left side of the brain. As this evidence accumulates, it appears more and more dubious whether we should retain the term "dominance" to describe the difference in the role of the two hemispheres in man. Perhaps one's major task at this stage is to enumerate the ways in which behavioral effects of lesions differ, depending on the side of the brain where a lesion is found.

In view of these subtle but pervasive differences in hemispheric function in man, the problem of hemispheric interaction is somewhat more complicated than in any of the infrahuman forms. We shall begin, therefore, with the problem of hemispheric differentiation and describe some of the effects of penetrating gunshot wounds of the human brain, from the standpoint of specialization in the role of the hemispheres. After that, we shall turn to the problem of hemispheric interaction.

SUBJECTS AND METHODS

The population of cases on which the present report and the subsequent one (Weinstein, this volume) are based has been under study at the Psychophysiological Laboratory, New York University-Bellevue Medical Center, for approximately 12 years.[2] This unit is concerned with investigations of brain function in man. To this end, the laboratory has studied effects of penetrating cerebral lesions, primarily in previously healthy adults. The effects of such lesions on sensory, motor, and intellectual functions have been assessed in the hope that disordered function, in the presence of fairly stable lesions in the nervous system, might bring us closer to an understanding of normal cerebral physiology.

In pursuing these studies, the laboratory has mainly relied on a group of 350 veterans with combat injuries of the nervous system: 232 of these (the experimental group) had sustained penetrating brain wounds;

[2] Since 1961, the Psychophysiological Laboratory has been located in the Massachusetts Institute of Technology and in co-operating hospitals in Boston, Mass.

the remaining 118 (the control group) had suffered similar missile wounds of one or several peripheral nerves, but not of the brain. These cases differ from those ordinarily included in studies of brain damage in several respects, since they were chosen irrespective of clinical needs and were followed for years after their wounding.

At the beginning of the laboratory program, these men had been identified as potential subjects by surveying rosters of all veterans residing in the Greater New York region who had been discharged from the armed services (during World War II or the Korean campaign) bearing diagnoses of brain or nerve injury. No known bias influenced their inclusion in the laboratory population, except that in the brain-injured group, loss of cerebral substance had to be proven by surgical records and x-ray evidence. Efforts were made to include all accessible cases of penetrating brain wound; the resulting group (from which the samples studied at the laboratory are drawn) probably represents four-fifths of all men with such injuries residing in or near Greater New York.

The co-operation of these subjects was enlisted initially by appealing to their altruism and was maintained over the years by stressing that the laboratory needed their help. Most of the men were approached in this way, for the first time, several years after being wounded, and testing continued at irregular intervals for ten years or more. The observations made on such a group are therefore based on late residuals of brain injury; the changes found are often subtle and, on the whole, rather less severe than those that could be observed in the early weeks or months after cerebral trauma.

There are several reasons why the laboratory has concentrated its efforts on these late aftereffects of penetrating brain wounds. The majority of the men had been in early adulthood when injured; their subsequent condition permitted detailed and protracted testing. They did not show the variable, and often progressive, pathology seen in cases of brain tumor or vascular accident, nor was there pre-existing illness, as in cases of psychosurgery, or in surgery for disorders of the basal ganglia. By testing the control group, norms could be obtained for a wide range of sensory, motor, and intellectual tasks, and deficits in the performance of the experimental group could be defined as deviations from these norms. By uncovering consistent deficits in the presence of certain lesions, one can then raise questions about the ways in which different aspects of behavior depend on the integrity of the brain.

To answer these questions, the cases of brain injury were classified in two ways: once, according to the presumed site of their lesions, and secondly, in terms of various key symptoms (e.g., visual field defects, or sensory or motor deficits). Thus, a given experimental task could be set for all men whose known injury implicated, say, the frontal region, or, to give another example, the right cerebral hemisphere. The performance of these men could then be contrasted with that of all other men whose known injuries seemed to spare the indicated regions. Similarly, one could compare all men with a given symptom, such as sensory deficits of the left hand, with those who lacked the deficit.

This dual approach is described in detail in the monograph by Semmes, Weinstein, Ghent, & Teuber (1960). Its essential feature, for the present purpose, lies in the independence of analyses, (a) according to presumed location of lesions (e.g., left vs. right cerebral hemisphere), and, (b) according to side of body affected (e.g., sensory or other deficits on right vs. left hand). These distinctions permitted us to ask in what major ways injuries of left and right hemispheres seemed to differ in their behavioral consequences. Furthermore, the approach made it possible to raise the question of whether lesions of one or the other cerebral hemisphere might not have unsuspected ipsilateral or bilateral effects, i.e., whether symptoms of unilateral lesions are invariably contralateral in their distribution over the patient's body. By setting a rather wide variety of tasks, we could also assess the patterning of symptoms: we could ask which symptoms appeared together and which ones were readily dissociated. This inquiry into various groupings of defects led to further, and equally unsuspected, differences in the effects of right and left hemispheric lesions.

HEMISPHERE DIFFERENCES: ANALYSES ACCORDING TO LOCATION OF LESIONS

If we look at our results in terms of the presumed site of the lesions, we encounter immediately some of the expected differences between hemispheres: Lesions of the left cerebral hemisphere—particularly the left parietotemporal region—produce significant and lasting losses on a (predominantly verbal) test of "general intelligence" (see Weinstein, this volume). Conversely, there are indications that certain perceptual changes appear to a disproportionate extent after lesions of the presumably lesser hemisphere, i.e., the right side of the brain.

Left Parietotemporal Symptoms: Verbal and Nonverbal

After left hemispheric damage, particularly of left parietotemporal regions (Weinstein, this volume), we find significant losses on the Army General Classification Test, when pre- and posttraumatic scores for the same men are compared (Weinstein & Teuber, 1957; Teuber & Weinstein, 1958). This is all the more important because the same test failed to disclose any losses in other subgroups, i.e., in those with known lesions elsewhere in the brain. Such a negative finding can be interpreted in two ways: It underscores, first, the notorious lack of sensitivity of such routine psychometric tests in revealing residuals of brain injury in man. Secondly, one could say that a test of this sort does seem to pick up certain aftereffects, provided the lesion involves the critical left parietotemporal region.

But what is the nature of the deficit revealed by the Army General Classification Test? It is not dysphasia, in any obvious sense of the term; as the subsequent report will show, the left parietotemporal deficit was still marked when analysis of test scores was repeated following elimination of scores from those cases which had previously been classified as dysphasic (by consensus of the staff) or as having shown signs of dysphasia at any time after their brain injury. This might mean that the AGCT reveals minimal traces of aphasia which are not noticed in any other way, or that there are consequences of left parietotemporal lesions which manifest themselves as an intellectual deficit independent of any demonstrable language loss.

The latter alternative is strengthened by the observation that our patients with left parietotemporal lesions also showed maximal impairment on a seemingly nonverbal task: A visual "conditional reaction" which has been described in detail elsewhere (Teuber, Battersby & Bender, 1951; Weinstein, Teuber, Ghent, & Semmes, 1955; Teuber, 1959). Briefly, the task requires that the patient choose a triangle rather than a circle, if both figures appear on a horizontally striped background; he must choose the circle rather than the triangle, if both figures appear on a background with vertical stripes. The task is complicated by varying the colors of the figures (triangle, circle) in a predetermined sequence irrelevant to solution. On this task which is given (and taken) without explicit verbal communication between experimenter and subject, there appears a differential deficit: men with left parietotemporal wounds show maximal impairment.

Right Hemispheric Symptoms

In the past, specific effects of lesions involving the so-called lesser hemisphere have been characterized as complex perceptual changes: visuospatial or visuoconstructive achievements are hampered (Lange, 1936; Dide, 1938; Hebb, 1939; Brain, 1941; Wagner, 1942; Paterson & Zangwill, 1944; McFie, Piercy & Zangwill, 1950; Hécaen & collaborators,

1951, 1956; Critchley, 1953; Milner, 1958; Zangwill, 1960) . More recently these peculiar deficits after right hemispheric lesions have been brought out with various kinds of pictorial material (picture absurdities, Milner, 1954; reversible figures, Cohen, 1959; tachistoscopy, Ettlinger, 1960; incompletely drawn faces, Landsdell, 1961).

There is, however, increasing evidence that these complex perceptual tasks need not be visual in order to reveal preponderant losses after lesions in the so-called lesser hemisphere. They may involve complex tactual tasks (Weinstein, this volume), and they implicate certain complex auditory achievements, (Milner, this volume). Accordingly, we shall give instances of certain visual, auditory, and tactual symptoms that appear to be more marked after right than left hemispheric involvement.

Visual fits. Within the visual modality, a subtle and curious disproportion may exist in the incidence of "visual fits," i.e., epileptic attacks, either beginning with visual manifestations, or entirely confined to the visual sphere (Teuber, Battersby, & Bender, 1960). Figure 1 shows the centers of the wounds of entrance in the 15 cases out of our total group, who had one or (usually) several of these attacks. Thirteen of these 15 had entrance wounds implicating the right hemisphere, primarily in the occipital and temporal regions. The number of cases is small, to be sure, and there are many with clearly bilateral involvement. Nevertheless, the disproportion of right hemispheric cases is suggestive: The Montreal group (Penfield, 1958) has a similar asymmetry in their cases of temporal lobe epilepsy with visual onset (10 of 11 cases have right temporal lesions); and Dr. Hécaen's (1951) material seems to point in the same direction: Of 24 cases with visual fits described by Hécaen and Badaraco (1956), lateralizing signs are mentioned for 16. Of these 16, 14 seemed to have a lesion in the right, rather than left, hemisphere.

Disproportionate auditory and tactual deficits. In the auditory sphere, slightly greater impairment of binaural localization with right parieto-temporal lesions has been noted in our group (Teuber & Diamond, 1956); this finding shall be described below, since it involves a special method of bilateral stimulation.

In the tactile sphere, we obtained a similarly suggestive difference (more impairment after right hemispheric lesions) in a simple study involving a formboard, i.e., a task which required the patient to fit variously shaped blocks (under exclusion of vision) into the appropriate holes in a board (Teuber & Weinstein, 1954). In this test, there were two runs of trials: In the first run, the formboard was placed upright before the patient; in the second run, immediately afterwards, it was turned

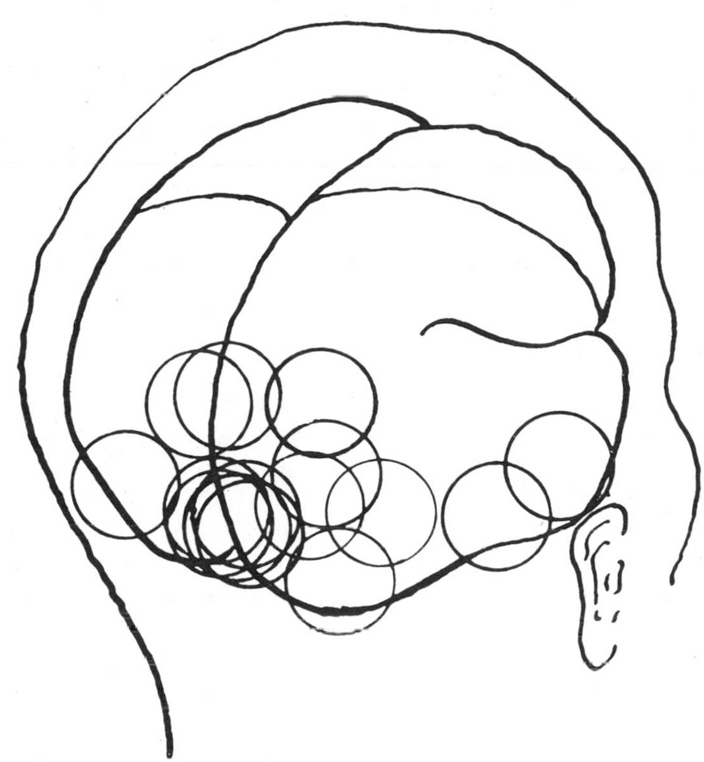

Fig. 1. Schematic representation of centers of bone gaps (wounds of entrance) in 15 cases of recurrent "visual fits" following penetrating missile injury of the brain.

180°, and the task repeated. The controls and all but one of the groups with brain lesion did better on this second run, in spite of the rotation of the board. Only those with right temporal lesions showed the reverse: they showed "negative transfer," i.e., their scores on the second run were significantly poorer than on the first. The next report (Weinstein, this volume) will describe a similar instance of disproportionate impairment for right-sided lesions on a haptic task involving the discrimination of tridimensional size.

It may be pointed out that the right-left differences cited so far are matters of degree rather than differences in kind, and that they tend to be small. Nevertheless, the right hemispheric symptoms (mostly right parietal and right temporal) should not be dismissed as trivial. In particular, one should not say that the differences are spurious, i.e., that these perceptual alterations are actually just as marked after lesions of the left hemisphere, but are masked, in left hemispheric cases, by simultaneous presence of aphasia. As is well-known, persistent aphasic disturbances are much less frequent in populations such as ours, where lesions are due to gunshot wounds, than in cases of vascular or neoplastic disease. In fact, none of our cases showed aphasia severe enough to obscure the perceptual changes we have reviewed here.

HEMISPHERIC DIFFERENCES: ANALYSES ACCORDING TO SYMPTOMS

Basic Sensory Thresholds

The case for genuine differences between the modes of functional representation in left and right hemispheres is strengthened further by recent discoveries about the state of elementary sensory thresholds after penetrating brain injury. For several years, Drs. Josephine Semmes, Sidney Weinstein, Lila Ghent, and I have studied the classical sensory thresholds of the brain-injured population by a variety of simple psychophysical techniques. Thus, we obtained thresholds for light pressure (by a modified von Frey technique), two-point discrimination, point localization, and ability to gauge passive motion of joints. The psychophysical methods employed have been described in detail in our recent monograph (Semmes, *et al.*, 1960); threshold values obtained for the patients were assessed against the distribution of scores obtained in 33 of our control subjects (without brain injury). These studies were carried out on 124 of the 232 patients; 88 of these had presumably unilateral lesions (44 right, 44 left) and 36 had clearly bilateral brain wounds, i.e., penetration of both hemispheres. Our principal findings, as summarized in the recent monograph, were threefold:

(a) Threshold changes of the right hand were associated, as expected, with lesions of the opposite hemisphere; these lesions were concentrated in the sensorimotor sector (pre- and postcentral as well as parietal regions.) By contrast, threshold changes of the *left* hand (though equally frequent) followed an aberrant pattern: the corresponding lesions were dispersed rather widely over the contralateral, and even, in many cases, the ipsilateral hemisphere. As has rightly been stressed (Ettlinger, this volume), a particularly high incidence of ipsilateral involvement (10 cases) was found for changes in point localization on the left hand, after left hemispheric lesions; in 4 of these 10 cases, both hands showed defective point localization. However, a similar differential pattern was seen for ordinary light-touch thresholds: abnormally raised thresholds of the right hand were associated with the expected lesions in the sensorimotor sector of the left hemisphere, but abnormal touch thresholds of the left hand were not analogous, since the corresponding lesions were scattered widely over the right, and sometimes even the left, cerebral hemisphere. In sum, tactile deficits of the right hand turned out to be much more easily localized in our population than those of the left.

(Only the results for sense of passive movement differed: they conformed to the expected, classical pattern of crossed representation.)

(b) Another aspect of the asymmetry we have described is the observation that left hemispheric lesions, more often than right, were followed by sensory changes in both hands. This, too, was found most often for point localization, and least (in fact, not significantly) for sense of passive motion.

(c) Finally, there were somewhat different kinds of sensory change in the right and left hands, respectively. Thus, disregarding the presumed site of the cerebral lesions, and merely correlating threshold values on each hand separately, it turned out that tactile deficits of the right hand were highly correlated: presence of one type of change, e.g., decreased pressure sensitivity, made it more likely that there would be abnormalities on the other three tasks. Conversely, for the left hand, there was *no* significant correlation between alterations in touch-pressure and those in point localization. This finding is of particular importance to us, because it shows a right-left difference quite independently of any assumptions about the exact site of the cerebral lesions.[3]

Although we are thus convinced that our statements are descriptive of the group we have studied, the findings are greatly in need of cross-validation for other groups of patients, preferably in those with brain lesions of different etiology. Should the asymmetry we described be sustained, one would like to know about its early development—that is, whether children show similar or different asymmetries, or none at all. In addition, one would like to know what would happen in the strongly left-handed patient. Isolated cases of bilateral sensory defect after unilateral cerebral lesions have previously been described (e.g., Foix, 1922), especially for left-handed patients (Guillain, *et al.,* 1925). In our own study, only nine men were apparently left-handed prior to their injury, and one was ambidextrous. These numbers are much too small for any analysis of the role of sinistrality.

It has often been suggested that the left-handed may show a more diffuse representation of language mechanisms than the right-handed (Chesher, 1936; Conrad, 1949; Humphrey & Zangwill, 1952; Goodglass

[3] Further analyses (Semmes, *et al., loc. cit.,* 1960) revealed that these differential results for left and right hands could not be attributed to any possible differential role of aphasia (15 cases), intellectual loss (21 cases), or epilepsy, although one-third of all patients with penetrating brain wounds had suffered one or more posttraumatic seizures.

& Quadfasel, 1954; Hécaen & Piercy, 1956; also A. R. Luria, in a personal communication). If this is so (and there are some who take issue with this view, e.g., Bingley, 1954), then the pattern of representation for language in the left-handed would be analogous to the pattern found by us, for sensory representation of the left hand in dextrals (Semmes, *et al.*, *loc. cit.*, 1960).

We should also point out that our somewhat unexpected results would not have been obtained, had we followed clinical usage, and combined the criteria of lateralization derived from knowledge of lesions and of symptoms. Only by keeping our classifications according to lesion and symptom apart did these peculiar results emerge.

HEMISPHERIC INTERACTION: UNILATERAL VERSUS BILATERAL LESIONS

The results just described were obtained by testing one side of the body at a time, and by considering lesions in one hemisphere as compared with equivalent lesions in the other. We now turn to the questions of interaction between hemispheres; first we shall cite some results bearing on the complex relations between effects of unilateral and of bilateral lesions; then we shall review certain results of unilateral versus bilateral simultaneous stimulation.

Autonomy of Hemispheres

Looking at lesions in either hemisphere, the simplest consequence one might anticipate would be strictly contralateral symptoms—such as the results we expected to find in the somatosensory system, but did not quite get, as has just been discussed. In the visual system, however, homonymous scotomata conform to the simple crossed pattern—lesions in the left optic radiation or optic cortex producing scotomata in the opposite homonymous halves of the visual field, and correspondingly for lesions on the right (Teuber, Battersby, & Bender, 1960).

Unilateral Deficits of Perceptual Learning

Rather less expected is such autonomy and equivalence of the two hemispheres for certain forms of learning. Yet this relative independence of the two halves of the brain can be demonstrated. For instance, we can present a tactile pattern learning task, separately, to the two hands (Figure 2): Here the patient holds a bidimensional pattern on his palm

Fig. 2. Bidimensional forms used in pattern discrimination test (Ghent, Weinstein, Semmes, & Teuber, 1955). For each trial, one of the patterns is placed for 5 seconds on the subject's palm, and then placed within the array. The subject then palpates the 6 patterns, attempting to identify the one which has just been placed on his hand. Vision is excluded by the simple device of screening the patterns with a black cloth. For further details, see text.

for 5 seconds and then attempts to identify this pattern in the array of 5 additional patterns displayed in the apparatus. Each hand is employed 18 times in this fashion, so that we can obtain (a) an average score, i.e., the overall proficiency for one hand in discriminating these tactile patterns, and (b) a learning curve indicating the gradual increase in proficiency, for that hand, from trial to trial. When results of this task are analyzed simply in terms of (a) average scores, one finds a deficit involving both hands (see next section); by contrast, when results are analyzed in terms of (b) learning curves, irrespective of the level of performance, one encounters a different kind of symptom (Ghent, Weinstein, Semmes, & Teuber, 1955): men with unilateral brain lesions (right or left) showed significant improvement (comparable to the control group) throughout the series of trials, for the hand on the same side as the injury. The hand opposite the lesion, however, did not show any significant improvement. This lack of improvement (i.e., failure to "learn" under these conditions) was not related to presence or absence of sensory defects as defined by the basic threshold measurements, nor was this lack of improvement related to the lobe injured.

Thus, an impairment of learning appeared after unilateral lesions, but the impairment was strictly confined to the hand opposite the lesion. These results speak for a certain equipotentiality within a hemisphere for this type of task, but they also indicate a surprising degree of independence between the two hemispheres.

INTERDEPENDENCE BETWEEN HEMISPHERES: BILATERAL IMPAIRMENT OF DISCRIMINATIVE ABILITY AFTER UNILATERAL LESIONS

These results are all the more remarkable since there are certain other and very pervasive signs of bilateral effects of unilateral lesions. We have frequently stressed (Teuber & Bender, 1949; Battersby, 1951; Teuber, Battersby, & Bender, 1960; Teuber, 1960) that subtle changes in basic visual functions (flicker-fusion, dark adaptation, motion perception) are found in both lateral halves of a visual field, in the presence of a scotoma in one homonymous half. In this respect then, the two halves of the field appear to be interdependent. Analogous results exist for certain tactile discriminations (including the pattern discrimination task just described). In the presence of sensory changes in one hand, subtle but significant changes in capacity for object quality discrimination through the tactile sense (for texture, bidimensional pattern, or solid form) have been detected in *both* hands (Ghent, Semmes, Weinstein, & Teuber, 1955; Teuber, 1959, 1960). These "bimanual effects" are disclosed by considering average scores for each hand, rather than learning curves. Such results suggest that it may depend on the level of performance required by a given task, whether the two hemispheres may seem to be interdependent or independent.

Bilateral Changes in "Time-Error" Function

A particularly effective way of demonstrating hemispheric interdependence in man is to require short-term temporal interaction between successive stimuli. When two light flashes, two clicks, or two pressure stimuli are presented one after the other, with intervals of one-half second to several seconds, the first of the two will be underestimated relative to the second, as if some trace process, set up by the first stimulus, had begun to dissipate by the time the second arrives (so-called "negative time-error," Köhler, 1923). This normal phenomenon—the overestimation of the second of two successive pressure stimuli—is abnormally enhanced after parietal lesions (Weinstein, 1955); this is found in either hand, after unilateral parietal lesion, right or left, thus indicating, again, a subtle change in function on both sides of the body, in the presence of a lesion that seems limited to one-half of the brain.

The possibility remains that such bilateral effects indicate an unknown bilaterality of the lesion, rather than diffuseness of functional representation. The possibility cannot be ruled out but is made less likely by the fact that these subtle bilateral effects here described occur with convexity lesions of the most varied etiology, i.e., not only after gunshot wounds, but also following vascular accidents or extrinsic tumors.

Paradoxical Effects of Bilateral Lesions

Interdependence between hemispheres may show itself in the form of an "overshoot," so-to-speak, of symptoms after unilateral lesions, so that the effects involve both sides of the body or of the visual field. But there is yet another sign of interdependence, rarer than the first, though much more revealing when it appears: certain bilateral lesions, under some conditions, turn out to be qualitatively different in their effects from those of their component unilateral lesions. Bilateral simultaneous removals of frontal eye fields in the experimental monkey do not produce a sum of the symptoms of unilateral neglect (the syndrome first described by Loeb, 1884) which follows either the right or left frontal removals, if these are carried out alone. In our studies with brain-injured patients, an analogous paradoxical result emerged.

Injury to the left or right hemisphere produced diminution in the rate at which a figure with ambiguous perspective (the double "Necker cube" shown on Figure 3) was seen to reverse itself (Figure 4); note that this diminution was maximal for lesions in the right hemisphere—as shown on the right side of the graph, and similarly maximal for frontal, as against postcentral, lesions. However, bilateral frontal lesions (top curve on the left side of the graph) produced the opposite of either of the component (unilateral) frontal injuries: men with bifrontal involvement differed from controls by showing abnormally frequent reversals, while unilateral frontals (right or left) showed maximal reduction in reversal rates (Cohen, 1959).

It may be important that a double figure (two cubes, placed side by side) was used in these experiments. If one uses, instead, a Rubin vase pattern, the unilateral frontals again show maximal reduction in

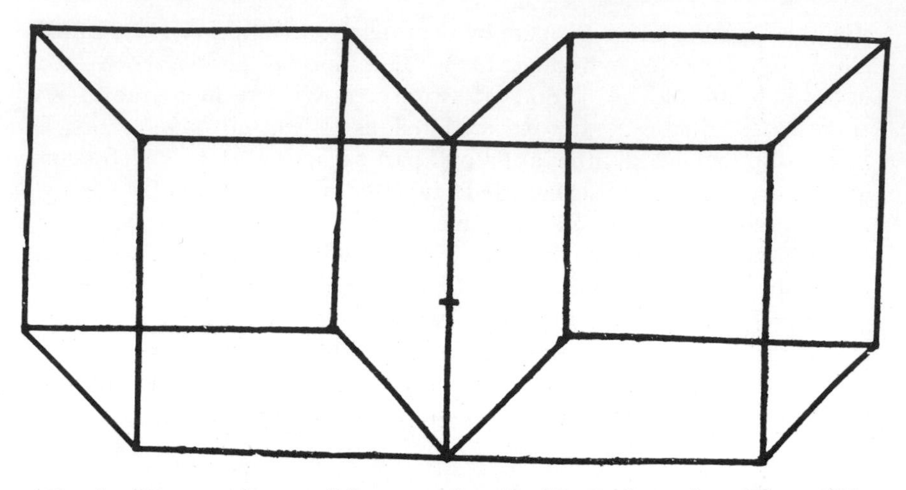

Fig. 3. Figure with reversible perspective (double Necker cube, Cohen, 1959; Teuber, 1960). The subject fixates on the short horizontal line which subdivides the central, vertical line of the figure. He is given buttons, one for the right, the other for the left index finger and instructed to depress the appropriate button or buttons upon each apparent reversal in the perspective of the right or left cube, or both.

reversal rate, but the bifrontal group shows rates equal to the controls; here the double lesion "undoes" what each single lesion would have done alone.

Such results require the assumption of some active influence between hemispheres which has become abnormal under the impact of a unilateral lesion but becomes modified again (or even normalized) when both hemispheres are symmetrically damaged.

HEMISPHERIC INTERACTION AS REVEALED BY BILATERAL STIMULATION

A particularly direct way of demonstrating bilateral interaction is the method of double stimulation. Instead of applying a single stimulus, or a succession of stimuli, to one side of the body (or one-half of the visual field) alone, one applies two or more stimuli, simultaneously, either in homologous or in nonhomologous regions. In principle, this method goes back as far as Loeb's animal experiments (1884), but interest in it has been revived repeatedly, especially by Poppelreuter (1917) during the first World War, and by Bender (1945) during and after the second.

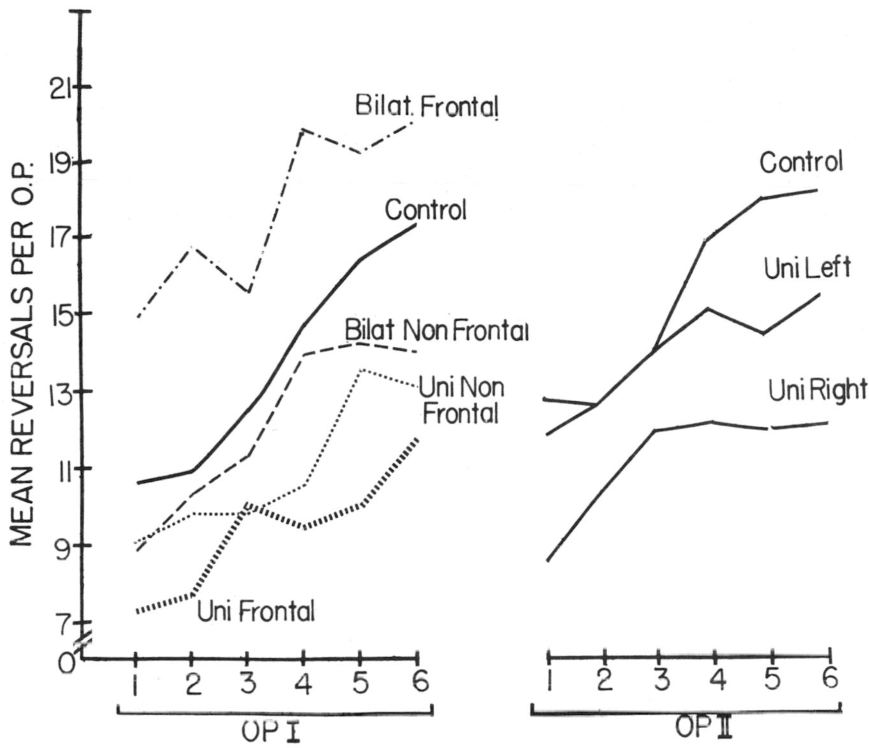

Fig. 4. Graphs showing average number of reversals for successive 15-second observation periods (OP 1–6) for the Necker cube illustrated in Figure 3. Patients with bifrontal lesions show more reversals, at all observation periods, than the controls without brain injury. Patients with uni- or bilateral brain lesions outside the frontal areas show fewer reversals than controls, and those with unilateral frontal lesions, least. The right side of the graph shows a similar comparison for controls without brain injury, and for brain-injured patients with left and right hemispheric damage, irrespective of lobe involved.

Extinction in Vision or Touch

The usual effect of such double stimulation, as shown in Figure 5 for vision, is the obscuration or disappearance of the impression in the half-field opposite a lesion (here a left parietal one, Teuber, Battersby, & Bender, 1960) as soon as both sides of the field are simultaneously stimulated. By contrast, exposing the stimuli one at a time leads to essentially normal perception. In a given patient, the phenomenon can exist for touch stimuli but not for vision, or conversely, for both vision and touch. The underlying change has been described as a form of lateralized inattention (Critchley, 1959), or as rivalry between the parietal lobes (Denny-Brown, *et al.*, 1952). However, the essential mechanism still eludes us: I am not aware of a convincing reproduction of this extinction phenomenon by experimentally placed lesions in animals; for man, we do not really know why extinction occurs when it does, nor why it fails to appear when it does not (Krueger, Price, & Teuber, 1954); it is seen perhaps more often after right parietal lesions than after lesions in other situations (Critchley, 1949, 1953), and it certainly occurs more readily in the acute phase, following an insult to the brain, than at later stages (Teuber, 1960).

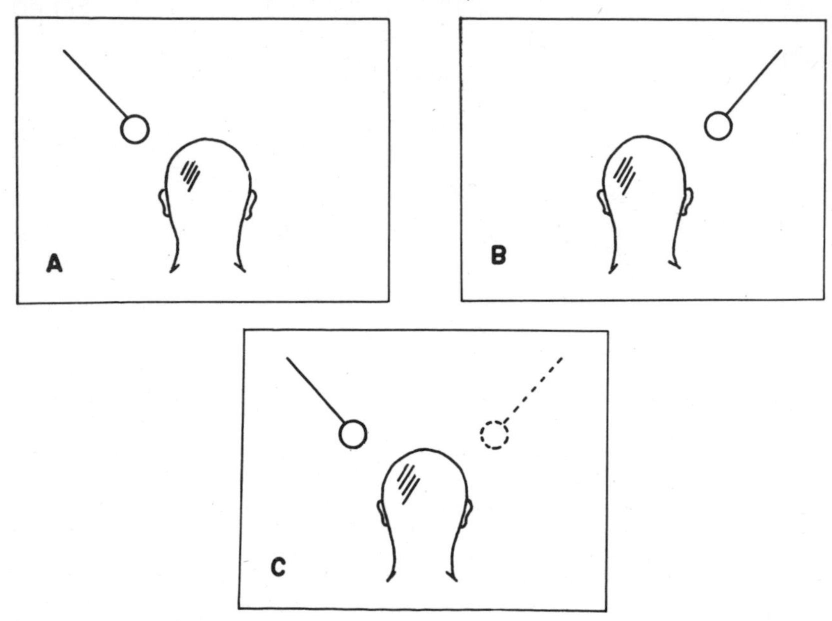

Fig. 5. "Extinction" in a case of left parietal injury on exposure of a single target in the left half (A) or right half (B) of the visual field; in both instances, the patient reports the target. On bilateral simultaneous stimulation in right and left halves of the field, the patient reports that the target on the right has vanished (Teuber, Battersby, & Bender, 1960).

Variants of Extinction: Bimanual Hefting of Weights

Phenomena akin to ordinary tactile extinction can be brought out in tests of weight judgment ("barognosis"), when unimanual and bimanual performances are compared. In the experiments illustrated in the next three figures, the patient is given a standard weight and a series of comparison weights. All weights look alike, but the series of comparison weights is so arranged that one of them is just as heavy as the standard, while the others are either heavier or lighter by small fractions (Fig-

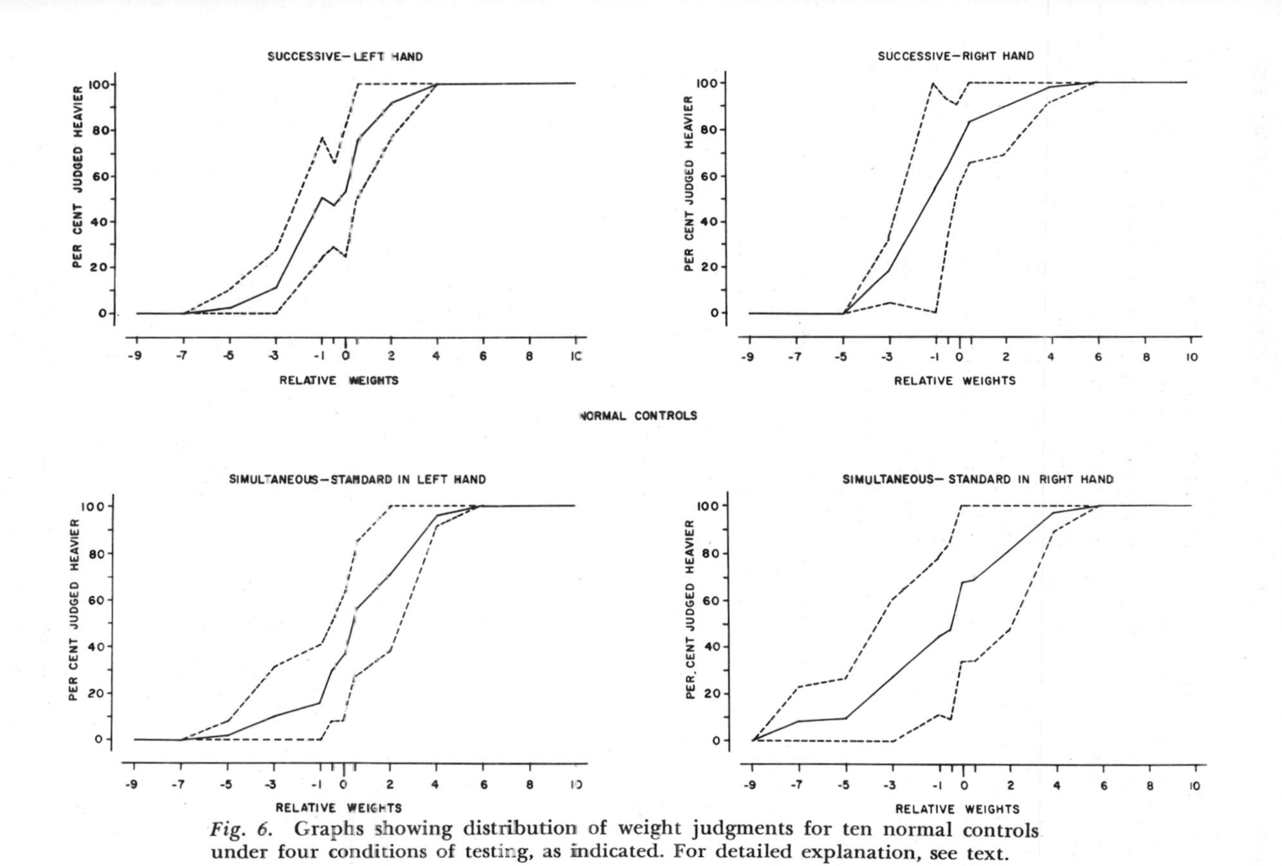

Fig. 6. Graphs showing distribution of weight judgments for ten normal controls under four conditions of testing, as indicated. For detailed explanation, see text.

ure 6). In this figure, the horizontal axis indicates the disposition of comparison weights, increasing to the right, decreasing to the left, so that those at the extreme right are very much heavier, and those to the extreme left, very much lighter than the standard.

The task is performed under four conditions: successive hefting of weights with one hand, successive hefting with the other hand, and simultaneous hefting with both hands, with the standard weight in the left hand, and with the standard weight in the right hand. Thus, in the unimanual conditions, the patient uses one hand alone, e.g., his left, hefting the standard and one of the comparison weights successively with the same hand and judging the comparison weight as "heavier" or "lighter" than the standard. This is repeated in random order, until every weight has been judged five times in relation to the standard. The resulting graph shows per cent heavier judgments, referring to the comparison weights, as a function of their objective weights.

An ideal curve produced by a supreme judge would look like this ___|‾‾. All weights actually lighter than the standard would be called lighter, and all that are heavier would be called heavier (with a 50–50 distribution in the middle where the comparison weight is identical with the standard). Since humans are imperfect, we obtain instead an S-shaped curve from our control subjects (Figure 6), whether they use their left hand alone, their right hand alone, or both hands simultaneously, with the standard weight in the left, or with the standard weight in the right. The dotted parallel lines to either side of the main function, in Figure 6, indicate the scatter of normal control values (for 10 control subjects) in terms of two standard deviations above, and two standard deviations below the mean judgments obtained at any point along these curves.

Results for brain-injured patients are shown in the next two figures. Figure 7 illustrates the findings for a man with a small left parieto-occipital gunshot wound, tested quite recently, i.e., over 15 years after the wounding. This man has normal thresholds for touch, two-point discrimination, and point localization and no abnormalities in sense of passive motion. His weight judgments performed with either hand alone are also normal, as can be seen in the upper half of the figure. However, as soon as he hefts weights with both hands together, he shows an abnormal performance: The weight held in the hand contralateral to the brain injury is consistently *under*estimated.

A more pronounced form of the same phenomenon is illustrated by the next figure (Figure 8). These are results for a man with a massive gunshot wound of the right postcentral and mid-parietal region who does show abnormal two-point discrimination and sense of passive

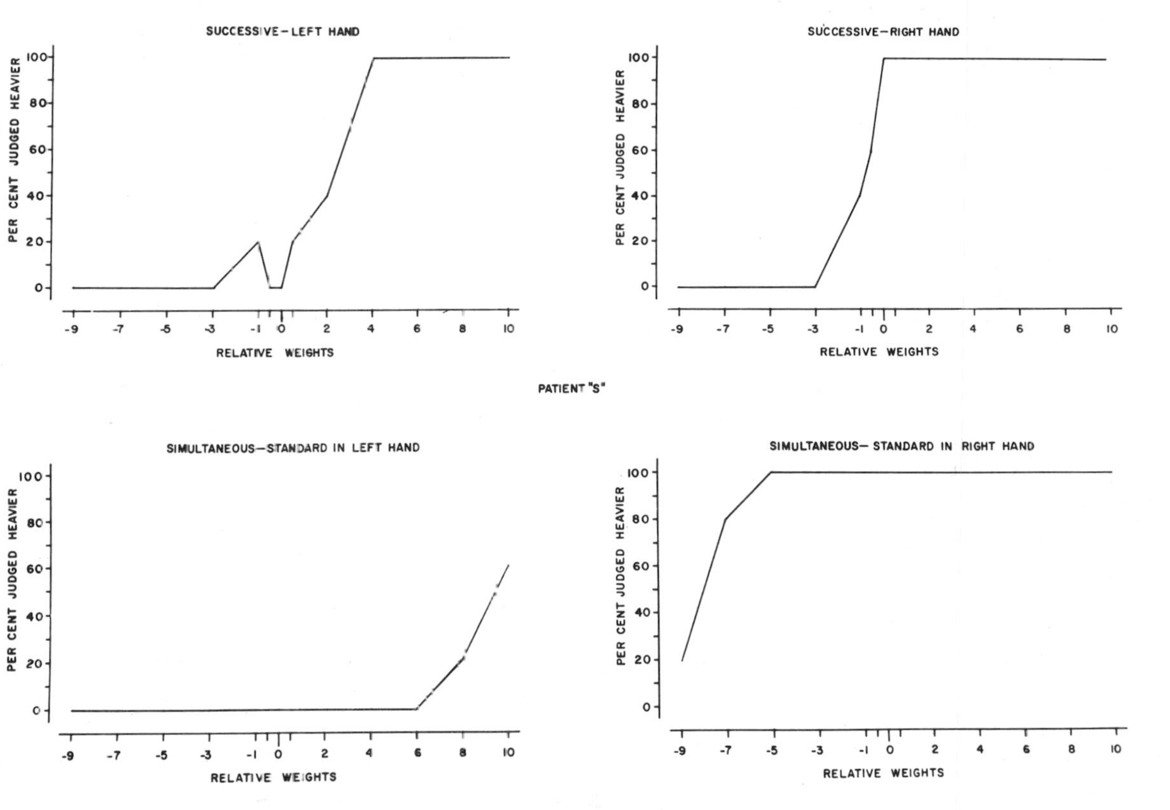

Fig. 7. Graph showing distribution of weight judgments for a patient with left parieto-occipital gunshot wound. Note consistent underestimation of weights held in the hand opposite the injury on simultaneous (bimanual) hefting. See text for details.

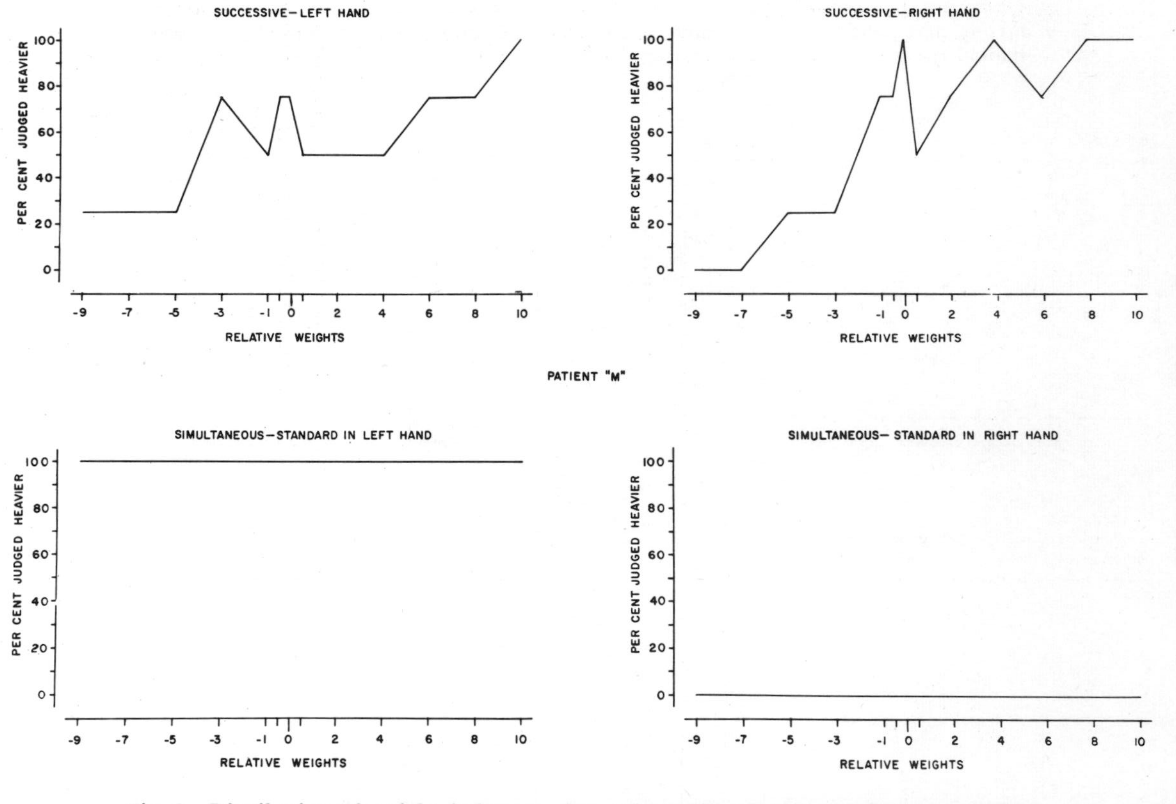

Fig. 8. Distribution of weight judgments for patient with massive gunshot wound of right postcentral and right midparietal region. Note marked underestimation of weights held in the left hand on simultaneous (bimanual) stimulation. Further details in text.

motion—both for his left hand. His touch and point localization thresholds, however, are normal.

As shown in Figure 8, this man does show somewhat defective weight judgments on using the left hand alone. The more striking abnormality, however, appears as soon as testing is bimanual: Every weight held in the left hand, no matter how heavy, appears lighter to him when it is hefted simultaneously with a standard weight held in his other hand.

In recent (unpublished) studies, in collaboration with Drs. Ildiko Mohacsy and Erich Krueger, we have noted that this peculiar change in barognosis, on bilateral simultaneous testing, can be a surprisingly independent sign of parietal lobe disease. Patterns such as those shown in the last two figures can be obtained in the presence but also in the absence of other, more basic, sensory signs, and there is no necessary connection between this alteration of weight judgment on bimanual hefting, and extinction for touch, pain, or visual stimuli.

Effects of Binaural (Dichotic) Stimulation

We have also inquired into possible analogous interaction between paired sense organs in the auditory sphere (Teuber & Diamond, 1956). The remarkable resiliency of many auditory functions, following large cerebral lesions in infrahuman forms, is well known (Neff, 1957). Nevertheless, slight changes in man are to be expected, and these should be accentuated by double (i.e., binaural) stimulation, especially if one selects those aspects of auditory performance that are known to depend on central interaction of neural processes arising in the right and left halves of the CNS.

Changes in hearing, after lesions of auditory structures outside the brain, are rather well understood; but little is known of auditory changes which might follow lesions restricted to the brain. This is in sharp contrast to the situation in the visual modality, where retrochiasmal lesions of the central pathways have their unmistakable (homonymous) consequences.

We have chosen to investigate binaural localization in brain-injured and normal subjects, employing dichotic clicks (i.e., pairs of clicks delivered with independent control over intensity and timing of each member of the pair). Others have used dichotic presentation of more highly structured material. Bocca (1958) used test words, presented through earphones, in such a way that one ear received the words without undue distortion, but with very low intensity; the other ear received the same words simultaneously, but with all frequencies above 500 cps removed. Under these conditions, each ear used alone yields only a 50 per cent articulation score (i.e., only half of the words are recognized), but binaural listening yields significantly better results. Such binaural interaction is diminished or absent in the presence of hemispheric lesions; in fact, Bocca (1958) believes that the impairment is specific for involvement of auditory cortex rather than brain stem structures, and that the test permits lateralization, since in his experience lower scores result from presenting the frequency-filtered speech to the ear opposite a cerebral lesion, and the low-intensity speech to the ipsilateral ear.

A similar binaural articulation test has been developed by Matzker (1958), who presented identical test words, through earphones, to the two ears; one ear, however, received only frequencies between 500–800 cps, the other those between 1500 and 2400. Matzker's normal listeners were able to perform a binaural synthesis under such conditions, thus obtaining an almost perfect articulation score, while each ear alone did quite poorly. In patients with cerebral lesions, the binaural synthesis was much diminished or absent, but it was also rather low in normal children, and nearly uniformly impaired in the aged (Matzker, *loc. cit.*, 1958). Current work in Montreal (Milner, this volume) is based on a much simpler method of binaural testing, derived from an experiment by Broadbent (1954).

In our own studies of binaural localization, we have employed thus far only 10 control subjects with nerve injuries of arm or leg and 20 men with penetrating brain wounds (7 of right hemisphere, 7 left, and 6 bilateral). Stimuli were delivered by earphones (PDR–10) which transduced pairs of pulses from a two-channel, square-wave generator into brief clicks. Relative arrival times at the ears could be set at simultaneity, or at varying delays. Intensity of clicks was separately controlled by attenuators.

In normal subjects, such pairs of clicks presented separately, one to each ear, will be perceived as a single (subjectively fused) click, as long as the interval between the two clicks is below a msec. These short time intervals are evaluated by the central nervous system instead, as variations in the spatial localization of the fused impression. The perceived click seems to be in the center of the head when the two clicks enter the ears nearly simultaneously but seems to shift toward the leading ear, as the time difference increases. Similarly, intensity differences between simultaneous clicks are perceived as a difference in spatial localization, so that the (subjectively fused) click seems displaced toward the ear which receives the greater intensity.

The experiment was performed in three parts: (1) Testing began with determination of absolute thresholds for monaural clicks. Stimulus intensity for each ear was then set at 25 db. above threshold for that ear, and binaural clicks presented. (2) With intensity held constant, relative time of arrival of clicks was varied in a predetermined sequence of delays covering a range of 0 delay to 2 msec. The subject indicated, for each trial, whether he heard the (fused) click in the center of his head, or to the left or right of center. Percentage judgment in each category was plotted as a function of time delay, and average errors, as well as constant errors of localization, were computed. (3) In the last part of the experiment, arrival time was held constant at simultaneity, and intensity of one click in the pair was varied relative to the other. Errors of judgment were computed as before.

When time was varied and intensity held constant, controls localized the sound with significantly greater precision (average error 105 μsec.) than the brain-injured (average error 225 μsec.). Some patients required a full msec. delay before reporting shifts in apparent localization. Subjects with frontal and frontoparietal lesions did somewhat better than subjects with temporal, parietal, and occipital lesions. (Similar results have been obtained in Russia by Gershuni and Blinkov.) Left hemispheric cases did slightly better than right hemispheric cases who did not differ from bilaterals (Figures 9 & 10). Larger numbers of cases are needed to test these differences among brain-injured subgroups. There

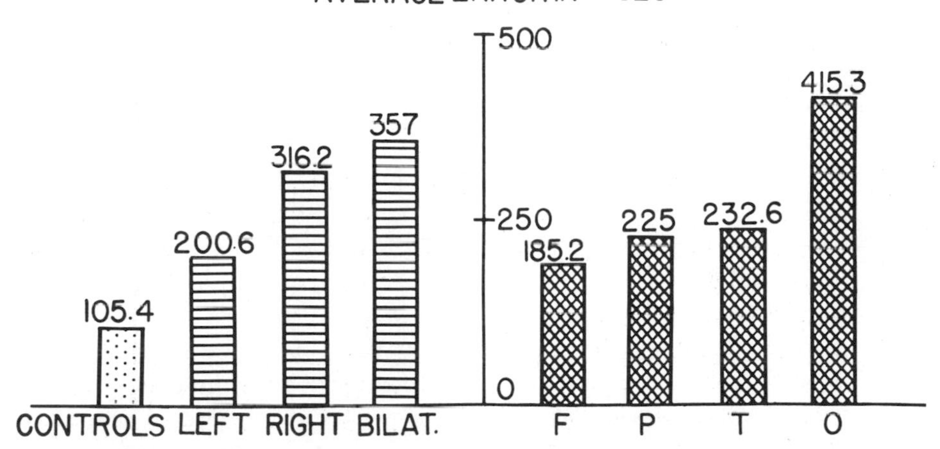

Fig. 9. Average error in microseconds in binaural sound localization for loudness-balanced clicks, with arrival time of clicks varied. "Left," "right," and "bilateral" refer to location of hemispheric lesions; F, P, T, O refer to frontal, parietal, temporal, and occipital, respectively.

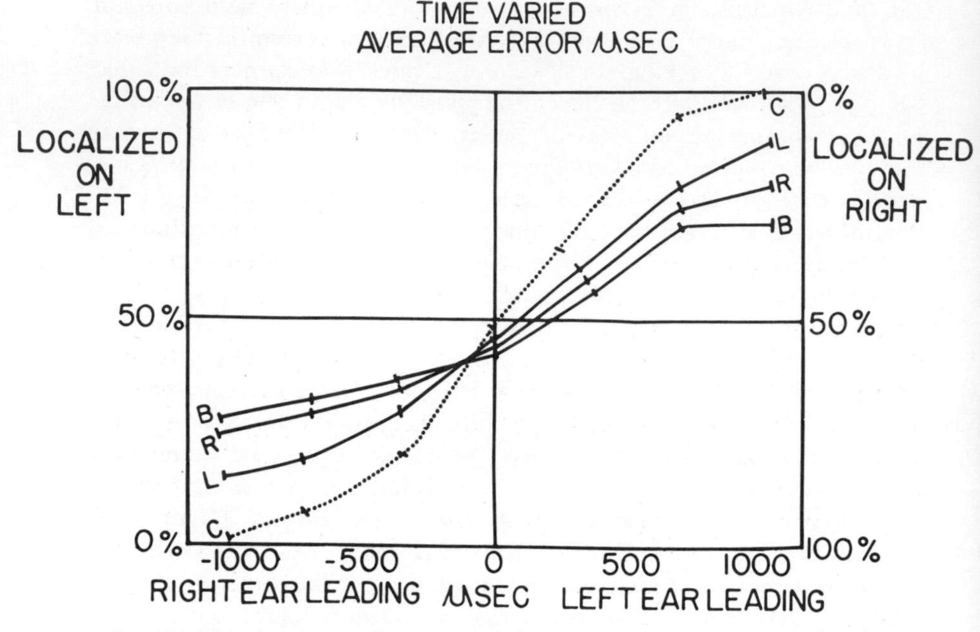

Fig. 10. Plot showing performance on binaural sound localization tests with time as variable for controls (C), and for brain-injured patients with involvement of left hemisphere (L), right hemisphere (R), and both hemispheres (B). See text for further explanation.

were no significant directional effects, i.e., constant errors did not differentiate the various groups.

With arrival time of clicks constant, and intensity varying, performance of patients was again significantly poorer (average 11 db.), than that of controls (5 db.). Subjects with postcentral injury did worse than frontals, and right hemispheric cases tended to be inferior to those with left unilateral lesions (Figure 11). There were rather marked directional effects: subjects with right unilateral lesions required more intensity on the left for mid-line judgments and conversely for men with left lesions (Figure 12). In this respect, judgments based on intensity behaved differently from those based on time. Moreover, individual subjects with marked difficulties for one type of judgment did better for the other, and conversely. Thus, brain injury can impair binaural localization based on time and intensity differences, but the effects are dissociable, suggesting at least partial separation of neural mechanisms underlying these two forms of localization.

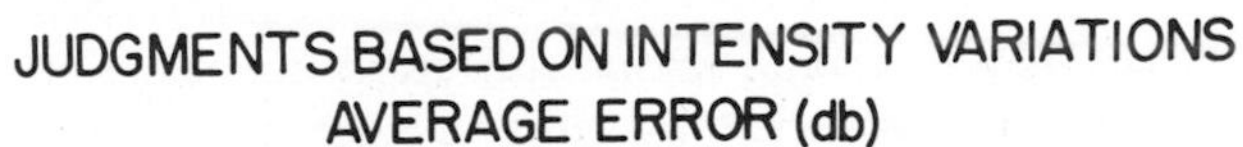

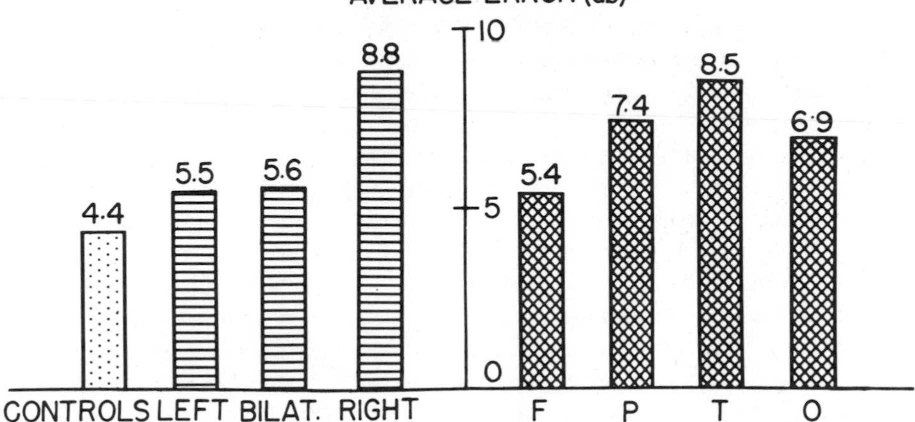

Fig. 11. Average error of binaural sound localization in decibels (db.), with intensity as experimental variable. See text and legend to Figure 9 for further explanations.

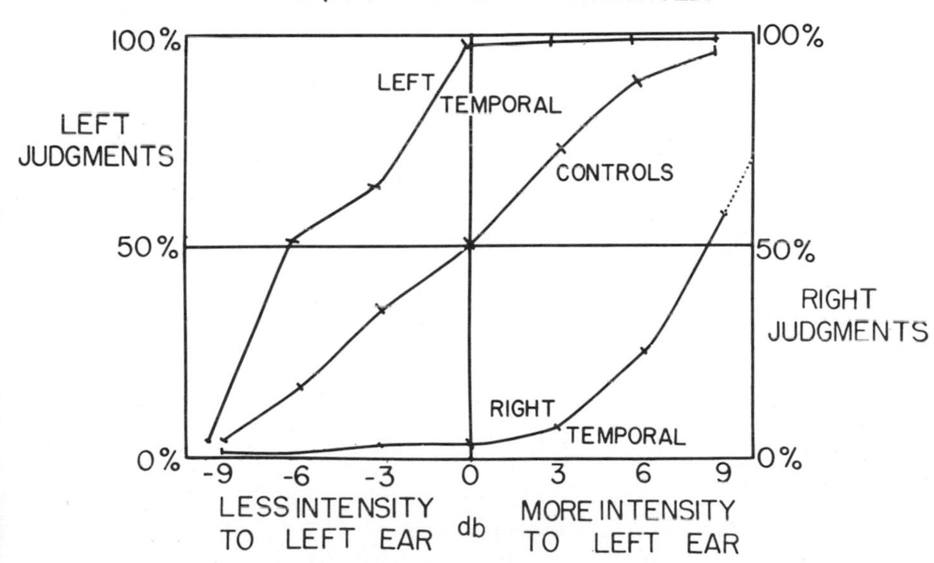

Fig. 12. Plots showing performance of controls, and of one patient with left temporal lesion and one with right temporal lesion on binaural localization test with intensity as experimental variable. See text for additional explanations.

An experimental arrangement employed in these studies permits assessment of still another value: the thresholds for separation of binaurally presented (dichotic) clicks. As the interval is increased beyond the range of binaural fusion, there appears the impression of two clicks—a loud one (referred to the leading ear) and a faint one (referred to the lagging ear). With a still further increase in the time interval, the click in the lagging ear seems to increase in loudness, until the subject hears definitely two separate clicks.

We have no adequate normative data on thresholds for recognition of duality in this situation. From our current exploratory work, we have reason to believe that the threshold, in the normal, lies between 1 and 2 msec., while many brain-injured patients require more than twice as much separation in time, before they hear the clicks as separate. These tests involving duality judgments for dichotic clicks form, in a sense, an auditory analogue of two-point thresholds in somesthesis. It will be of considerable interest to see whether impairment in one type of threshold is associated with impairment in the other, or whether the two types of impairment are again dissociable, being differentially vulnerable to lesions in different sectors of the brain.

CONCLUDING REMARKS

It is evident that much can be learned about differences between hemispheres, and about hemispheric interaction, if cases of cerebral lesions are studied with those psychophysical techniques that have been restricted in the past to work with normal subjects. Subtle losses in complex perceptual achievements turn out to be more frequent, or more pronounced, after lesions of the so-called "nondominant" hemisphere. Apparently, central representation of sensory functions for the left hand is not a simple mirror image of the sensory representation for the right hand. We have seen, further, that unilateral lesions, in either hemisphere, can have strictly contralateral consequences in some respects (homonymous scotomata, unilateral deficits of perceptual learning), or more diffuse, bilateral consequences (changes in flicker fusion in both halves of the visual field, in the presence of scotomata limited to one homonymous half; changes in tactile discrimination or time-error functions, in both hands, in the presence of parietal lesions in one hemisphere). Occasionally, lesions of both hemispheres have paradoxical effects which fail to represent a simple summation of those effects that would be expected after either of the component unilateral lesions.

The most intriguing signs of hemispheric interdependence, however, are the interactions between the two sides of the body or the two ears, or the two halves of the field of vision, on double or multiple simultaneous stimulation. Current work on subhuman forms employing split-brain preparations is addressed to the question of mutual facilitation and of transfer of training between hemispheres (see Sperry, Myers, Downer, Mishkin, this volume). Observations on brain-injured man add a variety of instances in which the hemispheres, in the presence of unilateral lesions, seem to get into each other's way. Impaired interaction can be shown on certain binaural tasks, and outright interference of varying degrees of severity appeared on bimanual judgment of weights.

So far, work of this sort does little to suggest how the hemispheres interact, but it underscores the vulnerability of this interaction, and adds further details to known differences in functional representation.

■□ VIII

Differences in Effects of Brain Wounds Implicating Right or Left Hemispheres:

Differential Effects on Certain Intellectual and Complex Perceptual Functions[1]

by SIDNEY WEINSTEIN

Albert Einstein College of Medicine, New York, New York

IN OUR STUDY of the effects of penetrating brain wounds on various sensory, motor, perceptual, and cognitive functions, although occasionally we found that the hemispheres did not differ with regard to effect of injury upon a patient's performance (Ghent, *et al.*, 1955a, b, c; Semmes, *et al.*, 1954, 1955; Teuber and Weinstein, 1955, 1956; Weinstein, 1954, 1955a, b, c; Weinstein, *et al.*, 1956, 1958a), we have also observed that injury to one hemisphere, but not the other, causes impairment on a given task (Semmes, *et al.*, 1960; Teuber and Weinstein, 1954; Weinstein, 1959; Weinstein, *et al.*, 1958b; Weinstein and Teuber, 1957). There are two specific functions I have selected to discuss today which demonstrate contrasting effects of right and left hemispheric lesions. The first demonstrates the effects of penetrating brain wounds in man on a test of general intelligence, the Army General

[1] All work reported was completed at the Psychophysiological Laboratory, Department of Neurology, New York University-Bellevue Medical Center. The study on size discrimination was done in collaboration with Drs. Josephine Semmes, Lila Ghent, and Hans-Lukas Teuber; the latter also collaborated in the study on intellectual functioning. During preparation of this manuscript, the author received support from the National Institutes of Health through the following grants: H-3838, M-2562, and A-2965. He is particularly indebted to OVR for their support under grant RD-427 and to the National Institutes of Health through grant B-3356.

Classification Test; the second concerns the effect of brain wounds upon a measure of three dimensional tactile size discrimination.[2]

Despite centuries of interest in the effect of cerebral lesions on intellectual function, there is little agreement as to the localization of those injuries that might produce maximal deficit on tests of general intelligence. One might suspect that any brain injury of sufficient size produces lasting deficits, in analogy to Lashley's (1941) results for rats. Against this view are recurrent claims that only lesions of certain areas of the brain, especially the frontal lobes, are followed by a loss. The uncertainty is increased by the large number of reports describing "negative" findings, that is, the absence of demonstrable deficits in test performance, despite the presence of large cerebral lesions, especially of the frontal lobes.

Most previous information derives from the testing of patients (often past middle age) with tumors or vascular accidents of the brain, and from cases of lobotomy or similar forms of psychosurgery in psychosis, severe neurosis, or intractable pain (Halstead, 1947; Hebb, 1939). Estimates of a decline in intelligence, based on a comparison with premorbid scores are rendered doubtful by the extent to which the disease process, e.g., brain tumor or psychosis, might have affected the patient's performance before operation, or continued to affect it afterward. As a result, the information is usually based on abnormal preoperative as well as postoperative scores.

To our knowledge, no studies exist which compare scores obtained on a standardized test of intelligence from patients, after relatively stable, localized brain injury, with corresponding scores achieved before injury, at a time when the patient could be considered physically and mentally intact. Nor are there studies in which a sufficiently long period elapsed after injury to allow maximum recovery from the effect of the brain wounds.

The opportunity for such a study arose in the course of a research program evaluating the effects of penetrating brain wounds on various aspects of behavior. We were able to obtain preinjury scores on the AGCT, a standardized test of general intelligence given each man on induction into the armed services, for 62 men who subsequently sustained penetrating brain wounds and for 50 controls, i.e., men who subsequently incurred peripheral nerve injuries of the upper or lower extremities. All men had been injured in World War II, one to three years after the initial testing. Approximately ten years after wounding, they were retested in our laboratory with a comparable form of the

[2] The population of brain-injured and control subjects has already been described elsewhere in this volume by Dr. Teuber.

AGCT (first civilian edition). Since all men had been given thorough physical and, at least cursory, psychiatric examination prior to induction, their preinjury scores can be considered as reasonably accurate estimates of general intellectual capacity, within the limits of such tests. Localization of the brain wound was based upon surgeons' notes at initial débridement, subsequent craniotomy, and upon roentgenographic evidence, i.e., bone defect and retained foreign bodies. In view of the lack of histologic verification of the lesions, all localizations are considered tentative.

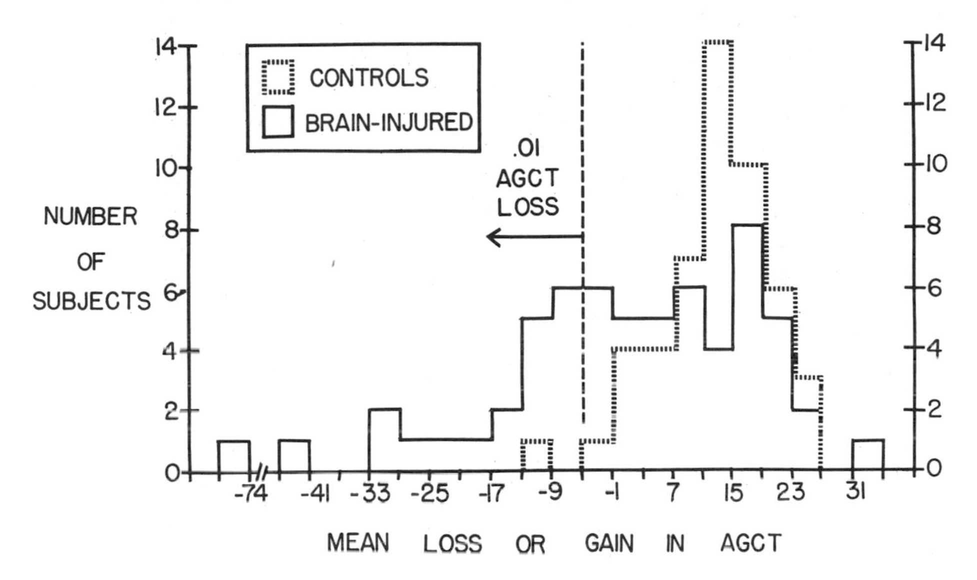

Fig. 1. Mean loss or gain in AGCT. The vertical dashed line is the .01 confidence limit, to the left of which are shown subjects with statistically significant loss in score.

The preinjury scores of our control and brain-injured groups were practically identical: the mean of the controls was 106.4; that of the subsequently brain-injured was 105.0. On the postinjury test, 48 of the 50 controls increased their score, yielding a mean of 119.4, or a mean increase of 13 points. This general tendency to gain was an orderly phenomenon, since the Pearson product moment correlation between pre- and postinjury scores was .902, indicating considerable retest reliability. Figure 1 shows the distribution of average losses or gains in AGCT scores for the 50 control subjects without brain-injury (broken line) and the 62 brain-injured subjects (solid line). Note first of all that the distributions overlap and that two-thirds of the brain-injured show the same pattern of gain following injury that is exhibited by all but 2 of the 50 controls.

The vertical broken line further indicates at what point a loss in score is statistically significant at the 1 percent level, for a one-tailed distribution. Only one control subject and 19 brain-injured subjects fell beyond this point, thus showing significant loss.

The next question is whether the losses occurred predominantly in any particular group of our brain-injured population. For this purpose the 62 brain-injured subjects were subdivided into groups according to the estimated location of their lesions (frontal, temporal, parietal, occipital, in left, in right, or both hemispheres), and the data were subjected to a series of analyses of variance. These analyses demonstrated that lesions of the frontal or occipital lobes did not produce a significant decline in score, and that only groups with wounds of parietal or temporal lobes of the left hemisphere showed a significant decrease.

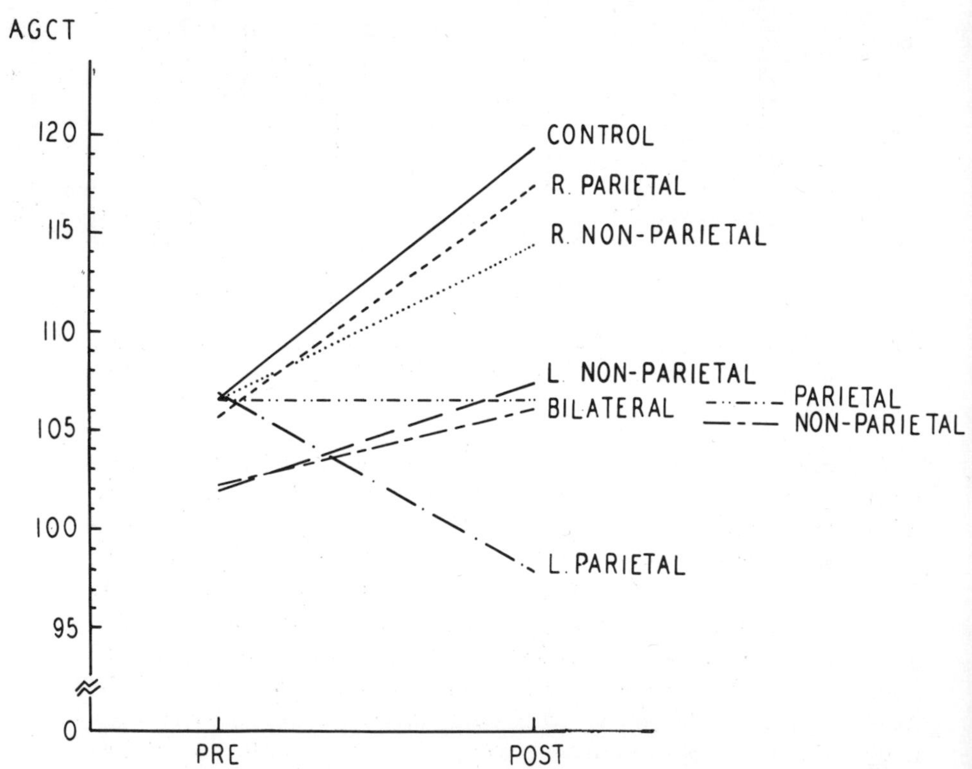

Fig. 2. Mean pre- and postinjury AGCT scores in controls and groups with parietal lobe lesions of either, neither, or both hemispheres.

Figure 2 gives the means of the pre- and postinjury scores for the various subgroups in the parietal analysis. It can be seen first of all that the preinjury scores of all subgroups tended to be within a few I.Q. points of each other. When one looks at the change in score from pre- to postinjury, it is apparent that five of the groups show a positive slope, (i.e., they show an improvement in score from the pre- to the postinjury testing); one group shows no change from pre- to postinjury tests and one group shows a striking decline in score. At the top are shown the control group and the two subgroups with wounds of the right hemisphere (i.e., the right parietal and the right nonparietal groups). Further down, demonstrating a somewhat lesser slope, i.e., a lesser increase in score, are the left nonparietal and the bilateral nonparietal groups. The group with bilateral parietal lesions shows very little change from preinjury to postinjury testing. However, the most striking finding concerns the group with left parietal lesions, which shows a marked decline from preinjury to postinjury testing.[3] Similar results were obtained when the analysis was applied to the group with lesions of the left temporal lobe. In order to investigate further the role of the two regions, a subsequent analysis was performed which compared men with lesions involving either or both of these lobes with those in whom these lobes were spared.

Figure 3 gives the mean increase or decrease in score after retest. The bars above the horizontal line show increase, those below, decrease. The black bars show the mean scores for subgroups of the total brain-injured population. It can be seen that the group with lesions of the left temporal lobe showed a slight decrease in score, and that the most striking drop was exhibited by the group with left parietotemporal lesions. In comparison with the large gain shown in the control group, the group with left parietal lesions showed only a slight increase on retesting; the groups without left parietotemporal lesions, or with lesions of the right hemisphere, showed greater gains, closer to that of the control group. The parietal, temporal, and parietotemporal groups with lesions of the left hemisphere were all statistically significantly inferior to the control group, and the left parietotemporal group was significantly inferior to every other brain-injured subgroup, with the exception of the left temporal group.

[3] The paradoxical finding that cases with bilateral parietal lesions were not impaired, whereas those with left parietal lesions showed profound losses has a simple explanation. Lesions of the left parietal lobe could be both massive and deep; lesions of both parietal lobes consistent with survival could only be restricted to superficial "gutter-type" wounds of the vertex. No cases were found with lesions of the lateral surfaces of both parietal lobes.

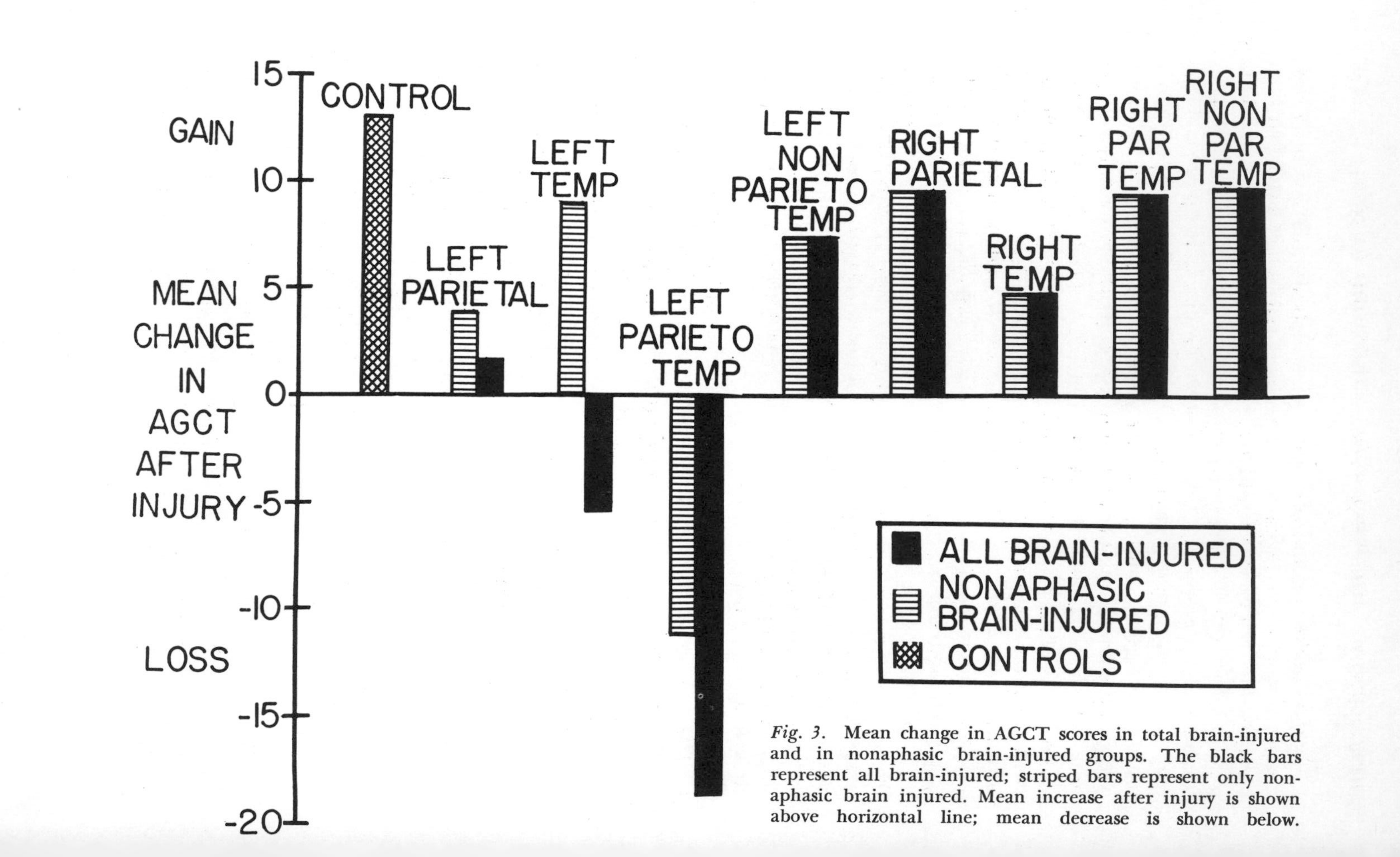

Fig. 3. Mean change in AGCT scores in total brain-injured and in nonaphasic brain-injured groups. The black bars represent all brain-injured; striped bars represent only nonaphasic brain injured. Mean increase after injury is shown above horizontal line; mean decrease is shown below.

One might suspect that the inferior performance of the groups with lesions of the left parietal and left temporal lobes (either or both) was entirely due to the presence of aphasia. Indeed, when the analyses were restricted to nonaphasics (the striped bars), the groups showed somewhat higher scores, and the group with the left temporal lesions now exhibited a gain rather than loss. The control group differed significantly only from the left parietal and left parietotemporal groups. The left parietotemporal group alone still showed a loss in score and was significantly inferior to every other group.

Essentially the same picture is shown in Figure 4. Here, the results are presented in terms of the number of individual subjects in each subgroup manifesting significant losses in score. The ordinate above the horizontal line shows number of subjects with statistically significant decline in scores; those below did not show this decline. It can be seen that only one of the 50 control subjects dropped significantly on retest. If we examine the black bars, we see that with the exception of the left parietotemporal group there were no more than two subjects in any group who showed this level of deficit on retest. In the left parietotemporal group, however, 9 of the 10 subjects dropped significantly. The striped bars give the same results after eliminating dysphasic subjects. It can be seen that the left parietotemporal group still contributes a disproportionate share of subjects with significant impairment.

The fact that there was a concentration in a particular area (the left parietotemporal) of those lesions which produced a demonstrable AGCT deficit in the absence of manifest aphasia, opposed the view that impairment is equal after lesions in any lobe, or that it should be maximal after injury to the frontal regions.

One obvious explanation which might be offered to account for the results is that groups with injury to the left hemisphere suffer from dysphasia, and that intellectual deficit on a verbal task merely reflects aphasic difficulties. There are three reasons why we believe that this is not the case. The first is that men with gross aphasic symptoms were not tested. The second is that all men had to complete 30 items of the AGCT correctly before they were permitted to take the test. The third reason is that in spite of the fact that some dysphasic subjects still completed the test, their elimination resulted in essentially unchanged results. The criticism that the impairment found was merely a "subtle" form of aphasia merely begs the question. The interpretation that injury to this region may have resulted in occlusion of the middle cerebral artery cannot be denied. If the implication of this statement is to invoke the theory of mass action *within this region,* then the argument may be valid. However, if such argument is invoked on behalf of

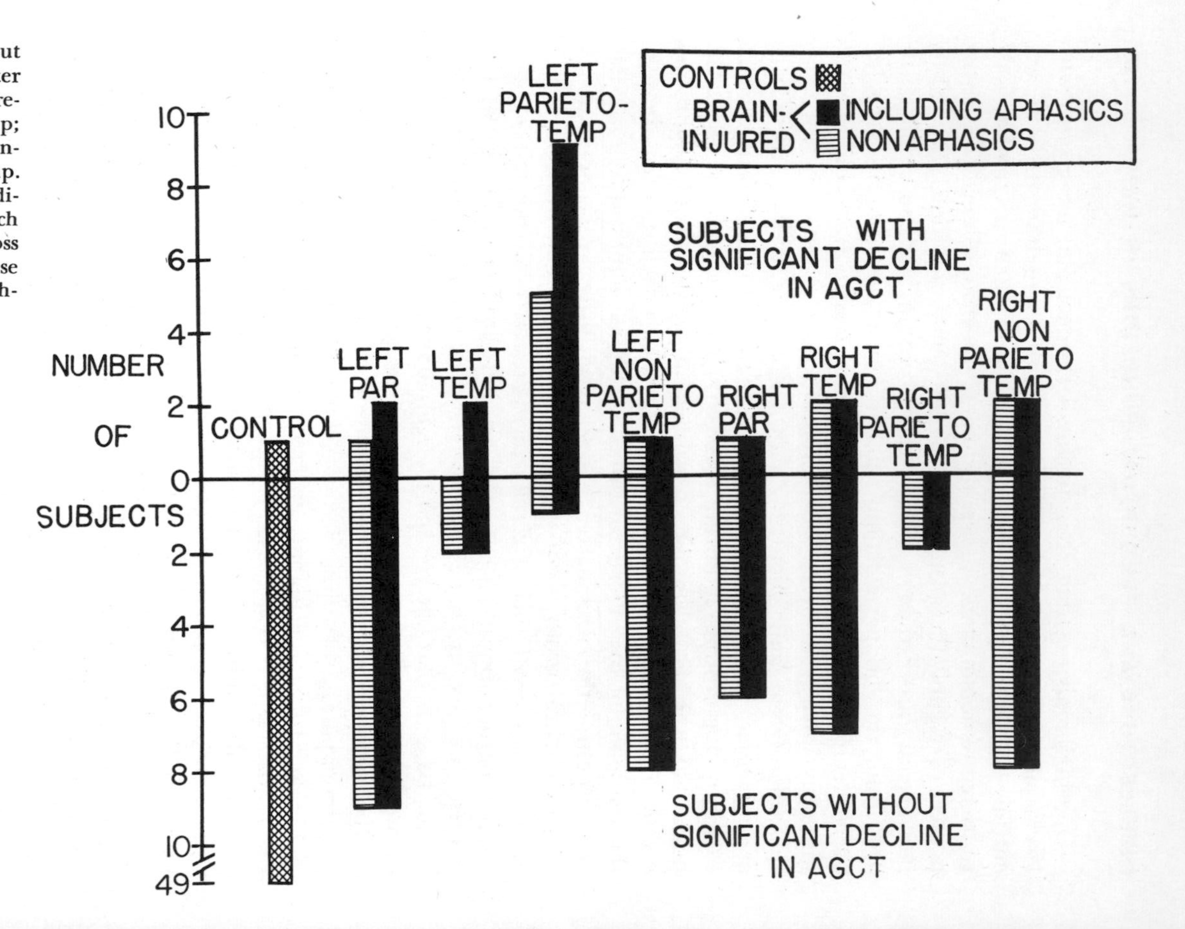

Fig. 4. Subjects with or without significant decline in AGCT after brain injury. Black bars represent total brain-injured group; striped bars represent non-aphasic brain-injured group. Bars above horizontal line indicate number of subjects in each sub-group with significant loss of score after brain injury; those below represent subjects without such loss.

mass action regardless of locus, then it can be denied. There were many cases with massive lesions of the frontal lobes which were not impaired on this test. Furthermore, the analogous group, i.e., the group with right parietotemporal lesions, was similarly subject to occlusion of the middle cerebral artery, and this group did not show the impairment demonstrated by those with left-sided injuries.

The conclusions to be drawn from these results are that, first, there were relatively few subjects who sustained an intellectual loss (as defined by the AGCT), in spite of the brain injury. The second conclusion is that some individuals suffered loss on this test after brain injury to any area of either hemisphere. The third conclusion is that injury to the left parietotemporal region resulted in greater intellectual loss than injury to any other single region.

The second study I wish to discuss deals with tactile size discrimination after penetrating brain injury.

There has been relatively little work on effects of brain injury on tactile size discrimination in man. Henry Head (1920) reported that size judgment is affected by cortical lesions. Evans (1935) interpreted his data as indicating that lesions of the posterior parietal lobule are especially detrimental for tactile size discrimination and related tasks. In an earlier study on two-dimensional size judgment (Weinstein, 1955a), the present author found significant impairment in a group of brain-injured men who had other types of sensory deficits, but could not confirm the earlier findings of Head (1920) or Evans (1935).

The present study was concerned with the effect of locus of penetrating brain injury and concomitant neurological deficits on three-dimensional size discrimination, i.e., discrimination of wooden cubes differing in size (Weinstein, *et al.,* 1958b).

There were 58 brain-injured subjects and 20 controls without brain injury, but with injury to the nerves of the leg; 16 of the brain-injured men had bilateral lesions; 19 had injuries to the right hemisphere alone; and 23 had injuries to the left hemisphere alone. Only those subjects were tested who could perceive and actively palpate the stimulus objects.

The subject's task consisted of palpating, with the fingers of one hand, a wooden cube, and then attempting to find, in a comparison array of 18 cubes, the one that was identical in size. (Figure 5.) The subject sat before a wooden box which contained a wooden strip, a meter and a half long. Mounted above this strip were 18 wooden cubes. These comparison stimulus cubes were arranged in order of size, with the largest on the subject's right and the smallest on his left. The sizes ranged in 1 mm. steps from 32 to 48 mm. The subject placed his hand under a black curtain which excluded from sight all of the cubes and

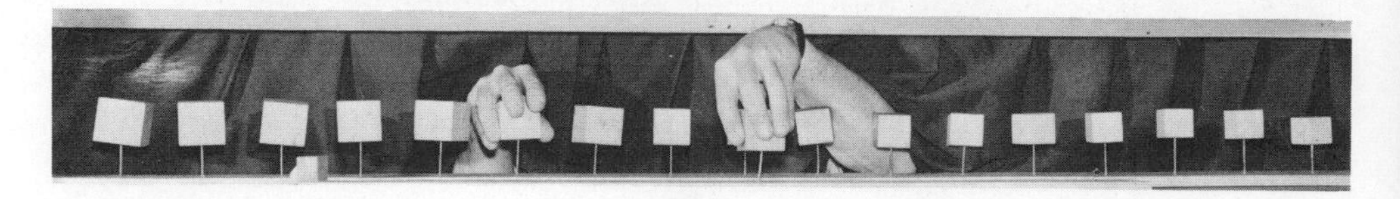

Fig. 5. Size discrimination test. A subject is shown with the left hand palpating the standard cube, while the right simultaneously seeks the mate in the comparison array.

palpated the standard cube, which was placed at the center and behind the comparison array. The standard cubes ranged from 37 through 43 mm., in 1 mm. steps. The subject was allowed to palpate the standard and comparison cubes as frequently and as long as he wished. There were four conditions of testing: two unimanual and two bimanual. In the unimanual testing conditions, the subject palpated the standard and comparison cubes with the same hand successively. The two bimanual conditions of testing were either successive or simultaneous. In the successive condition, the subject was required to palpate the standard with one hand, stop palpating, then find the mate in the comparison array with the other hand. He was permitted to return to the standard any number of times during testing, but only one hand could be in contact with either stimulus object at a given time, and he could not reverse the role of the hands under that condition. There were five trials in which the standard was presented to the right hand while the left searched for the mate, and five trials for the converse condition. The mean of these ten trials is the bimanual successive score.

The procedure for the bimanual-simultaneous condition was similar, except that the subject palpated the standard and comparison cubes simultaneously rather than successively.

The order of presentation of conditions was balanced in controls and brain-injured groups, so that comparison of the hands either contralateral or ipsilateral to the brain injury was unbiased with regard to laterality or order of testing in all groups.

The error score was the number of millimeters by which the response deviated from the correct choice. The data were analyzed by means of mixed, two-factor analyses of variance. The first series of analyses was concerned with the effects of locus of lesion, condition of testing, and their interaction in the various groups. In these analyses, three groups were compared: the controls, a brain-injured group with a given lesion, and the complementary brain-injured group without this specific lesion.

The brain-injured group was subdivided according to presence or absence of lesions in any given lobe: for example, subjects with frontal lesions versus nonfrontals, or subjects with lesions elsewhere. This subdivision was made separately for each lobe as well as for the central and posterior parietal subsectors of the sensorimotor region, and for the right versus the left hemisphere.

In a second series of analyses, the effects of somatosensory deficit were assessed. In these analyses, the brain-injured group was subdivided into three groups: a group with no evidence of somatosensory deficit (referred to as the nonsensory group), a group with one specific somatosensory deficit (of either sense of passive-movement, punctate pressure sensitivity, two-point discrimination, or point localization), and a group with somatosensory deficit excluding that under consideration. In the analyses concerned with locus of lesion, only brain-injured subjects with unilateral lesions were considered. In all analyses concerning somatosensory deficit, subjects with bilateral as well as unilateral lesions were combined.

Testing either hand alone produced significantly smaller average errors in all groups than testing both hands together. Essentially the same results were reported for an experiment involving roughness discrimination (Weinstein, *et al.,* 1955a). (Figure 6.)

In some analyses, brain-injured subgroups earned significantly lower scores than the controls; however, we shall consider only those analyses in which a brain-injured group showed a statistically significant difference from other brain-injured subgroups as well as the controls. There were two such analyses. The first was that concerned with the central, or Rolandic, region of the brain. Figure 7 shows the results of this analysis. It can be seen that the group with lesions of the central region of the brain was significantly inferior to both the control and the noncentral brain-injured groups. The control and noncentral groups differed only slightly from each other.

Figure 8 shows that the group with lesions to the right hemisphere made significantly greater average errors than those with injuries to the left hemisphere, or the control group. The control group and the left unilateral group did not differ significantly from each other. It might be thought that the inferiority of the right group merely reflects a greater proportion of men with injury to the central region in this group. This was not the case, since approximately one-third of the right, and one-third of the left unilateral groups comprised men with central lesions.

The following results were obtained when the groups were analyzed, not according to locus, but according to somatosensory status of the hand. When the various kinds of sensory impairment were considered, no differential effect was produced either by defective passive movement or by defective point-localization. However, Figure 9 shows that the group with impairment of two-point discrimination was significantly

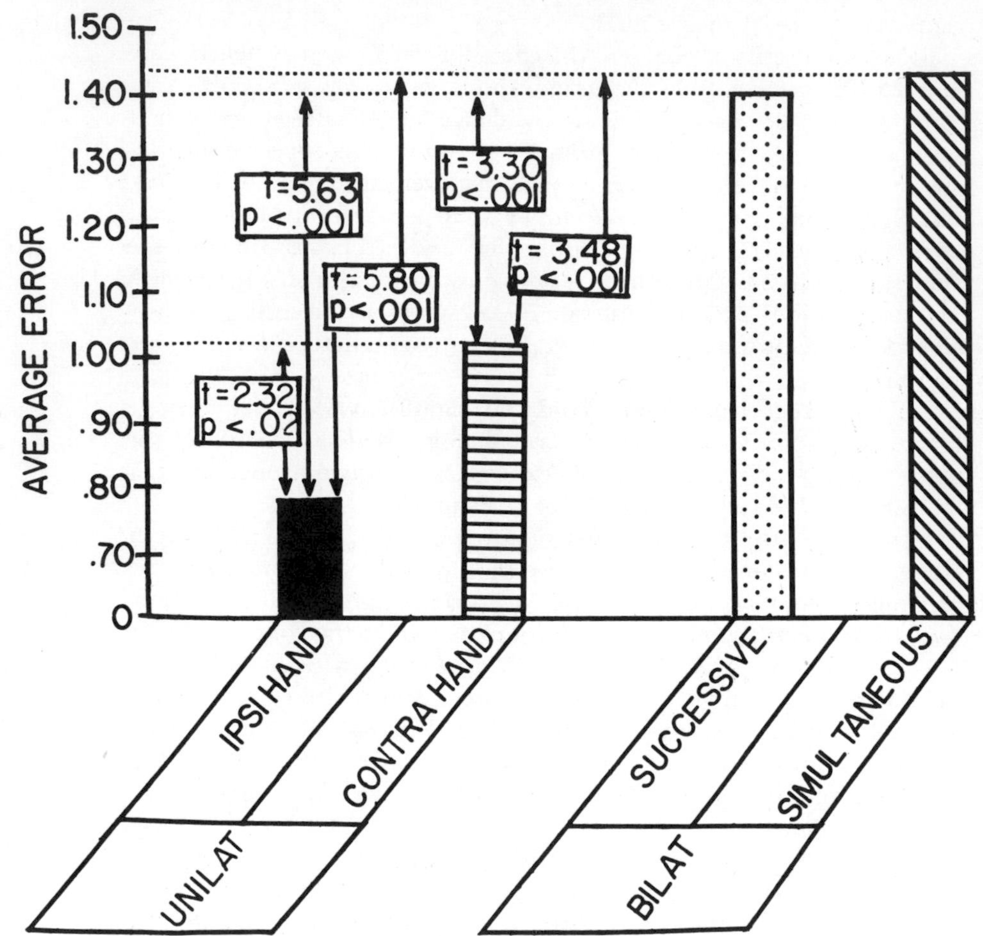

Fig. 6. Mean average errors for size discrimination in two unimanual and two bimanual testing conditions.

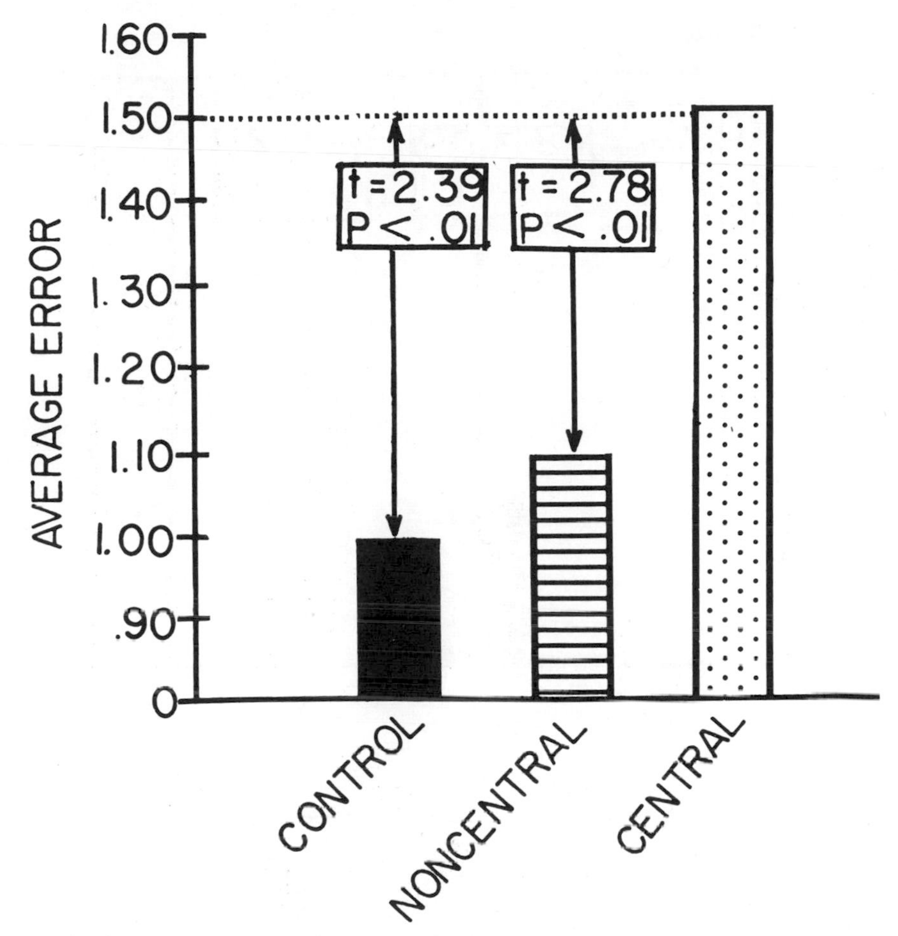

Fig. 7. Mean average errors for size discrimination in controls, and in brain-injured groups with lesions of central and noncentral regions.

inferior to the controls, to the nonsensory brain-injured group, and to the sensory defect group which did not have two-point deficit. The analysis also revealed that the inferior performance of the group with two-point defect manifested itself primarily in the defective hand, regardless of whether this hand was used alone or in the bimanual testing conditions.

In an attempt to understand more fully the relationships between defective size discrimination and the two independent variables (i.e., locus of lesion and the presence of a concomitant somatosensory defect),

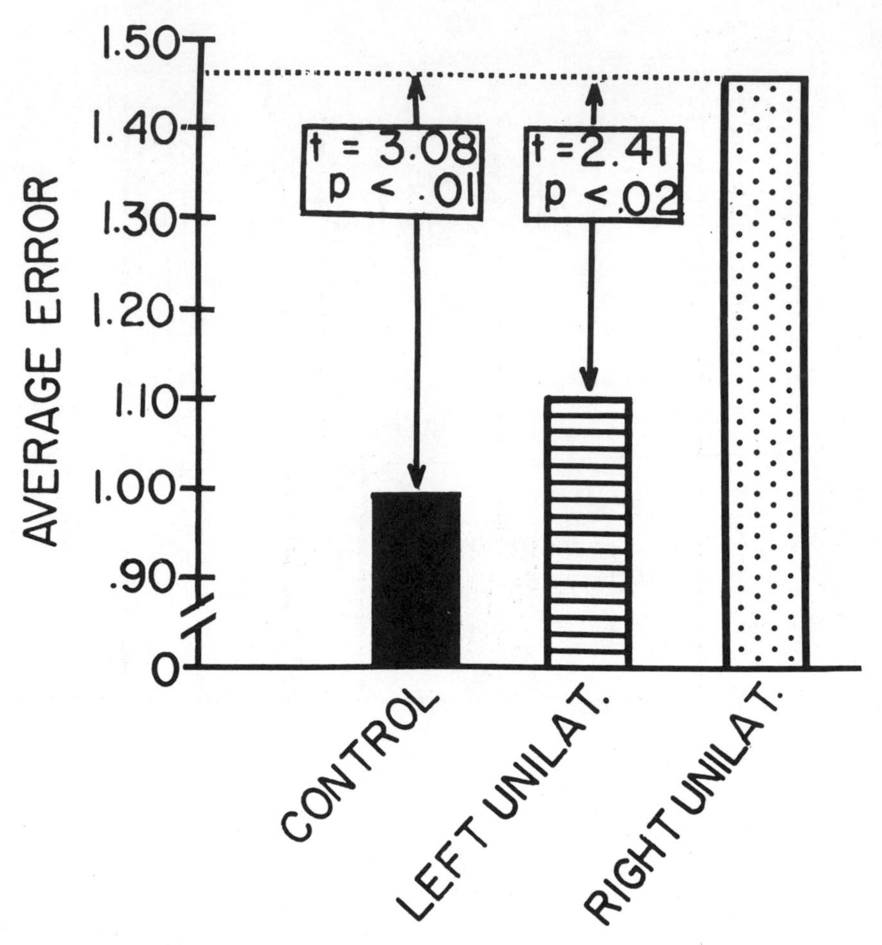

Fig. 8. Mean average errors for size discrimination in controls and groups with injury to right or left cerebral hemispheres. The group with right hemispheric lesions was significantly inferior to controls and to the group with left hemispheric lesions.

individuals were classified as being defective or not defective on the size discrimination test. This was done in the following way: the mean and standard deviation of the scores of the control group were determined for each condition of size discrimination. That is, we determined separately the mean and the standard deviation for the right hand alone, the left hand alone, for each bimanual testing condition alone, and for the total. All brain-injured individuals, whose score on any one of these

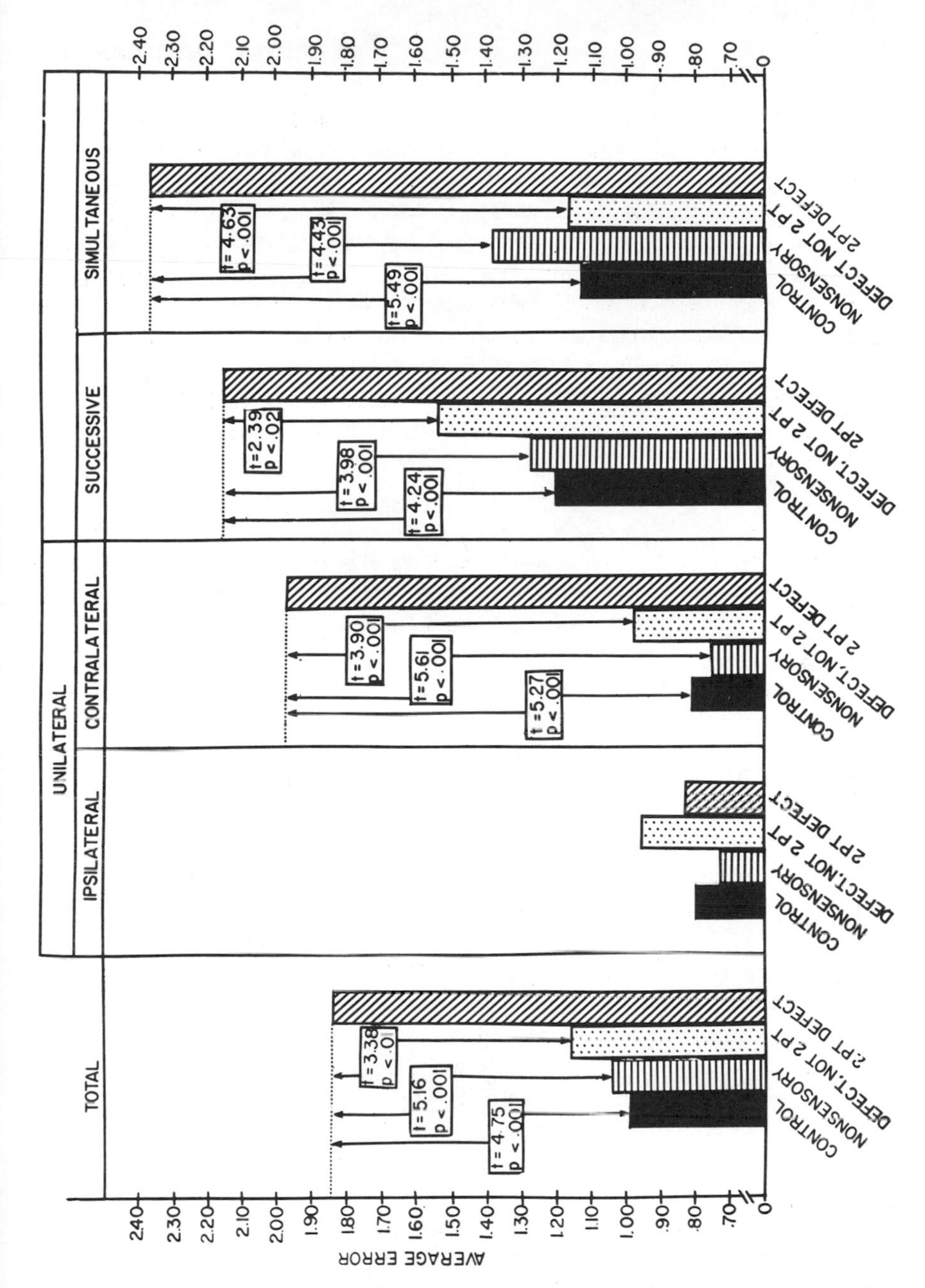

Fig. 9. Mean average errors for size discrimination in controls, and in brain-injured subgroups with defective two-point discrimination (2 pt defect), with somatosensory impairment exclusive of two-point discrimination defect (defect not 2 pt), and in a group without evidence of somatosensory impairment (nonsensory). The arrows indicate which groups differ significantly; the boxed figures show the *t* and level of probability (p), within each testing condition separately. It can be seen that the group with two-point defect was significantly poorer than each of the other groups in each testing condition except the ipsimanual.

conditions, or on the total, exceeded the one-tailed one per cent confidence limits, were designated as impaired on size discrimination.

We then considered the characteristics of these men with regard to the locus of lesion and their sensory status combined. Thus, chi-square tests demonstrated that men who had a sensory deficit of any form tended to be impaired on size discrimination in comparison with the brain-injured men without sensory defect. Of the 36 men with sensory defect, 17 showed defective performance on the test, whereas only 4 of the 22 men without sensory defects showed defect on the test. The existence of bimanual sensory impairment was no more detrimental than impairment limited to one hand, as shown by Figure 10. The two groups with sensory impairment were each significantly worse in size judgment than the control or nonsensory groups. However, little difference was seen between the two sensory deficit groups.

In contrasting individuals with right and left unilateral lesions, we obtained a highly significant chi-square: 11 of the 19 men with right unilateral lesions showed size defect; only 4 of the 23 men with left unilateral lesions showed defect.

We were further interested in the relationship between lesions to the right hemisphere and the presence of two-point deficit. The first thing we did was to compare men with lesions of either right or left hemisphere who had any sensory deficit. That is, we compared men who had an injury of the right hemisphere and a sensory defect with men who had an injury of the left hemisphere and a sensory defect, with regard to presence or absence of size defect. The chi-square was significant and indicates that men with lesions of the right hemisphere who had any somatosensory defect tended to be defective in size discrimination more frequently than men with left hemispheric lesions who had somatosensory defect. Moreover, when we contrasted men with injury of the right hemisphere who had two-point defect with men who had left hemispheric lesions and two-point defect, again a highly significant chi-square resulted. Thus, all six men with right-sided lesions and two-point defect were defective in size judgment, whereas only one of the five men who had left-sided lesions and two-point defect showed defective size judgment.

We then compared the men with right hemispheric lesions and two-point discrimination defect with men who had right hemispheric lesions and other forms of sensory discrimination deficit. Again, the chi-square was significant, indicating that the combination of right hemispheric lesion with presence of two-point discrimination defect resulted in a greater number of cases with defective size discrimination than presence of right hemispheric lesions with other forms of sensory impair-

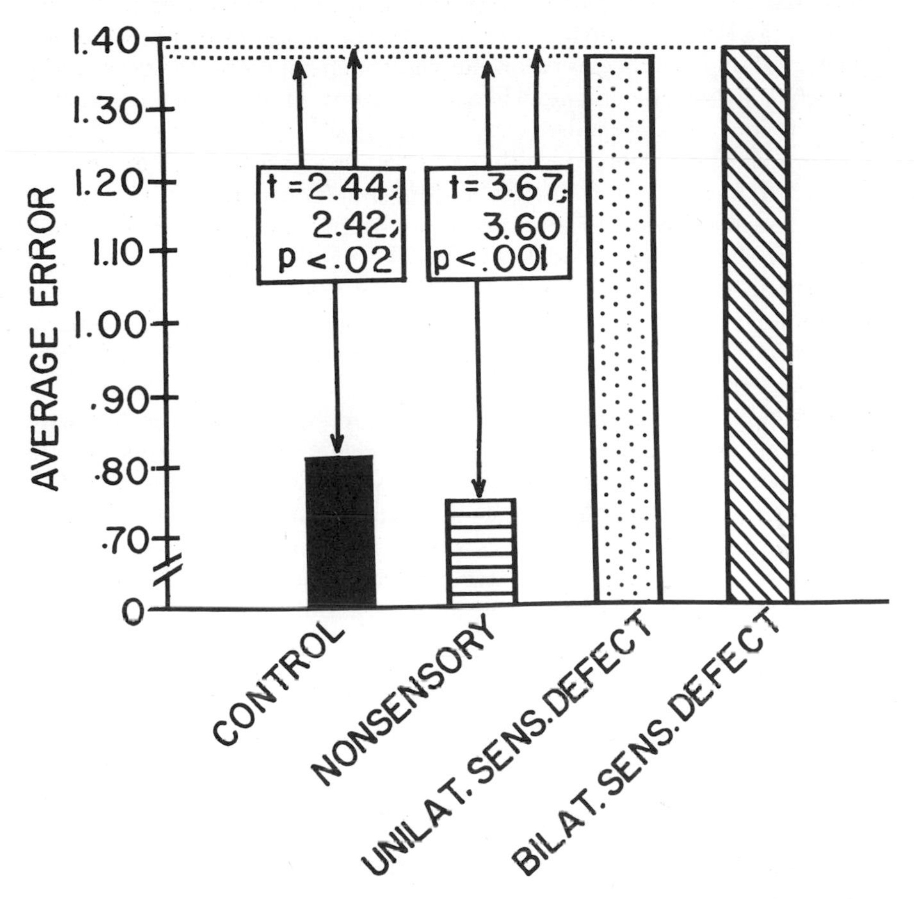

Fig. 10. Mean average errors for size discrimination in controls, brain-injured subgroups with unimanual, and bimanual somatosensory defect, and a group without somatosensory defect (nonsensory). Although the sensory defect groups were each significantly inferior to the control and nonsensory groups, they differed very little from one another.

ment. The converse situation for the left hemisphere did not produce a significant difference; that is, when we compared men who had unilateral lesions of the left hemisphere and presence or absence of two-point discrimination defects, we found no significant differences between these groups.

Finally, to investigate whether severe sensory impairment of any type was effective in producing defective size judgment (regardless of hemisphere injured), we compared the 7 men with right hemispheric lesions who had severe somatosensory impairment with the 7 men with left-sided lesions who also had severe somatosensory impairment. We found that all 7 men with lesions of the right hemisphere were significantly defective in size judgment, whereas only one of the 7 men with left-sided lesions was so impaired.

Thus, in conclusion, it is obvious that there are two factors related to deficit in tactile size discrimination after brain injury. The first of these is the presence of a lesion of the right hemisphere. The second factor is the presence of defective two-point discrimination. Although either one of these factors alone is effective in predicting defects in size discrimination, it appears that a combination of both factors results in the greatest frequency of defects in the tactile discrimination of three dimensional size.

In view of the many more cognitive and verbal deficits associated with left hemispheric lesions, the finding of a deficit in this perceptual task associated with lesions to the right hemisphere illustrates the principle that certain nonverbal achievements may depend more markedly upon the integrity of the right than of the left hemisphere.

In summary, I have shown two mutually exclusive effects of penetrating brain injury to the right, and to the left cerebral hemispheres. In so doing, I have demonstrated a double dissociation, i.e., individuals with right hemispheric lesions suffer from a perceptual impairment (tactile size discrimination), in the absence of significant intellectual impairment; conversely, those with left parietotemporal lesions suffer from intellectual impairment, but show little or no impairment in judgment of three dimensional size.

□■ IX

Laterality Effects in Audition[1]

by BRENDA MILNER

Montreal Neurological Institute of McGill University, Montreal, Canada

THE STUDIES which I shall describe today form part of a broader, long-term investigation of learning and perception in human subjects undergoing unilateral temporal lobectomy for the relief of focal epilepsy. These are patients with static, atrophic lesions of the cerebral cortex, dating from birth or early life, and do not include cases of brain tumor or vascular disease. Such subjects, in whom one temporal lobe is removed, provide a valuable opportunity for observing differences in function between the two temporal lobes. Although I shall be concerned here primarily with some recent observations which demonstrate an asymmetry of function between the left and right temporal lobes of man in auditory tasks, these studies can perhaps best be understood in the context of earlier work, which was not specifically auditory. I shall therefore begin by briefly reviewing these earlier findings.

VERBAL RECALL FUNCTIONS OF THE LEFT TEMPORAL LOBE

Perhaps the most clear-cut result to emerge from the study of human temporal-lobe function is the disturbance in the recall of verbal material,

[1] From the Montreal Neurological Institute, Department of Neurology and Neurosurgery, McGill University, Canada. This work was supported by Federal-Provincial Health Grant No. 604–5–49, and by U.S. Public Health Grant No. B2831 from the National Institute of Nervous Diseases and Blindness, Bethesda, Md. The author is indebted to Dr. Wilder Penfield, Dr. Theodore Rasmussen, and Dr. William Feindel for permission to study their patients.

which regularly accompanies lesions of the left temporal lobe when speech is represented in the left hemisphere. This has been shown both for verbal associative learning (Meyer & Yates, 1955) and for story recall (Milner, 1958). Although the defect is more pronounced after a lobectomy, even the presence of epileptogenic tissue in the left temporal lobe suffices to impair verbal memory selectively. We have known for some time that patients with left temporal-lobe epilepsy will recall significantly fewer items from a short prose passage that has been read to them earlier, than will patients with epileptogenic lesions in other parts of the brain. This has been tested with the two stories of the Logical Memory subtest of the Wechsler Memory Scale, first obtaining immediate recall (which may be normal), and then delayed recall after a 90-minute period filled with other activities (Milner, 1958). More recently, we have found a similar delayed-recall difficulty for verbal paired associates. Patients with seizures arising from the left temporal lobe are not clearly impaired in the rate of learning of word pairs (as measured by the Associate Learning subtest of the Wechsler Memory Scale), but their ability to reproduce these associations one and one-half hours later is inferior to that of patients with epileptic foci in other areas. If we now combine the delayed verbal recall scores for these two verbal memory tasks (the mean number of items correctly recalled for the two stories plus the number of correct word associations), we obtain a delayed verbal recall score for each subject which proves to be a more sensitive measure than either score separately. Table 1 gives the preoperative group means for this composite measure of delayed verbal

Table 1

Preoperative Delayed Verbal Recall

Group	No. Cases	Items Correct Mean	S.D.
Left Temporal	41	11.2	4.11
Right Temporal	33	14.9	4.04
Parietal	11	16.7	3.48
Frontal	11	16.5	4.76

recall for 96 subjects. The patients with left temporal-lobe epilepsy have significantly lower scores than patients with comparable damage to right temporal, frontal, or parietal cortex, and the difference between the left and right temporal-lobe groups is significant beyond the .001 level of confidence ($t = 3.72$).

There is, then, clear evidence of a verbal memory difficulty in patients with epileptogenic lesions of the left temporal lobe. When the left temporal lobe is excised, these patients have a transient dysphasia due to postoperative edema, and verbal memory difficulties are confounded with this more general linguistic disturbance. But if the patients return for follow-up study a year or more later, they are no longer dysphasic, yet their scores on verbal memory tests are lower than before operation. Moreover, there is now an impairment in the initial reproduction of the material presented. Table 2 illustrates this point for fifteen patients

Table 2

Verbal Memory Defect after Left Temporal Lobectomy
(Means for 15 Cases)

	Before Operation	Follow-up
Wechsler I.Q.	107.9	110.8
Verbal Recall		
Immediate	21.0	16.8
Delayed	12.7	11.0

who were first seen before operation and then re-examined, from one to four years after undergoing an anterior temporal lobectomy in the hemisphere dominant for speech. The mean I.Q. rating is slightly, though not significantly, higher at the second testing, but scores for immediate recall of verbal material are lower than before operation and the delayed recall difficulty persists. These patients now reproduce logically connected verbal material in a very fragmented way, and they may complain of difficulty in listening. If they are taking courses at school or university, they have more difficulty than formerly in apprehending the material presented. One girl who was working as a telephone operator became so confused at the switchboard that she had to change to a less exacting occupation.

These findings emphasize the auditory aspects of the problem, and it is true that the auditory mode of presentation was used for both story recall and associative learning. The severe deficit in verbal associative learning reported by Meyer & Yates (1955) was also demonstrated with auditorily presented material, and these authors have always termed the defect an auditory learning difficulty. We, on the other hand, have interpreted the impairment as a verbal one, affecting both assimilation and recall. If this is so, then one would also expect to find some impairment in the learning and retention of visually presented verbal material in patients with lesions of the left temporal lobe, and we have some preliminary data in support of this hypothesis. In the meantime, spontaneous comments from our patients strengthen the impression that this is not a modality-specific defect. Thus, one very intelligent young man returning for follow-up study, one year after a left temporal lobectomy, described his difficulties in the following way:

> You know, I can't remember things. I don't seem to be able to build up my vocabulary. I will tell you what I do. On Monday, let us say, I read part of a novel by Dostoevski. I find many words in it that are unfamiliar. When I meet such words, I look them up and rehearse them and try to learn what they mean. The next day I read a different book, a very interesting one; it is a geography book about Africa, and there are many words in it that I do not know, so I look them up, too, and rehearse them and try to learn them. The next day I read a section from a book on the psychology of women. This also is a very interesting book, and again there are many words that I do not know, and I try to learn them. Then, on the fourth day, Thursday, I go back to my Dostoevski and see if I can remember the words I had learned on Monday. If I remember one out of five, I think I am doing very well.

This, I think, illustrates admirably the kind of difficulty which these patients experience, and it does not seem to be specifically auditory, although it may be particularly easy to elicit by the auditory mode of presentation.

VISUAL FUNCTIONS OF THE RIGHT TEMPORAL LOBE

We have found no deficits on any verbal task after right temporal lobectomy when that hemisphere is nondominant for speech, but, as Dr. Mishkin has told you, we do find that right temporal-lobe injury is associated with impaired performance on a variety of visual, nonverbal tasks. Patients with epileptogenic lesions of the right temporal lobe are slow and inaccurate in detecting incongruities in sketchy, cartoon-like drawings (Milner, 1958); they also show a deficit in the recognition of overlapping nonsense figures and groups of dots tachistoscopically presented, although they can readily perceive objects to which a name can be attached (Kimura, 1960). Patients with left temporal-lobe lesions do not have these perceptual difficulties. Further evidence of the importance of the right temporal lobe for visual perception comes from Lansdell (1961), who studied a group of patients approximately three and one-half years after unilateral temporal lobectomy. Using Mooney's Closure Faces test (Mooney, 1956, 1957), he found that the group with right temporal-lobe lesions made significantly lower scores than those with left.

Turning to the domain of visual memory, we now have ample evidence of visual memory defect after right temporal lobectomy, but not after left temporal lobectomy of comparable extent. We find this for face recognition, using a one-trial procedure (Milner, 1960); for learning to recognize nonsense figures over a series of recurring presentations (Kimura, 1960); and for the delayed recall of geometric figures, even though these may have been accurately reproduced at the time of the original presentation (Milner, 1960). Thus the method of testing is unimportant, whether it be by recognition, rate of learning, or recall; what is important is the visual, nonverbal nature of the stimuli presented.

The evidence for impairment of visual perception and visual learning after right temporal-lobe injury in man accords well with the results of animal work, where bilateral lesions of the convexity of the temporal cortex cause profound impairment in visual discrimination learning (Chow, 1951; Mishkin & Pribram, 1954). For a deficit to occur in the monkey, a bilateral lesion is required, unless the task be very difficult. The fact that in man visual impairment follows unilateral temporal lobectomy on the right side, but not on the left, suggests that the development of language representation in the left hemisphere has disturbed the functional equivalence of the two temporal lobes for visually guided behavior, with the right now playing a proportionately greater role.

EFFECTS OF TEMPORAL LOBECTOMY ON AUDITORY DISCRIMINATION

This, then, was the background for our present work on auditory function. We had seen only visual, nonverbal defects from right temporal-lobe lesions and only a verbal defect from similar lesions on the left. The verbal defect had been most clearly demonstrated for auditorily presented material and might be thought to have a strong auditory component. It therefore seemed desirable to investigate the effects of right and left temporal-lobe lesions on some nonverbal auditory tasks, in order to determine whether left temporal-lobe lesions produced a general impairment of auditory discrimination, or whether the verbal or nonverbal nature of the task were the critical factor.

An additional stimulus for this work came from animal studies, showing that bilateral lesions of auditory cortex can impair the discrimination of tonal patterns in cat (Diamond & Neff, 1957) and monkey (Jerison & Neff, 1953), while leaving the discrimination of simple frequency or intensity differences undisturbed (see Neff, 1961 for a recent summary). Moreover, Goldberg, Diamond, & Neff (1957) have shown that in the cat, bilateral lesions of the insular and temporal cortex, anterior and ventral to the classical auditory areas, also impair tonal-pattern discrimination, and ablation of this area causes retrograde degeneration in the most caudal part of the medial geniculate nucleus (Diamond, Chow, & Neff, 1958; Rose & Woolsey, 1958). Recently, Akert, Woolsey, Diamond, & Neff (1959) have identified the homologue of this insular-temporal region in the monkey; it lies on the superior temporal plane, rostral to the traditional auditory area and to the ventral tip of the central sulcus. Bilateral lesions, involving this region in the monkey, impair the retention of tonal-pattern discrimination (Oder, 1959) and the comparison of compound auditory stimuli (Stepien, Cordeau, & Rasmussen, 1960). These findings encouraged us to look for similar deficits after temporal lobectomy in man, particularly since the removal invariably includes the anterior temporal region and, in a few cases, extends to invade the classical auditory projection area of Heschl's gyrus.

The tests chosen were the Seashore Measures of Musical Talents (Series A, 1939 revision; available on a single 33-1/3 r.p.m. record), since they sample a variety of tasks and preliminary work had already yielded some positive findings (Milner, 1958).

The subjects were 38 patients with temporal-lobe lesions, 22 left-sided, 16 right; in all cases the left hemisphere was dominant for speech. The main group consisted of 27 patients tested both before and two weeks after unilateral temporal lobectomy, 16 operations being on the left and 11 on the right. The remaining 11 subjects were available for postoperative testing only.

In the left hemisphere, the size of the removal (as estimated by the surgeon at the time of operation) varied from 4 to 7.5 cm. along the Sylvian fissure and from 4 to 7.5 cm. along the base of the temporal lobe. In the right hemisphere, the size of removal varied from 4 to 7.5 cm. along the Sylvian fissure and from 5.5 to 8.5 cm. along the base. The ablations on the right tended to be a little larger than on the left (averaging roughly 6 cm. of the temporal lobe as compared with 5.5 cm. on the left), but there was much overlap. In 6 patients with left temporal lobectomy and 5 with right, the transverse gyri of Heschl were said to have been completely excised. The Seashore tests were administered to each patient individually,[2] in order to insure that the

[2] The author wishes to thank Mr. L. B. Taylor for his assistance in administering the Seashore tests.

instructions were understood. The patient was seated about 7 feet from the loudspeaker and wrote down his responses.

The 6 tests, in the order of administration, are as follows (Saetveit, Lewis, & Seashore, 1940):

1. Pitch. Two pure tones in the region of 500 cps and of duration .6 sec. are sounded in rapid succession, and the subject has to judge whether the second note is higher (H) or lower (L) than the first. There are 50 pairs of tones, and the difference in frequency is gradually reduced, in 7 steps, from 17 cycles to 2.
2. Loudness. Two pure tones at 440 cps, but differing in intensity, are sounded in rapid succession, and the subject must judge whether the second tone is stronger (S) or weaker (W) than the first. There are 50 pairs of tones, and the intensity difference is gradually reduced, in 6 steps, from 4 db. to 0.5 db.
3. Rhythm. Two rhythmic patterns are tapped out in quick succession, and the subject has to judge whether they are the same (S) or different (D). The source was an oscillator set at 500 cycles. There are 30 pairs of patterns, and difficulty is increased by increasing the number of beats in each pattern from 5 to 7.
4. Time. Two tones at 440 cycles, but differing in duration, are sounded in rapid succession, and the subject must judge whether the second tone is longer (L) or shorter (S) than the first. There are 50 pairs of tones, and the difference in duration is gradually reduced in 7 steps, from .3 sec. to .05 sec.
5. Timbre. This test measures the ability to distinguish between complex sounds which differ only in harmonic structure. It consists of 50 pairs of tones, and for each pair the subject must judge whether the tone quality of the 2 sounds is the same (S) or different (D). Tonal structure is varied by reciprocal alteration in the intensities of the 3rd and 4th harmonics, the changes varying from 10 db. to 4 db., with total intensity constant.
6. Tonal Memory. In this test a sequence of notes is played twice in rapid succession, one note in the sequence being changed at the second playing. The subject must compare the two tonal patterns and identify by number the note which was changed at the second playing. There are 30 pairs of tonal patterns, and difficulty is increased by increasing the number of notes in each from 3 to 5. Intensity is held constant, and tempo carefully controlled. This is the task which we expected to be the most sensitive to cortical lesions.

Results: The mean error scores, for subjects tested before and after operation, are represented diagrammatically in Figures 1 to 3.

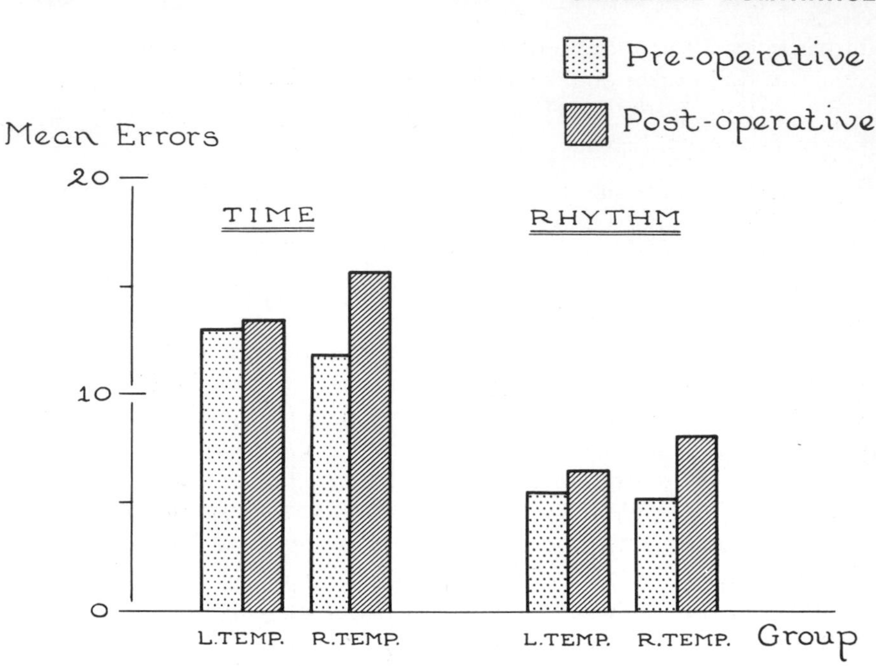

Fig. 1. Seashore Time and Rhythm tests: mean number of errors before and after operation for left (L) and right (R) temporal-lobe groups.

Figure 1 shows the error scores for Time and Rhythm, the two tests dealing with the temporal aspects of auditory stimuli. There is no difference between the performances of the right and left temporal-lobe groups before operation, and there is clearly no change on either test after left temporal lobectomy. The slight increases in error score after right temporal lobectomy are trivial, but, in the case of Time, the change is significant ($t = 2.38$, $p < .05$).

Figure 2 gives the corresponding data for Pitch and Loudness. There are no significant group differences before operation and no change after left temporal lobectomy; but again we see a tendency for error scores to increase after right temporal lobectomy. This change is not significant in the case of Pitch, where there is considerable individual variation, but, for Loudness, the change, though small, is significant ($t = 2.51$, $p < .05$).

Figure 3 gives the results for Timbre and Tonal Memory, and here the trend suggested in the earlier data becomes clear. There are no group differences before operation and no changes after left temporal lobectomy, but after right temporal lobectomy, the error scores on both measures increase markedly. For Timbre there is a 12.6 per cent increase

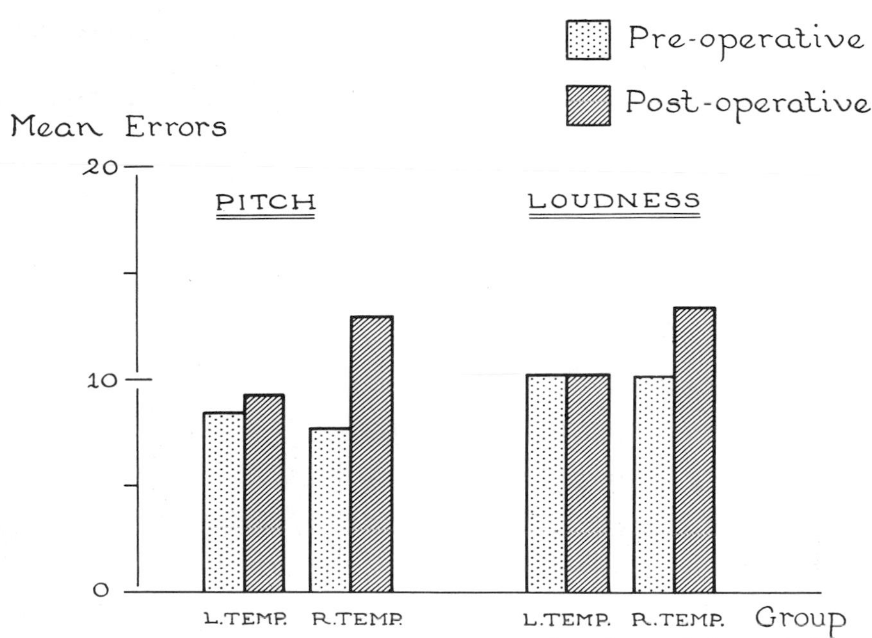

Fig. 2. Seashore Pitch and Loudness tests: mean number of errors before and after operation for left (L) and right (R) temporal-lobe groups.

in error score ($t = 3.84$, $p < .01$) and for Tonal Memory a 23 per cent increase ($t = 3.39$, $p < .01$).

The pre- and postoperative comparisons thus show increased difficulty in discrimination after right temporal lobectomy but not after left, on these nonverbal auditory tasks. The results for the 11 subjects who were only tested after operation also show higher error scores for the right temporal group. Since their scores closely resembled the postoperative scores of the other patients, they were combined with them for the purposes of further analysis. Table 3 shows that the resulting groups were well-matched with respect to both age and intelligence. On all

Table 3

Seashore Test: Subjects Tested Postoperatively

Group	No. Cases	I.Q.		Age	
		Mean	Range	Mean	Range
Right Temporal	16	103.1	(88–120)	28.8	(14–40)
Left Temporal	22	101.3	(84–123)	25.8	(18–39)

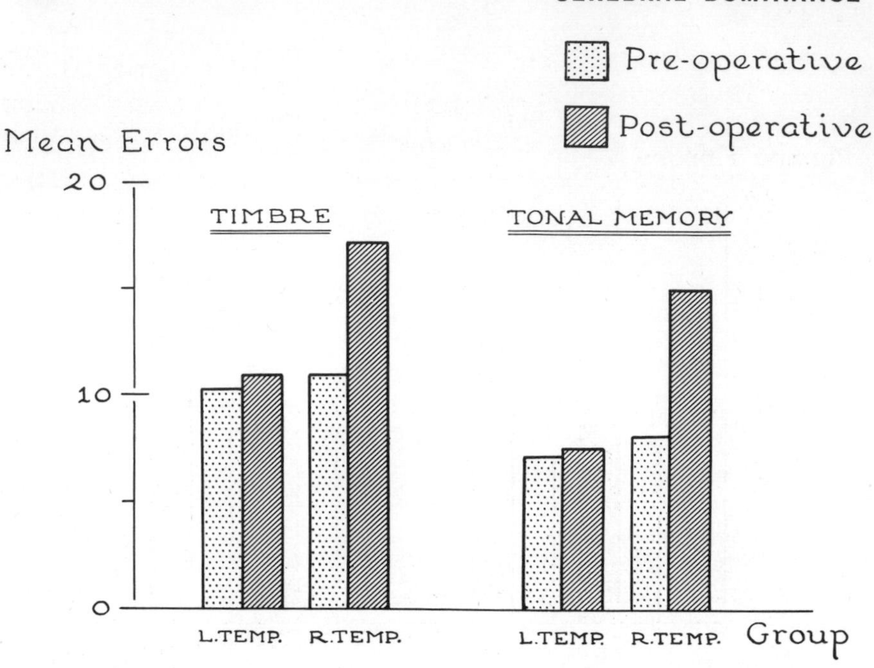

Fig. 3. Seashore Timbre and Tonal Memory tests: mean number of errors before and after operation for left (L) and right (R) temporal-lobe groups.

the Seashore tests, the right temporal group makes more errors than the left; the difference is most marked for Tonal Memory ($t \doteq 3.64$, $p < .001$) and for Timbre ($t = 2.98$, $p < .01$), but is significant for Loudness also ($t = 2.09, p < .05$).

Table 4

Seashore Test: Postoperative Per Cent Correct Responses after Right and Left Temporal Lobectomy Compared with Seashore Norms

Test	Group			
	Right Temporal Mean	Left Temporal Mean	Normal Mean	Normal S.D.
Tonal Memory	53.0	74.7	83.3	15.3
Timbre	63.4	76.8	77.2	10.2
Loudness	71.6	80.4	85.6	9.4
Pitch	72.8	81.0	80.8	13.2
Time	66.8	74.0	80.6	10.2
Rhythm	75.0	80.3	88.3	9.3

Table 4 presents these results in a slightly different way, showing the percentage of correct responses on the various tests for the right and left postoperative groups together with Seashore's normal data for a group of about 4,000 unselected young adults. Now it is certainly unsound to compare our data too closely with Seashore's norms, particularly since the conditions of testing were different, in that his were group tests. However, it will be noted that the scores for the right temporal group deviate by more than 1 s.d. from the normal on all tests but Pitch, and by 2 s.d. for Tonal Memory.

These Seashore norms were included for another and more valid reason: they provide an estimate of the relative difficulty of the 6 tests for a normal population. We note that Rhythm, Loudness, and Tonal Memory are relatively easy tests, Pitch and Time rather more difficult, and Timbre the most difficult of all. The sensitivity of the Timbre test to right temporal lobectomy may therefore be related to task difficulty, but the still greater defect on Tonal Memory cannot be interpreted in this way; it must rather depend on the particular nature of the task. It is therefore interesting that this test approximates most closely the tonal-pattern discriminations which are disturbed by cortical lesions in cat and monkey.

The results outlined above show conclusively that a right temporal lobectomy makes certain kinds of auditory discrimination difficult, comparisons of tonal patterns or judgments of tone quality being the most conspicuously impaired. We have no evidence of such loss after left temporal lobectomy and lesion-size cannot account for this difference. It is true that the removals on the right tended to be slightly larger than on the left, but there was considerable overlap in this respect. When we consider that all patients with right temporal lobectomy showed a postoperative loss on the Timbre test, it seems clear that we cannot invoke lesion-size to account for the marked asymmetry of effect between right- and left-sided lesions. A further unexpected finding was that the results were the same, whether or not Heschl's gyrus was removed. The only important variable seemed to be the side of the lesion.

These findings must be interpreted with caution. They may, in fact, mean that in man the right hemisphere makes a greater contribution than the left to those aspects of auditory discrimination known to be affected by bilateral cortical lesions in the monkey. This view would be consistent with the results of Teuber & S. Diamond (1956) and Shankweiler (1961) which indicate that in man there may be greater impairment of sound localization with right hemispheric lesions than with left. An alternative explanation, and one that would fit our data equally well, would be that auditory functions are more diffusely represented in the right than in the left hemisphere. Semmes, Weinstein, Ghent, & Teuber (1960, p. 27) have suggested that this is the case for somethesis, and it may be true for other modalities also. Our findings of deficits, after right-sided lesions but not after left, are limited to the anterior temporal region, but other cortical areas have been implicated in auditory function in the monkey (Weiskrantz & Mishkin, 1958), and it is quite possible that lesions in parts of the left hemisphere we have not studied (for example, the posterior Sylvian region) would impair auditory discrimination in man.

RIVALRY IN THE AUDITORY SYSTEM

We turn now to a slightly different problem, and one requiring a different testing technique. This time we ask what would be the effect of applying different auditory stimuli simultaneously to the two ears, thus putting the input from the right ear in competition, so to speak, with that from the left. Now at first sight, this might seem to be an unpromising line of investigation. The central auditory pathway involves both ipsilateral and contralateral connections, with each ear represented bilaterally at every level up to the medial geniculate body; one might therefore expect not to find any functional asymmetry in the normal brain, and it might also seem unlikely that an unilateral cortical lesion would cause any discernible contralateral defect. Moreover, it is known that in cases of unilateral temporal lobectomy standard audiometric studies reveal, at most, a slight high-tone hearing loss for the ear opposite the lesion (Sinha, 1959) and often show no loss at all (Jerger, 1960). Nevertheless, there is physiological evidence, from the work of Tunturi (1946) in the dog and Rosenzweig (1951) in the cat, that the contralateral auditory pathway is the stronger in terms of amplitude of evoked cortical response. Consistent with this, there are now a number of behavioral studies showing that under appropriate conditions of testing some loss in the contralateral ear can be detected. Penfield & Evans (1934) reported impairment of sound localization on the left side, in a case of right temporal lobectomy. Since then, Sanchez-Longo, Forster, & Auth (1957), Sanchez-Longo & Forster (1958), and Jerger (1960) have reported similar findings for series of patients with temporal-lobe tumors. The more recent negative findings of Shankweiler (1961) may merely reflect differences in locus of lesion, since Shankweiler does not state the extent or nature of the lesions in his patients. In any case, there is good evidence for asymmetry in other aspects of auditory perception after unilateral temporal lobectomy in man. Bocca, Calearo, Cassinari, & Migliavacca (1955), in Milan, showed that the recognition of words distorted by a low-pass filter was significantly impaired on the side contralateral to a temporal-lobe tumor, as was the perception of accelerated speech. More recent studies elsewhere have confirmed and extended these findings. Sinha (1959), working in the Audiology Department at McGill University, showed that, after temporal lobectomy for seizures, there was a defect in the recognition of speech arriving at the contralateral ear when the words were presented together with white noise. In the absence of this masking sound, no difference between the ipsilateral and contralateral ears was found, nor was any defect found for either condition after radical frontal lobectomy. Jerger & Mier (1960) also reported deficits in the perception of speech for the ear contralateral to a lesion of the auditory cortex, under conditions in which an irrelevant conversation was being channelled to the ipsilateral ear. The studies by Kimura (1961a; 1961b), to be reported below, provide further evidence that the crossed connections to the auditory cortex are more effective than the uncrossed, while at the same time revealing an unexpected asymmetry in normal hearing.

The subjects in Dr. Kimura's main study (1961b) were 65 patients admitted to the Montreal Neurological Institute for the investigation of seizures. There were no cases of brain tumor or diffuse cerebral disease. They were classified as left temporal, right temporal, frontal, or subcortical, according to the locus of EEG abnormality. Forty-five patients were tested twice, before and two weeks after unilateral brain operation; the remaining 20 were tested once only, at the time of their admission to hospital.

The technique used was that devised by Broadbent (1954), in which different digits are simultaneously presented to the two ears by means of a dual-channel tape-recorder with stereophonic earphones. In this study, digits were presented in groups of 6, 3 digits to one ear and 3 to the other. In what proved to be the most discriminating condition, 2 digits, say 4 and 7, would be presented simultaneously, 4 to the left ear and 7 to the right, followed by another pair a half-second later and then by a third pair. The subject merely reports all the digits he hears, in any order. This yields a total score for the test (with a maximum of 192) and also separate scores for the left and right ears.

Table 5 gives the mean total scores for the different groups preoperatively. A simple analysis of variance yielded an F-ratio of 3.57 ($p < .02$) and subsequent *t* tests showed the left temporal group to be inferior to the right beyond the .01 level of confidence. Since these two groups did not differ in age, IQ, or seizure-frequency, we have here (as in the case of story recall) an auditory task on which left temporal-lobe injury produces impairment; unlike the Seashore tests, the stimuli here are verbal.

Table 5

Broadbent Test: Preoperative Mean Scores

Group	No. Cases	Total Digits Correct
Left Temporal	30	157.4
Right Temporal	16	171.9
Frontal	9	165.3
Subcortical	10	161.8

Table 6 summarizes the effects of temporal lobectomy. Six subjects with Heschl's gyrus excised are excluded from this analysis, as are two patients who were markedly dysphasic after left temporal lobectomy and therefore had difficulty in repeating digits under normal conditions. It can be seen that there is a mean reduction in total score of 7.1 points after left anterior temporal lobectomy ($p < .02$), but no change in total score after right temporal lobectomy. Thus, in patients with epileptogenic lesions of the left temporal lobe, removal of the epileptic focus enhances, at least for a time, the pre-existing defect.

Table 6

Broadbent Test: Mean Losses after Temporal Lobectomy

Group	No. Cases	Total Loss	Ipsilateral Ear	Contralateral Ear	Relative Loss on Contralateral Ear
Left Temporal	19	7.1	0.7	6.4	5.7
Right Temporal	11	−0.1	−2.7	2.6	5.3

If we now consider the effects of the temporal lobectomy on the relative efficiency of the two ears, we find a loss on the contralateral ear for both groups (Table 6). For the left temporal group, there is a relatively large loss on the contralateral ear and a small and insignificant loss on the ipsilateral ear. For the right temporal group, there is a small gain on the ipsilateral ear and a correspondingly small loss on the contralateral ear. There is thus a relative loss of about 5 points on the contralateral ear for both groups; this is significant beyond the .02 level. If Heschl's gyrus is included in the excision, then the loss on the contralateral ear is considerably greater. The results of this study are consistent with those of Bocca, *et al.,* (1955), Sinha (1959), and Jerger & Mier (1960) in showing that after temporal lobectomy, provided the conditions of testing are made difficult enough, there is a selective impairment in the discrimination of stimuli to the contralateral ear. In the present study, as in that of Sinha (1959), no such trend was found after frontal lobectomy.

In the course of this investigation Dr. Kimura (1961b) noted a curious asymmetry in the preoperative scores for the right and left ears. She observed that her subjects tended to make higher scores for the right ear than the left, irrespective of the locus of origin of their seizures. Table 7 illustrates this finding for the various clinical groups; the difference between the scores for the right and left ears for all patients is significant beyond the .001 level. Dr. Kimura (1961b) has subsequently confirmed this finding for a group of normal adults and also for normal children, varying in age from 9 years down to 5 years, which was the youngest group tested.

Table 7

Broadbent Test: Preoperative Mean Scores for Right and Left Ears

Group	Left Ear	Right Ear
Left Temporal	76.8	81.5
Right Temporal	81.4	86.0
Bitemporal	77.9	80.2
Frontal	82.7	86.4
Subcortical	74.7	80.6

The only hypothesis we could offer to account for the superiority of the right ear was that verbal stimuli presented to the ear opposite the dominant hemisphere for speech would tend to be more accurately perceived than stimuli to the ipsilateral ear, under these conditions of competition between the two ears. This would be consistent with the demonstrated importance of the left temporal lobe for performance on this task as a whole, and with the greater effectiveness of the contralateral auditory pathway. It would follow from this interpretation that subjects with speech represented in the right hemisphere would show greater efficiency on the left ear. Fortunately it was possible to test this prediction, since there were 13 patients known to have speech representation on the right,[3] and whose data had therefore been excluded

[3] The right-sided speech representation was demonstrated in all cases by the Wada technique of intracarotid injection of sodium amytal, the right and left sides being injected on different days (Wada & Rasmussen, 1960). The injection produces a brief contralateral hemiplegia: if it is in the dominant hemisphere for speech, it also produces a dysphasia which typically outlasts the hemiplegia by a few minutes; from the nondominant side there is hemiplegia but no dysphasia.

Table 8

Broadbent Test: Hemisphere Dominance and Mean Preoperative Scores for Right and Left Ears

Locus of Speech	No. Cases	Left Ear	Right Ear	Right minus Left
Left Hemisphere	107	76.6	83.0	6.4
Right Hemisphere	13	85.0	74.9	−10.1

from the preceding analysis. Table 8 shows the preoperative mean scores for these 13 subjects, contrasted with those for the main group with speech on the left (Kimura, 1961a). It is clear that when speech is represented in the left hemisphere, the right ear is more efficient ($p < .001$), and when speech is represented in the right hemisphere, the left ear is more efficient ($p < .02$).

A further point to be elucidated was that of the relationship between handedness and the relative efficiency of the two ears on the Broadbent test. This is of particular importance, since there was a higher proportion of left-handers in the group with speech representation on the right than in the group with speech on the left. Dr. Kimura (1961a) therefore subdivided her groups into right-handers and left-handers (omitting 5 subjects classified as ambidextrous), and the mean scores for the right and left ears for the resulting 4 subgroups are shown in Table 9. It is clear that for both right- and left-handed subjects there is greater accuracy of report for the ear opposite the hemisphere dominant for speech. A simple analysis of variance for the difference scores for the two ears yielded an F-ratio of 10.42 ($p < .001$). The difference between the left-handers with speech in the left hemisphere and the left-handers with speech in the right hemisphere is significant beyond the .001 level, and there is no difference between the two groups with speech in the left hemisphere but differing in handedness ($p > .40$). Thus laterality of speech, rather than handedness, appears to be the main factor in producing these results.

The findings on the Broadbent test show that digits are more efficiently reported when they stimulate the ear contralateral to the dominant hemisphere for speech, and that temporal lobectomy in this dominant hemisphere impairs performance on the test as a whole, this being a verbal task. When we set these findings in the context of the deficits seen on the Seashore auditory-discrimination tests after right, but not after left temporal lobectomy, the question arises whether the efficiency of the ears might not be reversed for nonverbal material; i.e., efficiency of report might be greater for the left ear than for the right.

Table 9

Broadbent Test: Speech vs. Handedness
(Mean Scores)

Handedness	No. Cases	Left Ear	Right Ear
	Left-Dominant Group		
Right-handed	93	77.03	83.73
Left-handed	10	72.50	77.00
	Right-Dominant Group		
Right-handed	3	83.67	81.67
Left-handed	9	85.00	71.44

The difficulty was to find some nonverbal auditory stimuli which could be presented to the two ears simultaneously and elicit an immediate response. We have not solved this problem very satisfactorily yet, but Dr. Kimura (1961b) has gathered some preliminary data for recorded groups of clicks. In this variation of the Broadbent task, 2 different groups, each comprising from 1 to 6 clicks, are presented to the 2 ears over a 2-second or a 1-second time-span, and the subject has to report the number of clicks arriving at each ear. Thus, he may hear 3 clicks in 1 ear and 5 in the other, in which case he would report "3 and 5." This test yields a total score, which is the number of correct estimates for the 2 ears, and also separate scores for the left and right ears. Clicks were used partly for ease of report, and partly because patients with right temporal-lobe epilepsy are inaccurate in estimating the number of dots flashed on a screen tachistoscopically (Kimura, 1960). It seemed possible, therefore, that this click test, which also requires an immediate estimate of quantity, would be more dependent upon the right temporal lobe than the left, and hence that subjects might show greater efficiency on the left ear.

The preliminary findings are summarized in Table 10, which gives the mean scores for 14 normal subjects (student nurses) who were tested with both digits and clicks. In all cases, the clicks test was given first and the digits at least one day later, since we did not wish the strong right-ear dominance for digits to influence the performance on clicks. It will be observed that the results for the 2 tests are quite different. For the digits, there is the expected higher mean score for the right ear ($p < .02$) but, for clicks, there is a slight, though insignificant, difference in favor of the left ear.

Table 10

Mean Scores for Right and Left Ears for 14 Normal Subjects Tested with Both Clicks and Digits

Test	Left Ear	Right Ear	Right minus Left
Clicks	28.3	26.6	−1.7 N.S.
Digits	85.2	89.8	+4.6*

* $p < .02$

A different, and perhaps more meaningful, way of looking at these data is to compare performance on the 2 tests for each subject. This is particularly important in a normal group, since we have no means of knowing which subjects, if any, have speech representation on the right; and there were 2 left-handed and 1 ambidextrous subjects in the group. According to our hypothesis, subjects in whom the right hemisphere is dominant for speech should tend to make higher scores on the left ear for digits and on the right ear for clicks. Thus the critical test would be that the difference between the scores for right and left ears should be of opposite sign for the 2 tasks. When we analyze the individual scores for our 14 subjects from this standpoint, we find that for 10 subjects the difference scores are of opposite sign, and for the remaining 4 the signs are the same. This work is still in progress, and we hope to adapt some other nonverbal auditory task such as tonal-pattern perception to the Broadbent method. Already it is clear that all auditory stimuli are not more accurately perceived if they are channelled to the ear opposite the dominant hemisphere for speech; it is probably only verbal material that is thus favored.

I believe that these diverse results, obtained for different kinds of auditory stimuli with the Broadbent technique, afford a parallel to some of the results of tachistoscopic work in vision. Yesterday, Dr. Mishkin pointed out that tachistoscopically presented words and letters tend to be more accurately perceived in the right than in the left visual field, and that this holds for a wide variety of conditions, though not for all. However, this superiority of the right visual field applies only to alphabetical material; under the same conditions, geometric forms and nonsense figures are recognized equally well in both right and left fields (Bryden, 1960; Heron, 1957; Terrace, 1959). Hence, when we try to understand how the two hemispheres work together in perception and learning, we have to keep in mind the nature of the stimulus material which the nervous system must handle; this means not only the sensory channel, but also the verbal or nonverbal nature of the information being processed.

Conclusions and Summary

These observations on human temporal-lobe function have emphasized differences between the left and right temporal lobes. The visual and auditory deficits seen after right temporal lobectomy resemble those produced by bilateral temporal-lobe lesions in the monkey; they are however less severe, presumably because the lesion is unilateral. It is known that in man bilateral temporal-lobe lesions cause profound perceptual and memory disturbances (Terzian & Dalle Ore, 1955; Milner, 1959). The clinically rather trivial, though statistically reliable, disabilities, seen after right temporal lobectomy in man, suggest that the right temporal lobe plays a major, the left an ancillary role in nonverbal visual and auditory functions. The deficits produced by left temporal lobectomy are verbal, and here the functions are more strongly lateralized, although we have evidence from the use of the Wada intracarotid amytal technique that there may be bilateral representation of speech in some individuals, with one hemisphere relatively, rather than absolutely, dominant.

At first sight, these verbal and nonverbal deficits may seem quite unrelated, but they have a formal similarity in that both deal with perceiving and learning, auditory and visual. Patients with temporal-lobe lesions show, for example, no consistent deficits in reasoning or problem-solving, or in the maintenance of prolonged attention. There seems then to be much in common between the functions served by temporal cortex in man and monkey, but with the important distinction that in man an asymmetry renders one hemisphere dominant for the perception and learning of verbal material, leaving it less important than the other hemisphere for the perception and learning of some nonverbal, visual and auditory patterns.

Discussion Third Session

A.

Differences in the Functions of the Two Cerebral Hemispheres

WILLIAM D. NEFF

Psychophysiology Laboratory, Bolt Beranek and Newman Inc., Cambridge, Massachusetts

THE EVIDENCE presented by Drs. Teuber, Weinstein, and Milner shows quite clearly that, on certain tests of sensory discrimination or of intellectual ability, a greater deficiency in performance of human subjects may occur after damage to a given region of one cerebral hemisphere than after similar damage to the corresponding region (as defined by gross anatomical landmarks) of the opposite hemisphere. The kinds of performance for which differences have been found are not limited to tasks which involve use of language. Teuber, for example, has mentioned impairment of binaural sound localization and of performance on a tactual form-board test after different lesions of the right cerebral hemisphere. Weinstein described deficits of tactile size discrimination resulting from damage to the right hemisphere. And Milner has reported changes in certain auditory discriminations (Seashore tests of tonal memory and timbre)—again, after damage to the right hemisphere. All three have mentioned other deficiencies which occur after destruction of tissue of the left hemisphere; in most instances, these defects were measured by tests which make use of spoken or printed verbal material.

For man, then, we must conclude that there are measurable differences in the functioning of the two cerebral hemispheres; that the differences are not confined to behavior which involves language; and that the differences cannot be accounted for readily in terms of the manner in which sense organs project to, and motor organs receive innervation from, contralateral and ipsilateral hemispheres.

In the time which I have been allotted for discussion, I wish to comment briefly on the contribution which animal experiments have made or may make to understanding the problem of cerebral dominance, or stated more broadly, the problem of differences in the functions of the two cerebral hemispheres.

Impairment in performance, as measured by behavioral tests, has been observed in mammals after unilateral ablations of the motor, somesthetic, and visual areas of the cerebral cortex. The deficiencies noted are similar to those found for man in clinical investigations, and differences in effects produced by lesions in the right and left hemispheres appear to be explainable, for the most part, in terms of the known anatomical relationships, and in particular, the fact that all or most of the neural connections are between all or part of a given peripheral organ and one cerebral hemisphere. Excluding results of experiments which have (a) examined movement of a limb after ablation of contralateral motor cortex, (b) measured tactual discrimination after ablation of somatic cortex contralateral to the side stimulated, or (c) plotted the visual field after ablation of optic cortex, there are almost no reports of animal experiments in which a behavioral change has been noted after an experimental lesion confined to one cerebral hemisphere. The kinds of behavior which have been studied in animal experiments—learning, problem-solving, activity related to motivation or emotion, and most sensory discriminations—have not been measurably affected by unilateral ablations. Typically, lasting behavioral changes are found only after complete or nearly complete bilateral ablation of anatomically defined regions.

It would be premature, however, to state that animal experimentation has nothing to contribute to the problem of understanding differences in the functions of the two cerebral hemispheres. With appropriate selection of behavioral tests and of ablation procedures, it seems not unlikely that changes can be measured after ablations in one hemisphere, and that differences between the two hemispheres may be discovered. Let me give one or two illustrations of experiments which may lead in this direction.

In recent years, a number of investigators have reported that the ability of animals to make learned complex sensory discriminations may be impaired by bilateral ablations of cortical areas outside the primary projection areas, anterotemporal and inferotemporal regions in the monkey (Neff, 1961; Stepien, Cordeau, & Rasmussen, 1960) and insular-temporal region in the cat (Goldberg, Diamond, & Neff, 1957) and dog (Chorazyna & Stepien, 1961). To the best of my knowledge, changes after unilateral ablation have not as yet been shown. It may be profitable to give further attention to these "association" areas, to look for possible changes in more complicated discriminations after unilateral ablation and to compare the effects of lesions of the left and right hemispheres.

Dr. Teuber reported that, in man, localization of sound in space was impaired by damage to the right cerebral hemisphere. Other investigators have also reported deficiencies in localizing sound after unilateral lesions in human subjects (Sanchez-Longo & Forster, 1958). There are, on the other hand, reports of studies in which no changes were found (Shankweiler, 1961; Walsh, 1957). Dr. Norman Strominger and I have tested the localizing ability of cats after large unilateral ablations of the temporal lobe. Impairment of localization has been found in a number of cases. No differences have been noted between lesions of the right and left hemispheres. It is of interest that localization of sound in space is the only kind of auditory discrimination which we have found to be affected by a unilateral ablation of the temporal lobe.

The organization of the auditory system is such that one might expect to find some differences in the functions of the cortex of right and left cerebral hemispheres under the appropriate experimental conditions. Each cochlea projects to both hemispheres, but anatomical and electrophysiological findings suggest some differences in the projections to the two sides. By destroying one cochlea and training and testing an animal with only one ear intact, a comparison can be made between the effects of ablating contralateral and ipsilateral cortical areas. Behavioral tests to be used should include discriminations of complex temporal patterns.

Experiments on lower animals have not, with the exceptions noted above, contributed appreciably to an understanding of differences in function of the two cerebral hemispheres. This does not mean that no significant contribution can come from such experiments. It may only mean that researchers, studying brain function by means of laboratory experiments on animals, have been concerned with other problems which are more readily attacked, and that they have only recently obtained knowledge and developed techniques which may lead to experiments which will look for interhemispheric differences. This line of research will be encouraged by the shift in emphasis of clinical investigations from examination of disorders of language to the study of other kinds of perceptual and intellectual behavior.

B.

HAROLD G. WOLFF[1]

Cornell University Medical College, New York, New York

I WOULD LIKE to begin by expressing my appreciation and admiration for the ingenuity and devotion and the sustained purposefulness of those who have been working with this veteran material for so many years, and particularly to Drs. Teuber and Weinstein. In the days immediately after World War II, I had the opportunity to consider the ways in which we might learn the most by the study of these unfortunate individuals. The continuing studies of Dr. Teuber and his group have been productive beyond our wildest hopes. That is to say that they have studied carefully the veterans with brain damage in an exhaustive manner, in order to discover what lessons that group could give.

Nevertheless, I want to say at once that I believe it would be an injustice to overinterpret these results. I have myself been working in this same field for about ten years, and I have gradually evolved a series of criteria which I believe must be met before we can draw inferences about the functions of the cerebral hemispheres in man, from studies of these brain-injured individuals. First, there must be an accurate estimate of the site and extent of the anatomical defect, at the very least within the limits of gross measurement. It is impossible to make such estimates for these men, regardless of the notes which are available, for they are often very sketchy and were made very quickly at the time of injury, or shortly after it. Second, it must be established that there are no lesions elsewhere in the brain, or, if there are, these other lesions must be accurately described. Third, the effects of the loss

[1] Dr. Wolff died unexpectedly on February 21, 1962, before an opportunity had arisen for him to correct the record of his remarks made at the conference. I have undertaken to do this, and to preserve so far as possible the spirit and factual content of his stimulating discussion. The errors are mine, not his.—The Editor.

of not only local aggregates of neurons, but the untoward effects of the injury upon arterial supply and venous outflow must be known, as well as the directly damaging effects upon adjacent or underlying structures as sequelae of the operative procedures or of the original injury itself. Incidentally, it is often important to recognize that people with left-sided lesions receive medical attention a little sooner than do those with right-sided ones because of the signs and symptoms resulting from disturbances of speech. Further, surgeons are more likely to make more extensive removals or debridements on the right side of the brain than on the left.

Fourth, the remaining cerebral hemisphere must be known to be free of any progressively destructive process, including that of seizure disorder; and the group of brain-injured veterans described includes many individuals who have seizures. Fifth, one function should not be singled out for study, and the implication made that all other functions are intact, unless these other functions are adequately measured. This is an all-too-common practice when investigators discuss memory function in relation to certain areas of the brain. The methods of study of functional defects must include not only the relatively simple or low-level sensory and motor tasks of learning discriminations and the expressive and receptive features of speech function, but must also include a study of the subject's reactions relevant to human adaptation, especially as regards his interpersonal and social relations. It must be appreciated that most test procedures involve, directly or indirectly, the function of speech.

Sixth, the effects produced by the loss of cerebral tissue must be appraised with reference to the premorbid life experience of the individual, his prevailing moods, attitudes, his adaptive versatility, his schooling, social experience, and especially his goals and aspirations. A man with a fixed aspiration beyond his capacity may be exposed to an underlying frustration—an unending frustration. It would be unfortunate indeed if we used that gross screen known as the Army General Intelligence Test as an indication of the adaptive versatility of an individual, and on the basis of such a criterion decided whether or not the loss of brain substance had impaired that adaptive versatility. I believe this would lead us back to those unfortunate days when it was believed that the brain had very little function other than to cool those passions which were thought to arise from the heart.

Therefore, I believe that the important observations made by Drs. Teuber and Weinstein as regards certain lower-level, relatively simple functions are valid. One could not quarrel with these, if we can assume that language function is not impaired and that seizure disorders play no role, and that the premorbid equipment of the individuals was the same, and so on. But when one attempts an estimate of the overall adaptive capacity of the individual made on the basis of these criteria, I think a profound error can be made. The speakers have pointed with satisfaction to the fact that some of the subjects studied have done well at the professions and in industry. I can cite with equal relevance one of our subjects who, with 150 grams of brain missing, writes an important financial column for a New York newspaper. However, conversations with his family, his wife, and his friends give an entirely different kind of estimate of this man's adaptive versatility. One of my subjects is a psychiatrist whose functioning, so far as I can tell, is adequate, though 120 grams of his brain is missing. His performance is not adequate, however, if one takes into consideration the opinions of his family and friends.

A well-grooved pattern, and especially one learned earlier in life, can carry a man already established in life for a long time without a perceptible fall-off. That does not mean that his adaptability is not altered by brain damage. The effects of the loss of cerebral substance must be appraised with a knowledge of the subject's environment. Does he return to a high-powered world where much is expected of him? Or does he, on the other hand, go back to a simpler situation where his limitations are less conspicuous? In the first case, the opportunities for frustrations may be maximal, and the effects of that frustration upon high-level functioning may be appreciable.

I would like to summarize briefly our own experience, and I hope that you will allow me to pass over a detailed description of our methods, which have included the usual methods for the so-called testing of intelligence, studies of conditional reflexes, of frustration tolerance, as well as many other measures of performance which we have devised or abandoned or changed. Subjects with the loss of different amounts of their cerebral hemispheres show significant variations in the degree of impairment of the highest integrative functions. Impairment is less for those who, before injury, disease, or brain removal, had demonstrated a high order of adaptive versatility, and it was greater in those who, before loss of brain tissue, had exhibited difficulties in prolonged, overall adaptation with associated anxiety.

The individual variations in the degree of impairment were most striking when the amount of cerebral tissue lost was small, i.e., less than 60 grams. The variations between individuals as regards the degree of impairment were much less marked when the amount of cerebral tissue lost was great, i.e., 90–150 grams or more. Persons with a loss of brain substance of up to 90 grams may not score poorly on conventional, psychological screening tests. Such tests are too gross for the type of impairment of which I am speaking. These losses or changes in function become apparent when careful studies are made of the environment in which the individual makes his day-to-day adjustments. Such studies are, at least to me, far more valid than the army intelligence test, which was done under the pressing circumstances of sweeping large numbers of men into the services when they were most needed, to say nothing of the defects of the test itself.

However, in a series such as we have studied, in which the premorbid, overall adaptive capacities were comparable, the mass of tissue lost varied from 15 to 150 grams. The form and content and the degree of impairment of the highest integrative functions were directly related to the mass of tissue lost from the isocortex. It was independent of the site of the lesion. I add quickly an exception to this general principle: subjects with large nonfrontal lesions were somewhat more impaired than were those with similarly large frontal lesions. We infer, perhaps incorrectly, that impairment of lower and intermediate level functions, in subjects with large nonfrontal lesions, is responsible for this difference.

Our studies of patients with various types of less well defined degrees of diffuse loss of cerebral tissue, from slight to severe, indicated a direct relationship between the amount of tissue lost and the impairment of the highest integrative functions. Individual variations were less striking in those individuals with moderate to severe diffuse loss, that is to say when the loss of tissue was minimal, there was a great deal of variation which appeared to depend upon the premorbid equipment and experience of the individual. These variations were much less marked when the lesions were large.

The implications from these on-going studies is that there is a reasonably predictable relation between the site and size of brain tissue loss and the resulting defects in relatively simple sensory and motor functioning, as well as defects in sensory-motor patterns of learning and discrimination, and that the expressive and receptive aspects of speech function are mainly dependent upon such local function, namely that of the left hemisphere. However, the degree of impairment of the highest level of integrative function which I have been discussing has no such regional dependence and, barring individual differences in premorbid equipment, is more closely related to the total number of adequately functioning cortical neurons after the loss of brain tissue, regardless of the site of the lesion and regardless of whether the absent or defective nerve cells are missing from or within one area of the isocortex or distributed diffusely throughout the hemispheres.

I think it is a triumph that the frontal lobes are at last left alone! They have hardly been mentioned in this conference in the sense of being loci of all sorts of mystical qualities, and at least we are now talking about those qualities, less in terms of the magic formerly attributed to the frontal lobes, and more in terms of attributing the highest level functions to other parts of the brain. So, I repeat. I am certainly in complete sympathy with the effort made by the previous speakers. I am in accord with their recognition of defects and of the disturbances of relatively low level functions, and of the expressive and receptive aspects of speech function by relatively local lesions. However, when we come to discuss the highest integrative functions, and particularly that of the capacity of humans to adapt, I think we should be extremely cautious in drawing general, and what I fear may be premature, conclusions from the study of these brain-injured men.

C.

HANS-LUKAS TEUBER

Massachusetts Institute of Technology, Cambridge, Massachusetts

WE ARE GRATEFUL to Dr. Wolff for his discussion of our reports. There are many points on which we agree with him, and a few where we differ. Dr. Wolff's questions fall into two parts: he has stressed problems revolving about one's choice of subjects, and problems related to the choice of experimental tasks.

Concerning the choice of subjects: Dr. Wolff has stressed the desirability of working with cases of brain damage where site and size of the lesions are exactly known. He has warned us rightly that surgeons, in debriding a brain wound, might remove more tissue from the right than from the left hemisphere. He has pointed to the possible complications resulting from posttraumatic seizure disorders.

With regard to the choice of tasks, he stressed (and we fully agree) that one should study more than one aspect of behavior after brain injury, at any one time; that one should take a man's preinjury history and his postinjury adjustment to social situations into account; and that one should *not* accept a "good" score on a routine test of intelligence, after brain injury, as evidence of integrity of the "highest adaptive functions." Lastly, Dr. Wolff described, in brief, some of his own studies in this area: he has employed tumor cases, measured the amounts of tissue removed at operation in each case, and correlated these amounts with the degree of loss estimated by means of a great multiplicity of psychological tests. He found, as might be expected, that there was a high correlation between grams of tissue removed, and general impairment as assessed by a composite score taken from the many psychological tests.

Let me try to respond to these comments and questions in the same order in which they appeared in his detailed discussion. The choice of subjects for studies such as ours is beset with difficulties. Missile wounds of the brain are often seen to have widespread effects in the cerebral substance when studied at autopsy, but we should remember that autopsies, performed soon after such injuries, are selective for maximal damage, i.e., brain damage sufficient to lead to death. The method for arriving at tentative localization of lesion in surviving patients is open to doubt, but this doubt does not detract from the differential effects we have reported. As you recall, we contrasted, in every comparison, patients with penetration through a given area of the skull—say the right frontal region (as seen in their X-rays)—with all other men with known penetrations through other parts of the cranium. In this way, errors in defining the lesion tend to be primarily errors of underestimation. This means that such errors would diminish, rather than enhance the probability of obtaining focal (differential) results, since, in every comparison, complementary lesion groups are pitted against each other; mutual overlap of their lesions would thus blur, rather than produce a difference.

It seems to us that the further problem raised by Dr. Wolff—that of a possible tendency, on the surgeon's part, to engage in more extensive debridement from right as compared with left hemispheres—is a much more serious question. The same problem can arise, of course, in dealing with tumor cases or in those with epileptogenic scars such as the group of cases studied so thoroughly in Montreal. Yet even if such a bias did exist (resulting in more massive tissue loss from right than left hemisphere), I cannot see how it would account for some of the differential effects of right *vs.* left hemispheric lesions. For instance, in the monograph by Josephine Semmes, *et al.,* we described a conspicuous tendency for tactile deficit of the left hand to be associated with lesions of right or left hemisphere; tactile deficits of the right hand, by contrast, were due almost exclusively to contralateral involvement (i.e., involvement of left hemisphere). Such a result suggests to us differential patterns of functional representation, and not unknown differences in extent of lesions in right and left hemispheres.

The same results can be cited in illustrating how we dealt with the problem of posttraumatic epilepsy: Dr. Wolff suggests that cases with epilepsy should be excluded. We approached this problem quite differently; on every comparison among test results, all patients are considered, but comparisons are made in such a way that we assess performance of those with a given symptom (e.g., posttraumatic epilepsy, aphasia, visual field defect), as against those without that symptom—so that we could say what difference, if any, resulted from the presence of a given consequence of the brain wound. In fact, such analyses permit us to treat the results of our experimental tasks without reference to location of lesions: we could (and did) ask whether all men with field defect had certain other quantitatively established symptoms or not, and correspondingly for other functional changes. Thus, cases of this sort can be studied in terms of an analysis according to association and dissociation of symptoms, irrespective of site or size of their lesions—a possibility clearly seen (and exploited) by Sir Henry Head three and four decades ago.

Dr. Wolff made a strong case for the study of tumor cases, and for the weighing of tissue removed in such cases at operation. Our experience with such cases is more limited than his, but we are not convinced that the weighing of tissue (which may include varying combinations of neoplastic and relatively healthy tissue) can really counterbalance certain disadvantages that cling to studies of neoplastic cerebral disease. Such cases ought to be studied, but if one finds (as have several of our students) that these cases tend to show much more diffuse impairment than cases of gunshot wounds, then one is forced to conclude that tumor cases on the whole exhibit less focal involvement of the brain, and that arguments about diffuseness in the representation of function should be advanced with great caution: it may be the disease, rather than the pattern of representation, that is diffuse in such patients.

We believe that it is of greatest importance to study both kinds of cases (traumatic and neoplastic) in sufficient numbers and with objective techniques, so that definitive statements can be made about possible differences in the outcome of human brain damage depending on its etiology. It is for this reason that we are currently investigating groups of tumor cases, using the same tasks we have employed with our cases of penetrating trauma. So far, the results do suggest a less differential, i.e., more diffuse, impairment in the tumor cases as contrasted with those of missile wounds. However, whether one finds specific (focal) or nonspecific (nonlocalizable) effects of brain lesions, in animal or man, is not only a function of the lesion but also of the task employed.

This brings us to the second part of Dr. Wolff's discussion: The problems centered around the nature of the behavioral tasks to be used in studies such as his or ours. We agree completely, of course, on the desirability of using more than one index of behavioral change; only by using many and diverse tasks can one come closer to a proper analysis of altered performance after brain injury. We are just as much in agreement with regard to certain standard tests of so-called general intelligence (such as the Army General Classification Test). These tests, as Dr. Wolff pointed out, depend maximally on overlearned information and skills which can survive after considerable destruction of cerebral tissue.

In fact, we have frequently stressed the shocking insensitivity of such intelligence tests to the presence of massive brain lesions. Unless the lesions encroach on the left parietotemporal area as Dr. Weinstein pointed out, these tests can give a spurious impression of normal performance. If one uses other types of tasks, however, then the same cases which seemed unimpaired after lesions, say of the right temporal, or right frontal region, turn out to have lasting and significant deficits. So far then we do not differ in our interpretation from Dr. Wolff. We agree furthermore on the desirability of life history data (I am currently engaged in a survey of life histories of our gunshot wound cases), but we would add that in such investigations of social adjustment, equally detailed studies of a matched control group are essential. We are therefore comparing here, as elsewhere, cases of penetrating brain wounds with cases of peripheral nerve injury.

The only real divergence in approach between Dr. Wolff and ourselves becomes manifest in what he calls changes in overall adaptation, or "highest level functions." He expressed a concern that our methods are, on the whole, restricted to assessment of low-level sensory and motor functions; he expressed a fear that we might underestimate the seriousness of other aftereffects of such brain wounds—aftereffects revealed in a patient's day-by-day interaction with his fellowmen. We do not intend to make light of these injuries, and if this impression was created, we would like to amend it. But here there is another problem, a logical one which has troubled this field for over a century: As Flourens and many others before him, Dr. Wolff has proposed that specific localization of function may be restricted to what he called low-level sensory and motor functions. The highest "adaptive" functions, he suggested, are quite differently mapped; for these aspects of behavior, it is the mass of available neurons rather than their location that matters. Positive proof for such nonspecific or "general" functions of the hemispheres, however, is much more difficult to obtain than is the demonstration of more focal representation of specific functions. We have used a number of complex problem-solving tasks (including tasks involving transfer of logical solutions from one sense-modality to another), yet have found, even for these, surprisingly specific patterns of representation (e.g., maximal losses after parietal lesions). Still, there are symptoms, in our own work, that seem to be nonspecific, and these nonspecific symptoms coexist with the numerous specific (localizable) ones. Some years ago, Dr. Weinstein and I reported such nonfocal changes for a seemingly simple task: that of discovering visual figures hidden within embedding contours. Impairment on this hidden-figure task appeared in our group of men with penetrating brain wounds, regardless of the site of their penetration: whether in frontal, parietal, temporal, or occipital regions, and regardless of whether the right or left hemisphere seemed to be involved. Nor did it matter whether or not the men had visual field defects, or sensory impairment, or epilepsy; all of these groups showed significant losses as contrasted to the control cases without brain injury. Such a general symptom may mean that both specific and nonspecific modes of representation coexist.

However, compelling proof for the existence of such a general factor presupposes that the task employed be unitary and that the lesions be sufficiently restricted; it is here where the serious difficulties begin. If the lesions are not as focal as we think they might be, then the interpretations of nonfocal behavioral changes has to be held in abeyance. Still more serious, however, is another and purely logical argument, made most forcefully many years ago by Professor W. S. Hunter in his criticism of Karl Lashley's claim for cerebral mass-action: The more numerous and complex the tasks that are employed to bring out nonfocal effects of brain lesions, the greater the probability that each lesion will contribute in a different way to an aggregate of impairment. What looks like a nonspecific mass-effect may turn out to be, instead, the combined outcome of many specific deficits which all enter into the poor performance on the manifold tasks employed.

A high positive correlation between mass of tissue lost, and some composite score denoting general impairment is thus compatible with a principle of cerebral mass action, but unfortunately cannot prove it. It is for this reason that we have put a great deal of emphasis, elsewhere, on the nonspecific (nonlocalizable) impairment we found with a single, and apparently simple task: the performance on hidden-figure tests. However, the main chore of this symposium has been to trace the contrast between right and left hemispheres, and their facilitory and inhibitory interaction. Dr. Wolff's discussion introduced broader issues in the central area of localization of function. He has reminded us of the unusual difficulties in this field; his discussion underscores the need for employing many different behavioral methods; the need for looking at brain damage of different etiology, and the need for great care in one's interpretations. For all this, we are very much in his debt.

D.

Speech and Speech-loss in Relation to the Duality of the Brain

MACDONALD CRITCHLEY

The National Hospital, Queen Square, London, England

AS DR. LILLY pointed out, it really was not until 5:30 yesterday evening that the word "speech" first cropped up in a discussion upon cerebral dominance. It is perhaps a pity that a whole session could not have been devoted to problems of speech and aphasia. Rather than try to sum up the remarkable papers we have heard this morning, I will adhere to my original instructions and devote just ten minutes to language in the context of cerebral dominance.

I hope you will forgive me if I start of necessity on a historical note. This important colloquium held today, 1961, in Baltimore, logically stems from the pioneer observations made 150 years ago.

In the center of the wine-growing region of Gard, in the south of France, stands the tiny walled town of Sommières. There, at the turn of the eighteenth century, lived an obscure general practitioner, Dr. Marc Dax. It was he who—as the result of inspired clinicopathological correlation—first realized that as far as language, at any rate, was concerned, the two cerebral hemispheres are not equipotential. In 1836, he delivered a short address upon this topic before the Congrès Méridional. The paper attracted no attention: it was never published; the manuscript lay forgotten in a drawer, long after his death the following year. Nearly 30 years later, and a century ago, Paul Broca was slowly beginning to realize that every single one of his cases of aphemia were the result of lesions of the left half of the brain. In 1865, he wrote a paper to that effect, which came to the notice of Gustave, the doctor son of Dr. Marc Dax, also a medical practitioner at Sommières. Dax junior wrote a peevish letter to the medical press, claiming that Broca had deliberately ignored his father's pioneer work. Broca replied in similar vein, protesting that he had never heard of Marc Dax or read any of his works; and that furthermore he had just made particular search of the press reports of the 1836 Conference and discovered that no mention was ever made of any paper by Dax. The son responded to this taunt by unearthing the original manuscript of the lecture, given by his father in 1836, and he proceeded to reprint this paper and incorporate it within an article of his own in the *Gazette hebdomadaire* for 1865.

Such is the unusual story of the beginnings of our ideas as to the lateralization of certain cerebral functions to one hemisphere only. Though the conception rapidly gained acceptance, the two Doctors Dax themselves remained neglected figures. They became identified with national politics, and the son was forced to give up his post at the local hospital, an appointment which he and his father held for 52 consecutive years.

Hughlings Jackson accepted this doctrine that the left hemisphere was principally concerned with speech, but with certain reservations. Mindful of the logical distinction between positive and negative consequences of disease, he ascribed the defects in self-expression to the left-brain lesion, while attributing the fragmentary utterance of an aphasiac to the operation of the intact hemisphere. Jackson spoke of the left half of the brain as the "leading" hemisphere as regards the faculty of speech, concerned with creative aspects of language, while the right hemisphere was tied up with the "automatic" use of words.

Jackson's views as to the modest role of the nondominant hemisphere in the physiology of speech did not attract very much sympathetic attention. The more striking phenomenon of the correlation of language with the left hemisphere usurped the notice of all who were interested in aphasia. For a long time the matter rested, as it were, but early in the present century, neurologists began to enquire why it was that right-handedness, left cerebral dominance, and the lateralization of speech-endowment to the major hemisphere, should all three be associated in this striking fashion. The mere acquisition of superior motor skills by the right hand did not in itself appear enough to account for the importance of the left hemisphere *quâ* speech. The difference between the function of the two hemispheres was so much greater than the relatively smaller difference between the daily work of the two hands. Gradually the idea developed that it was the acquisition of the art of writing—an artificial and wholly asymmetrical activity within the domain of language—which determined that the opposite hemisphere should develop a special symbological importance. This view was first stated explicitly by Ernst Weber in 1904, who proclaimed that to explain the left-sided importance of the brain as regards speech, mere right-handedness was not enough. Right-handed children do not become aphasic after left-brained disease—unless old enough to have learned to write. Similarly, illiterate persons do not develop the same left-brained preponderance and therefore are liable to show little, if any, aphasia after disease of the left-brain. In other words, there was a greater likelihood of bilateral cerebral representation in the speech-functions of illiterates. Although this notion is of course a naïve and gross oversimplification of the problem, it is an idea which cannot be completely brushed aside and forgotten.

Interest afterwards turned to the problem of cerebral dominance, and the inherent complexities of this apparently simple topic soon became evident. Left-handedness and right-brain dominance no longer was regarded as a mirror-opposite variant of the normal state of affairs. Degrees of cerebral dominance; cross-laterality; correlation of inadequate dominance with cerebral immaturity; ambidexterity as a state of bisinistrality—all these topics came up for discussion. These ideas profoundly influenced our interpretation of such clinical phenomena in sinistrals as aphasia, and also the effects of right parietal disease. A considerable amount of work has been done on the pattern of aphasia in sinistrals, following lesions of either the right or the left half of the brain. Data have been collected by such authors as Conrad, Subirana, and Zangwill and his group, and many others, of course. The exciting results are now well-known, and I need not narrate them here.

At the same time, there has grown up a tendency to focus attention upon the minor hemisphere, and to posit a number of specific nonverbal properties to its pathology. The trend was, and still is, toward parcelling certain neuropsychological endowments, some to the major hemisphere, and others to the minor. With increasing concentration of interest, this latter group seems to be steadily increasing in number, perhaps, it may be said, to an inordinate degree.

The role of the minor hemisphere in such presumed major brain activities as speech had meanwhile been somewhat overlooked. The position as expressed in 1935, by Weinberg and McBride, might be taken as still representing current opinion. They wrote:

> The right brain, while not directly concerned in language in the right-handed individual, nevertheless is in a state of receptivity for language acquisition, the degree varying in accordance with the use of the left hand in writing. In addition, nonlanguage functions and behavior, which are almost always implicated in aphasia, have admittedly a bilateral cerebral basis. This is as far as we can go from the evidence obtained in this research. There is nothing to show that the right brain has any specific language function as indicated by Hughlings Jackson and some more recent investigators.

But is this really and truly the last word in the problem? Quite apart from the question of left-handers and acquired disease, there is the rare appearance of aphasia after lesions in the right hemisphere in subjects who have shown no personal nor familial evidence of sinistrality whatsoever. The notion of "ectopia" of the speech centers, from the left half of the brain to the right, has been argued on and off since the work of Bramwell in 1899, and the subject was ably discussed by Kurt Mendel in 1912. This phenomenon of genuine "crossed aphasia" must be regarded as uncommon, and recently Penfield and Roberts have gauged that less than one per cent of right-handed persons have some representation of speech in the right cerebral hemisphere. In 1955 a paper by Ettlinger, Jackson, & Zangwill discussed a series of sixteen such cases collected from the literature. The impression still exists that cases of "crossed aphasia" are associated with some degree of familial sinistrality—the "stock-brainedness" of Foster Kennedy.

Perhaps we still tend to neglect the possible role of the right half of the brain in the faculty of speech. Some neurologists, conspicuously Dr. Eisonson, are beginning to think that appropriate testing of a sufficiently searching character might well elicit defects, within the sphere of language, which are too subtle for ordinary routine techniques to bring to light. I would like to plead for neuropsychologists to pay closer attention to the linguistic capacities and incapacities of right-handed victims of right-brain disease. Already a number of suggestive clinical data can be mentioned in this context:

(1) Disordered articulation is commonly a very striking sequel of disease of the minor hemisphere, though it may be transient. Of course, dysarthria of this kind is to be regarded as a manifestation of a disorder of speech or speaking, rather than of language. But if the dysarthria is very severe, there will result a poverty of speech which mimics closely

an aphasia and may cause difficulties in bedside diagnosis, even at the hands of very experienced neurologists. In so far as gross dysarthria hampers or hinders articulate self-expression, it can be looked upon as a disorder in the act of communication.

(2) Creative literary work, demanding a particularly high level of performance, may, I submit, be severely affected in such circumstances. I have seen striking examples of this phenomenon in professional writers who have been afflicted with disease of the minor hemisphere.

(3) Appropriate techniques may reveal hesitancies or actual blocking in word-finding. The patient may surmount the naming-difficulty by resorting to very unusual circumlocutions whereby approximate pseudo synonyms emerge, and odd explanations and circumstantial comments are gratuitously offered. This phenomenon, which differs somewhat from the orthodox verbal behavior of a patient with amnestic aphasia, may be spoken of as "metonymous paralogia."

(4) Again, appropriate testing procedures such as tachistoscopy, for example, may demonstrate inordinate delays in the identification of language by the patient, along either auditory or visual channels.

(5) Right-brain disease may perhaps lead to difficulties in the learning of novel linguistic material.

(6) One may also mention the interesting phenomenon described by Nathanson, Bergman, and Gordon in 1952, associated with lesions of the nondominant parietal lobe. Here the patient shows a variety of hesitancies and inaccuracies of speech, but only when the present disability is the topic under discussion. This phenomenon recalls Weinstein's "nonaphasic disorders of naming."

(7) Difficulties in the full understanding of the ultimate meaning of pictorial matter is a common phenomenon of brain disease, and some workers are already tending to associate this more specifically with lesions of the minor hemisphere. Pictorial material may be deemed a far cry from speech, but both can be looked upon as modalities of symbolic formulation.

We recall Penfield's experimental work, whereby either vocalization or else temporary interference with speech can be secured by electrical stimulation either of the dominant or the nondominant hemisphere, but the relationship of these findings in the context of language is still not clear.

The foregoing phenomena, it may be noted, are mainly intensifications of what may occur as temporary difficulties under physiological conditions. In this way it accords with the findings of Howes and Geschwind, who have demonstrated by statistical methods that an aphasia merely represents a random disturbance of the processes underlying the production of normal language.

We may extend this notion to a conception of a spectrum of speech defect depending upon the intrinsic difficulty of the test situation, and ranging from the "normal" subject at one extreme, through the linguistic pattern of nondominant hemisphere defect, up to—at the other limit—a fully fledged aphasia from disease of the dominant half of the brain.

■□ X

Clinical Symptomatology in Right and Left Hemispheric Lesions

by H. HÉCAEN

Les Hopitaux Psychiatriques de la Seine, Paris, France

THE PROBLEM of the functional specialization of each hemisphere of the brain occurred with the first works on aphasia. In an unnoticed publication, Marc Dax, in 1836, had already insisted on the connection between aphasia and lesions of the left hemisphere of the brain. Broca (1865), in his first publications, admitted that both hemispheres might be involved with the language function; later in other works, he proved the existing left cerebral pre-eminency for this function. This proposition was soon confirmed by the works of Bastian, Jackson, and Wernicke. Exceptions to this rule were soon brought forward and explained as resulting from a left manual pre-eminency. Broca (1865) said in this way that certain individuals, with a left manual predominance, "spoke with their right cerebral hemisphere."

So the predominance of the left hemisphere of the brain, in the right-handed subject, was recognized. From this, it was more or less implicitly considered that, with the right-handed patient, the left hemisphere of the brain was pre-eminent for all symbolic functions. In a parallel direction, the works of Liepmann (1900) on apraxia seemed to confirm this opinion, showing the importance of the left hemisphere of the brain for the gestual function. As for the visual gnosic disturbances, one inferred from this opinion, rather than concluded from anatomico-clinical facts, the importance of the left lesional localization with the right-handed patient.

In spite of a few anatomicoclinical facts and hypotheses about the role of lesions of the right hemisphere of the brain in producing apraxia or spatial agnosic disturbances, the role of this hemisphere was generally never recognized in the field of symbolic functions.

With the first descriptions of disturbances of the body-image, the role of the right hemisphere was admitted; one contrasted the somatognosic symptomatology with right lesions and the one provoked by left lesions.

R. Brain (1941) described a symptom of neglect of one side of the visual field and space, insisting on the role of the lesions of the nondominant hemisphere. Patterson & Zangwill (1944), in lesions of the minor hemisphere, described constructive difficulties similar to the ones seen with left parieto-occipital lesions, but without any semantic aspect in the disorder. McFie, Piercy, & Zangwill (1950) established that lesions of the nondominant hemisphere could give disturbances of spatial perception and of constructive activities, a short time after I could confirm such facts with de Ajuriaguerra & Massonnet (1951).

In 1945, apraxia for dressing, described by R. Brain (1941), was connected with lesions of the nondominant hemisphere (Hécaen & de Ajuriaguerra, 1945).

Thus an opinion was reached not only of the possibility of apraxic and agnosic symptomatology with lesions of a hemisphere considered so far as "mute," but also of some qualitative difference from the one due to lesions of the left hemisphere.

As further observations were made, still in the same way, contrary opinions arose refuting the specificity of the praxic and gnosic disturbances; some authors considered them to be produced by diffuse lesions or by lesions of either hemisphere of the brain.

Nevertheless, the anatomicoclinical facts so far gathered seem to give reason for concluding that there exists a specific symptomatology for each hemisphere, without so far having the right to infer from that the existence of particular functions.

Our study then can only be schematic, emphasizing in that way the rather arbitrary character of some of our opinions. We still think that the arguments are sufficiently strong to justify such a classification, in spite of arbitrary opinions which may cause some reservations.

Whatever the pertinent criticisms on the notions of agnosia and apraxia, terms that are indeed only kept as clinical terms consecrated by use, it is a fact that the symptomatology is different according to the hemisphere disturbed, thus obliging us to consider a certain functional organization of the cortex that would be different for each hemisphere. In doing so, it seems necessary to reject the theories which reduce the symptoms to a more diffuse and global perceptual disturbance, as well as the theories connecting the symptom with only an elementary sensory disturbance.

Before considering what could be called the disturbances of the symbolic functions, which is specifically the field of hemispheric lateralization of the lesion, two remarks could be made: a negative one and a positive one. It is a fact that one must insist that when there is a disturbance of the activities of synthesis (such as the personality disturbances derived from cerebral lesions), no difference can be found between left and right lesions. Such a specialization was first supposed for the frontal lobes; it was not confirmed later. More recently, in our study with de Ajuriaguerra (1956) on the mental disturbances resulting from intracranial tumors, we could never show any difference of frequency or of quality in the psychical disorders according to the lesioned hemisphere, whether it concerned the frontal lobes or the other lobes.[1]

On the other hand, very recently, Semmes, Ghent, Weinstein, & Teuber (1960), in studying cortical sensory disorders, could point to a difference according to the lateralization of the lesion. The sensory representation does not seem to be organized in the same way in each hemisphere. In the same way, Teuber, Battersby, & Bender (1960) showed that visual epileptic paroxysms, especially the elementary hallucinatory ones, were connected with lesions principally situated in the right occipital lobe.

APHASIA

Nowadays it is impossible to question the fact that the region of language is situated in the left hemisphere, with the right-handed subject, and there is no need to discuss such a point. Nevertheless,

[1] Nevertheless, it should be pointed out that a kind of affective reaction to failures, varying according to the hemispheric lesions, seems to exist. Indeed the Italian authors, Terzian & Cecotto (1959), Alema & Donini (1960), Perria, *et al.* (1961), have mentioned that after intracarotid injection of sodium amytal, the modifications of mood seem different according to the side of the injection, either on the dominant or nondominant side: depressive-catastrophic reactions on the former, euphoric reactions on the later.

In our material we have also found a greater incidence of catastrophic reactions in left-sided lesions, 55 times out of 206 cases (25.69 per cent), while in right-sided lesions, 20 out of 154 (12.98 per cent). On the contrary, indifference to failures was found in 34 out of the 206 left-sided lesions against 51 in the 154 right-sided lesions.

These differences statistically are quite significant, both in the catastrophic reactions ($X^2 = 10.10$) and in the indifference reactions ($X^2 = 13.67$).

However, we should point out that the confusional and demential disturbances are more frequent in right-sided lesions (35.71 per cent) than in left-sided lesions (20.38 per cent). Therefore the type of reaction to failures was perhaps under the influence of this modification of consciousness for which other factors than the lateralization could play a part (larger lesions are found in right-sided lesions than in left-sided lesions due to the earlier appearance of aphasic disturbances in the dominant hemispheric lesions).

we should mention the possibility of producing an arrest of speech without any aphasic character, by stimulating either hemisphere of the brain in a region where the buccophonatory organs are represented, and also in the region of the supplementary motor area (Penfield). Although true disturbances of language have been produced only by stimulation of the dominant hemisphere, the former fact had to be mentioned in view of the theoretical ideas of Pierre Marie on anarthria, and of the frequent and important regression of the symptoms after a lesion of the posterior end of the left third frontal convolution.

The related problem of musical language and of the hemispheric representation of amusia is not settled yet and still is at the origin of arguments about the possibility that such a symptom may be produced by right-sided lesions of the brain.

The motor amusia, or "avocalie," is connected with a lesion of the base of the second frontal convolution and the top of the third; it seems that it can also be seen with lesions situated only in the right hemisphere. Mann gave the first description of such an expressive form of amusia, insisting on the right-sided lesion lateralization; the literature on the subject shows other cases of lesions situated in either hemisphere. Probst & Kleist (1934) insist on the possibility of a bilateral representation. Recently, Botez & Wertheim (1959) have observed a patient who was operated upon for an oligodendroglioma situated in the third posterior part of the first two frontal convolutions; this patient showed an expressive vocal and instrumental amusia that seemed essentially of a dyspraxic nature.

Receptive amusia cases have also been described with right-sided temporal lesions, and most of the authors admit such a possibility, but insist at the same time on a higher frequency with left-sided lesions. Kleist (1934) thinks that the hemispheric dominance varies from one subject to another. It is possible to note certain differences between the aspects of sensory amusia according to the side of the lesion; with a lesion of the nondominant hemisphere, it seems that the patients are unable to recognize correctly musical sounds (Kohl & Tsabitscher, 1953) and present disorders of the sense of rhythm (Potzl); with a lesion of the left hemisphere, there seems to be essentially a disorganization of musical understanding.

APRAXIA

Liepmann (1900) admitted the predominance of the left hemisphere and particularly of the inferior part of the parietal lobe, in the praxic functions; this opinion was connected with the idea that the corpus callosum was essential for the transmission of the gestural command to the nondominant hemisphere.

Several authors rejected such a conception. Kleist (1934) admits the existence of a praxic territory in the right hemisphere. Foix (1916) insisted on the frequency of a right-sided lesion when the apraxia is predominantly left-sided and thought that the lesions must be bilateral when the apraxia is bilateral; later Foix (1916) admitted that a unilateral lesion could also give a bilateral apraxia. Morlaas (1928) thinks on the contrary that a left-sided lesion can only give a right-sided apraxia, as if the praxic activity of the left limbs was depending only on the right hemisphere; this last conception is obviously very far from the initial one, the conception of Liepmann (1900). It seems that such a contradiction amounts to too strict a conception of an existing, specific praxic function; the description of new forms of apraxia obliged us to revise the problem and put it another way; is there any connection between the clinical form of apraxia and the location of the lesion?

We recently tried, together with Angelergues & de Ajuriaguerra (1960), to reply to such a question by studying our clinical records, that is, 415 cases of retrorolandic lesions. According to the lateralization of the lesion, we found the following percentages of the various clinical forms (Figure 1):

ideatory apraxia:

9 times out of 206 left-sided lesions (4.46 per cent)
twice out of 55 bilateral lesions (3.81 per cent),

ideomotor apraxia:

39 times out of 206 left-sided lesions (18.93 per cent)
8 times out of 55 bilateral lesions (14.54 per cent),

constructive apraxia:

93 times out of 151 right-sided lesions (61.58 per cent)
82 times out of 206 left-sided lesions (39.8 per cent)
40 times out of 55 bilateral lesions (74.07 per cent),

apraxia for dressing:

32 times out of 147 right-sided lesions (21.76 per cent)
8 times out of 205 left-sided lesions (3.9 per cent)
11 times out of 55 bilateral lesions (20.0 per cent).

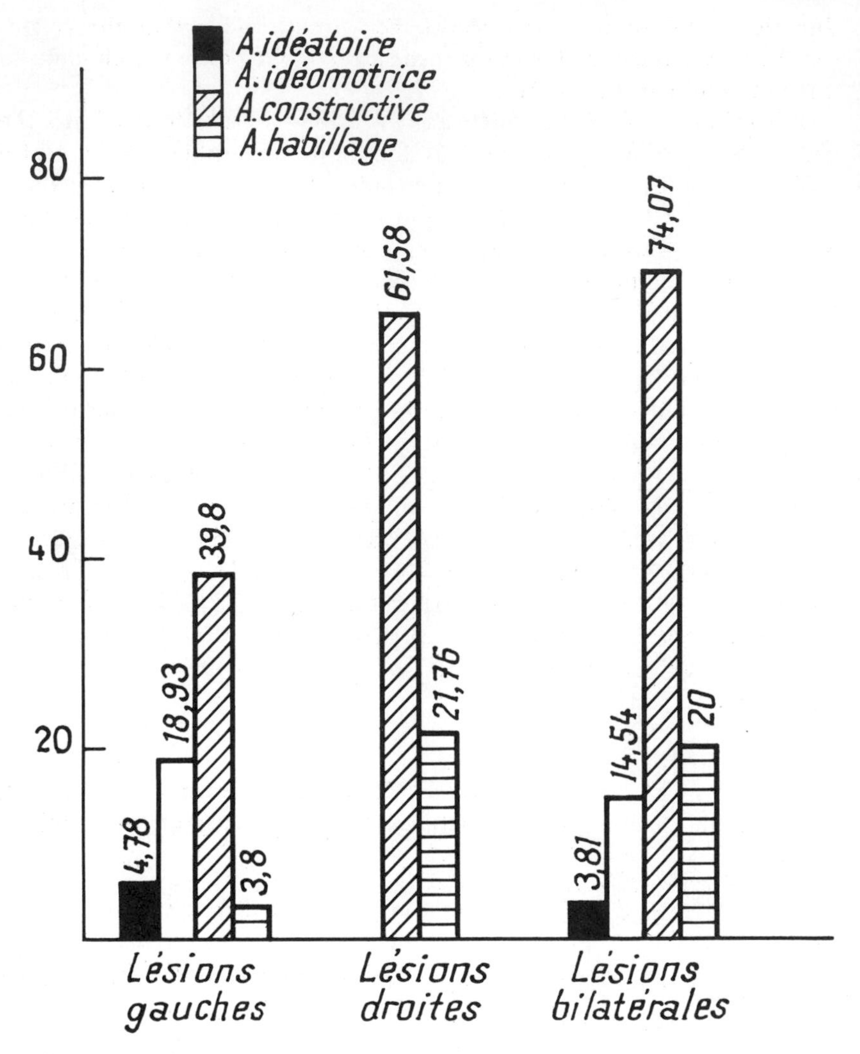

Fig. 1. Frequency of varieties of apraxia according to the injured hemisphere.

Ideatory and ideomotor apraxia are thus only encountered with left-sided or bilateral lesions, which is in accordance with the classical findings. The association of such forms of apraxia with aphasic symptoms is very frequent (about 90 per cent of the cases). Association with intellectual disturbances (deterioration, confusion, . . .), with a state of indifference, is much more frequent in the case of the ideatory apraxia; it must be noted besides that ideatory apraxia is usually connected with large lesions and even with diffuse ones.

Constructive disturbances were first attributed to left-sided lesions, in accord with the first anatomical findings, and with a frequent association with the symptoms of Gerstmann's syndrome. After the earlier studies of Paterson & Zangwill (1944) and of McFie, Piercy, & Zangwill (1950), Hécaen, de Ajuriaguerra, & Massonet (1951) describe a syndrome connected with right-sided lesions which was made up of visuospatial disturbances and constructive disorders. Critchley (1953) suggests the possibility of constructive apraxia with lesions of either hemisphere and shows its greater frequency with bilateral lesions; he also concludes, from the study of a very large series of cases, that such disorder could be less frequent with left-sided lesions than with right-sided ones. Duensing (1953) makes a complete distinction between the constructive disorders amounting to a visuospatial agnosia in right-sided lesions and the same disorders amounting to left-sided lesions; in the last case he considers the disorder to be explained as a deficiency of execution. It must be noted that such a distinction is based on four cases only, among which three had bilateral lesions predominating on one side. Denny-Brown, Meyer, & Horenstein (1952) think that constructive apraxia, such as the ideatory and ideomotor ones, is a conceptual disorder produced by lesions of the dominant hemisphere; and they say that the visuoconstructive disturbances observed with right-sided parietal lesions depend only on a perceptive deficiency, nonagnosic, either tactile or visual, limited to one side of the body or space (amorphosynthesis). The same disturbances also exist with left-sided lesions, but are then masked by the aphasic-agnosic disorders.

Ettlinger, Warrington, & Zangwill (1957) studied carefully 10 cases with right-sided lesions, presenting visuospatial and constructive disorders; they consider these symptoms as a visuospatial agnosia amounting to a restriction of visual attention and to a disorganization of the spatial orientation at a conceptual level. Later on, McFie & Zangwill (1960) insisted on the difference between the clinical aspect of the constructive disturbances, according to the lateralization of the lesion.

The first point that should be made from the study of our own cases is a more frequent possibility of constructive disorders with retrorolandic lesions of the nondominant hemisphere (61.48 per cent) than of the dominant hemisphere (39.8 per cent, with X^2 giving 12.023).

Such a difference was already significant in the clinical group studied with de Ajuriaguerra & Piercy (1960); it was 37.8 per cent against 16.7 per cent, the X^2 giving $5.98 > 0.2$. Clinical associations also show a difference according to these two groups (Figure 2).

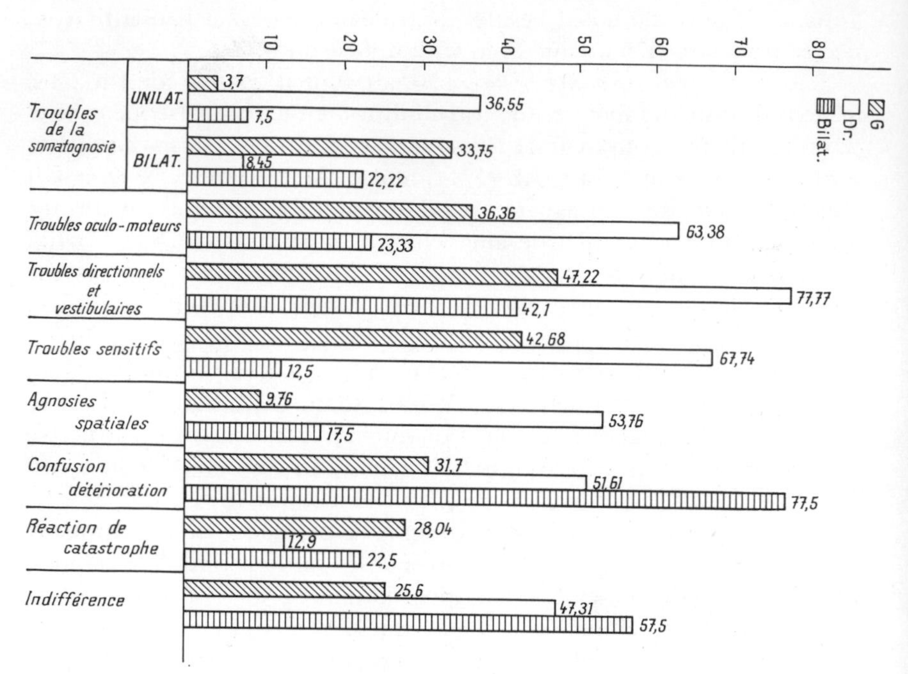

Fig. 2. Frequency of clinical associations in constructive apraxia, according to the injured hemisphere.

With right-sided lesions, associations are more frequent for directional and vestibular symptoms (77.77 per cent), for sensory disorders (67.74 per cent), for oculomotor symptoms (63.38 per cent), spatial agnosia (53.76 per cent), consciousness disorders 51.61 per cent), and hemiasomatognosic disorders (36.55 per cent). The affective reaction mostly encountered is indifference (47.31 per cent).

With left-sided lesions, we find in order: aphasia (71.95 per cent), directional and vestibular troubles (47.22 per cent), sensory disorders (42.68 per cent), oculomotor disorders (36.36 per cent), bilateral somatognosic disorders (33.75 per cent), disturbances of consciousness (31.7 per cent). The abnormal affective reactions are equally often the catastrophic one (28.04 per cent) and indifference (25.6 per cent).

So, with right-sided lesions giving constructive apraxia, there is a predominance of spatial agnosia (X^2 giving 70.929), directional and vestibular disorders (X^2 giving 12.654), indifference of mood (X^2 giving 9.035), oculomotor disorders (X^2 giving 8.606), confusion and deterioration (X^2 giving 5.712), sensory disorders (X^2 giving 4.633).

With left-sided lesions there is a more frequent catastrophic reaction (X^2 giving 4.188).

The following table taken from McFie & Zangwill (1960), comparing the clinical associations in both groups of constructive disorders, shows also a very significant difference; but we shall note a contradistinction for the intellectual disorders that predominate with left-sided lesions in their material, while they predominate with right-sided lesions in our own cases.

Comparison between left- and right-sided lesions

	Left		Right	
	No. examined	No. with disability	No. examined	No. with disability
Unilateral neglect	8	1	21	14
Dressing disability	8	1	15	10
Cube counting	6	(1)	7	6
Paper cutting	4	0	10	9
Topographical loss	8	1	18	9
Right-left discrimination	8	5	21	0
Weigl's sorting	6	5	16	1

Is there any possibility, moreover, to distinguish specific characters in the constructive disorders of these patients, according to the side of the lesion? McFie, Piercy, & Zangwill (1950) already insisted on the way patients with right-sided lesions made a copy: line by line, without any general planning, which they called a piecemeal approach. Hécaen & de Ajuriaguerra (1951) suggested that certain features of their patient's performance set them apart from the comparable left-hemispheric syndrome: neglect of the left side of a model in copying; diagonal orientation of drawings; inability to represent perspective in drawings of three-dimensional objects; inability to articulate different parts of a two-dimensional drawing.

Together with Piercy & de Ajuriaguerra (1960), we tried to make more precise these particularities in the mode of constructiveness, insisting on the fact that it was vain to try to give a lateralization of the supposed lesion by only considering the production of the patient.

Troubles in drawing are generally more severe in patients with right-sided lesions, and if as intense a disorganization can be observed as a result of a left-sided lesion, it can easily be fitted into the framework of a more global apraxia, with ideatory or ideomotor disturbances. The same difference of degree affects copying, whether it is a question of a drawing which remains, in general, more easily identifiable during constructive left-sided apraxias, or of a reproduction with sticks which is usually more disturbed during constructive right-sided apraxia.

In the structure of the drawing itself, differences are to be seen: left-sided lesions appear to entail particularly a simplification of the design as compared with the model, while as a result of right-sided lesions, the copy, very far from being an exact reproduction of the model, takes nevertheless a form of an equivalent complexity, and the number of lines drawn by the patient is noticeably greater than in constructive left-sided apraxia. The number of lines remains more or less constant on the right, whether the copy is fairly accurate or no longer recognizable, whereas on the left, the number of lines decreases as the resemblance diminishes. The inaccuracy of copying in a right-sided apraxic patient appears to be related to certain fundamental errors: inaccuracy of proportions; lack of perspective; faults in the arrangement of the different parts of the drawing. The right-lesional apraxic, on the other hand, tends toward a diagonal orientation of his constructions.

We encountered the phenomenon of closing in, in the study of bilateral lesions. When it existed in unilateral lesions (six times on the left, twice on the right), there occurred also other very intense apraxic symptoms.

This study appeared, on the contrary, to show that the left-lesional apraxic patient benefits by a model which allows him better to construct his copy after paying close attention to the model, while no matter how often the "right-lesional apraxic" consults the model, there will be no improvement in the reproduction of spatial relationships.

APRAXIA FOR DRESSING

We are indebted to Brain (1941) for the description of apraxia for dressing, and for insisting on its presence apart from any disturbance of ideatory or ideomotor praxia.

With de Ajuriaguerra (1945), we took up once more the semeiological description of the disorder underlining its right-lesional lateralization. Our later observations, along with those of most writers on the subject, have confirmed the lesional lateralization of this disorder on the minor hemisphere in the parietal or parieto-occipital region.

Thus Arseni, Voinesco, & Goldenberg (1958), considering 32 parietal tumors (20 right, 12 left), find 17 cases of apraxia for dressing, all as a result of a right-sided lesion.

In our series, as we have seen, the percentage is 21.76 per cent for right-sided lesions as opposed to 3.9 per cent for left-sided lesions. This difference has a considerable statistical significance ($X^2 = 20.304$), and it must also be noted that out of the 8 observations of apraxia for dressing, resulting from a left-sided lesion, in 6 cases the patients were left-handed. Notice too that McFie & Zangwill (1960) find apraxia for dressing only once in 8 left-sided cases and 10 times out of 15 right-sided lesions.

If, in our series, we consider the clinical contexts, we observe a high percentage of association with unilateral somatognosic disturbance (35.29), spatial agnosias (50.98), directional and vestibular disorders (67.50 per cent), and indifference to failure (45.09 per cent); that is to say, a clinical context very similar to that encountered with constructive apraxias from a right-sided lesion.

There is therefore, it would seem, a group of arguments in favor of a right-lesional origin which allows us to admit this hemispheric lateralization of the lesions producing apraxia for dressing, contrary to the opinion of Denny-Brown (1958). For this writer, in fact, they would be no more than the result of amorphosynthesis and could be dependent on injuries to one or the other hemisphere.

We shall attempt to classify the facts as thus presented, studying the praxic syndromes belonging to each hemisphere; in so doing, we shall notice some other aspects of disturbances in gesture passed over until now in silence.

Apraxic Syndrome Due to Left Retrorolandic Lesions

This is formed in the first place by constructive apraxia, with the semeiological nuances explained above, next by bilateral ideomotor apraxia, finally by ideatory apraxia, with perhaps a necessary condition for this last: the association of more diffuse lesions or the general disturbances caused by the lesion. It must also be noted that temporal lesion appeared to us to be more frequent than that of the other lobes, in case of apraxia due to left-hemispheric lesion.

Apraxic Syndrome Due to Right Retrorolandic Lesions

Foix (1916) and Morlaas (1928) have called attention to the existence of right-sided lesions in certain forms of left-sided ideomotor apraxia, attributed since Liepmann (1900) to corpus callosum lesions. With Gimeno Alava (1960), following a study of the literature on the subject and of personal cases, we have deduced that a group of these observations depended on right-sided retrorolandic lesions, with which, however, certain less important lesions of the left hemisphere were associated. The disturbance then seemed very close to hemiasomatognosia.

But the apraxic syndrome due to nondominant hemispheric lesions, is in fact characterized by two essential elements: constructve apraxia in the first place, with its particular characteristics which make it a visuoconstructive disorder, and apraxia for dressing. Parietal injury here seemed to us to be most frequent.

Apraxias due to frontal lesions cannot be passed over in silence, while the lesional lateralization cannot be envisaged other than for bucco-linguofacial apraxia. As for the part played by corpus callosum lesions, it appears that this must no longer be retained, chiefly after the negative results of surgical sections. Bucco-faciolingual apraxia depends on lesions of the left ascendant frontal convolution. However, it can be encountered in cases of right-sided lesions in a right-handed patient, but their apraxic nature is then called in question. (Alajouanine & Lhermitte, 1960.)

Melokinetic apraxia is also of frontal origin, but it seems that it cannot be considered as a disturbance in gesture.

There is equally a variety of left unilateral ideomotor apraxias which correspond to homo- or contralateral medial frontal lesions; they must be distinguished, as we have shown with Gimeno Alava (1960), from those to which we have alluded when speaking of right-parietal lesions. This type of disturbance corresponds, we believe, with what Denny-Brown (1958) has described as frontal kinetic apraxia, to be formally distinguished from conceptual apraxias, but to be placed on the same level as parietal kinetic apraxia. These two varieties of unilateral disturbances in movement would correspond with the predominance of avoiding or grasping reactions on one side of the body, and would be determined by lesions of one or the other hemisphere. It remains to discover whether it is in fact a question of true apraxias, in their nature as a disturbance bearing on the purposiveness of movement.

SOMATOGNOSIC DISTURBANCES

In spite of certain cases which seem to us to be exceptional, and for the most part to be explained by the ambidexterity of the patients, anatomicoclinical experience allows us to say that disturbances of the body scheme appear under very different aspects according to whether the lesion is situated upon one or the other hemisphere (Hécaen & de Ajuriaguerra, 1952).

After injury to the posterior parietal region of the minor hemisphere, we encounter disturbances of the somatognosia of one side of the body or of a single contralateral limb. The different clinical pictures can be grouped under three principal headings, which are indeed very often closely allied:

Hemiasomatognosia which can range from simple negligence, forgetfulness, to complete unawareness of one half of the body;

Anosognosia which consists essentially of the negation of the motor deficit where left hemiplegia occurs;

Feeling of absence of a part or a side of the body, which includes variations such as a feeling of strangeness, of belonging to a strange person, or even of a phantom limb.

Closely associated with these facts, there seems to be pain hemiagnosia, a syndrome consisting of the nonrecognition on one half of the body of the nature and place of painful stimuli which are none the less felt.

Without wishing to go into details of the physiopathological explanations offered for these disorders, we must, however, call attention to two groups of explanations which by internal necessity postulate the presence of these symptoms with lesions of the one and the other parietal lobe.

The first group considers them to be only the result of sensory disturbances, and Denny-Brown (1958), who has brought this explanation up to date, admits that anosognosia is only the result of an absence of synthesis of the multiple sensory stimuli coming from one side of the body (amorphosynthesis): anosognosia is not an agnosia, for it lacks the conceptual character proper to this type of disorder.

It will be understood that this thesis necessarily implies the possibility of hemiasomatognosia determined as much by the lesions of the dominant hemisphere as by those of the minor hemisphere. Thus Denny-Brown & Banker (1954) believe that hemiasomatognosia is not to be found during left-sided lesions solely in proportion to the aphasia; he cites, moreover, a very typical observation of the feeling of nonownership of the right upper limb in a right-handed person who had no trace of aphasia. It will be noticed, however, that the somatognosic disturbance lasted only two days. Gentilli (1955), who sticks to the thesis of Denny-Brown, has also published an observation of unawareness of the right upper limb, but, we must note, with finger agnosia and autotopoagnosia.

Conversely, other writers considered these symptoms as witnessing only to a generalized psychic disturbance close to Korsakow's syndrome. Currently this old thesis has been taken up again by Weinstein & Kahn (1955), for whom anosognosia is only an aspect of the negational behavior of the disease; this negation equally affects other physical deficiencies, incontinence for example, as much as recent operation or unhappy circumstances in previous life. Anosognosia would always be associated with other changes in behavior such as disorientation, reduplication, and paraphasia. This denial, which applies to multiple deficiencies, would thus translate the patient's desire for a state of perfect health and would be the result of the new reorganization pattern of the lesioned brain. In the thesis of Weinstein & Kahn (1955), the mechanism of anosognosia therefore becomes very close to that intervening in the Korsakow's syndrome; anosognosia is therefore only a part of a generalized disturbance in behavior and personality. Writers on this subject find no separation between the observations of denial or unconsciousness of hemiplegia and the negations of deficiencies of all kinds with confabulation appearing to fit into the framework of Korsakow's syndrome.

On the other hand, at no time do they discuss the problem of the lateralization of the lesion. When considering the summaries they give of observations, one is amazed at the number of left hemiplegias affected by the mechanism of negation, while one only finds three cases of negation of the right hemiplegia. In two of these observations, if the few clinical notes given allow us to assume the presence of a syndrome close to that of Korsakow, they are also cases with diffuse lesions. The third of these cases would deserve discussion, if we were in possession of elements other than the idea of a simple denial of hemiparesia.

Although these theses each add important elements to the discussion, they meet a stumbling block in the problem of lesional hemispherical preference, and, to surmount it, must go on to deny it in spite of the important mass of facts arguing in favor of it.

After injury to the major hemisphere, somatognosic disturbances are bilateral, either localized (finger agnosia) or generalized (autotopoagnosia). Finally, a particular disturbance of the appreciation of pain in relation to the body, asymbolia of pain, is equally encountered during left posterior parietal lesions.

Lunn (1948), reviewing all the published cases of finger agnosia, was able to conclude that apart from cases of ambidexterity or diffuse lesions, no demonstrative observation of Gertsmann's syndrome had been shown with a right-sided lesion.

Autotopoagnosia appears to result from more diffuse lesions, and many of the published observations result from bilateral injuries. However, on the basis of the cases cited by Nielsen (1937, 1946), Potzl (1928), Hécaen & de Ajuriaguerra (1952), we can say that a lesion of the left hemisphere can by itself produce this syndrome, but that it must be extensive although necessarily reaching the parieto-occipital region.

For Denny-Brown, Meyer, & Horenstein (1952), these disturbances are true symbolic agnosias and are conditioned by a conceptual disturbance. But there is nothing to prevent their being associated with unilateral somatognosic disturbances, simple nonlocalized perceptive disturbances.

It will be noticed that Benton (1959) does not admit a direct relationship between the "finger schema" and the dominant hemisphere, but that the greater importance of this hemisphere, in relation to the minor hemisphere in finger identification performances, is, for him, due only to the relationships which exist between this hemisphere and the symbolic processes.

What does the global study of our material add to these discussions? Out of 206 left-sided lesions, 44 times we find asomatognosic syndromes applying to both sides of the body: most frequently finger agnosia, in several cases autotopoagnosia, and only in 8 cases disturbances lateralized on the right side, but in 5 instances in paroxystical form (feeling of absence, of illusion of movement . . .); in 3 cases the hemiasomatognosia is permanent, but in two cases the patient was left-handed.

On the contrary, out of the 154 right-sided lesions, in 44 cases there existed contralateral disturbances of the somatognosia, and in 11 cases bilateral, but in 7 instances in left-handed patients. Out of the 4 cases of finger agnosia from a right-sided lesion in right-handed patients, 3 times the symptom is slight.

If left-handed patients are excluded from the series, the percentages are as follows:

Unilateral somatognosic disturbances:

with right-sided lesions:	28.46 per cent	(39/137)
with left-sided lesions:	3.46 per cent	(6/173).

Bilateral somatognosic disturbances:

with right-sided lesions:	2.91 per cent	(4/137)
with left-sided lesions:	20.23 per cent	(35/173).

These figures appear to us to speak for themselves. However, the relative frequency of unilateral paroxystic disturbances with left-sided lesions will be noticed. Several times already we have emphasized that the right-lesional localization is not necessarily present here, as it is in permanent hemiasomatognosic disturbances. Thus, reviewing 51 observations of somatognosic auras with unilateral topography, made by ourselves or else cited in the literature on the subject, we found that 15 of them affected the right limb or limbs. However, study of the results of stimulations carried out during operations for ablation of the epileptogenic scar by Penfield allowed us to confirm the fact that all the points, the stimulation of which had induced an illusion of movement in a contralateral limb, were situated in the right hemisphere (Hécaen, Penfield, Bertrand, & Malmo, 1956).

Finally, if Wada & Rasmussen (1960) only notice a negation of hemiplegia following an intracarotid injection of sodium amytal in patients to whom it was given on the nondominant side, Terzian & Cecotto (1959), on the other hand, have confirmed a hemiasomatognosia with right injections as much as with left ones, although they add that it was more pronounced on the nondominant side.

VISUAL AGNOSIAS

Whatever the concepts of agnosia, whether one attempts to reduce it to a fundamental disturbance or to a sensory disturbance, there appears to be sufficient clinical anatomical evidence to link certain clinical aspects of visual nonrecognition to lesions of one or the other hemisphere, or at least to give rise to discussion of the question.

We shall consider successively spatial agnosias and agnosias of objects. In fact, hemispherical lateralization, localization in one lobe, and physiopathological problems take on different aspects in each of these two varieties of disturbances of visual recognition.

SPATIAL AGNOSIAS

For some time now, writers such as Dide, Lange, & Potzl have insisted on the important part played by the right parietal lobe in spatial functions. Brain (1941) described agnosia for the left half of space. In their description of the visuoconstructive disturbances due to right-sided lesions, McFie, Piercy, & Zangwill (1950) insisted on the frequent association with disturbances in the perception of spatial relationships.

It would therefore appear that currently there can be recognized as a specific of posterior injuries to the minor hemisphere, along with visuoconstructive disturbances, a series of symptoms translating the perturbation of "spatial thought," that is to say unilateral spatial agnosia, and disturbances of topographical notions (orientation on a plan or geographical map). It would seem also that the loss of topographical memory can be connected with identical lesions, as proved by the observations made by Hécaen, Penfield, Bertrand, & Malmo (1956).

It is only right to add that although these conclusions are admitted by a large number of writers, they are still contested by some. Thus for Denny-Brown & Chambers (1958) unilateral spatial agnosia is no more than amorphosynthesis and can be encountered in left-sided lesions as often as in right-sided lesions. On the basis of their examinations of 122 patients with cerebral lesions, Battersby, Bender, Pollack, & Kahn (1956) consider that, if spatial disorders are more frequent with right-sided lesions, the difference is not, however, significant. This disorder is indeed, for them, the result of a disturbance in consciousness and of a unilateral sensory deficiency.

Our experience does not agree with their conclusions, any more than it does with those of Zangwill, or Hoff. Denny-Brown himself (1958) recognizes the greater frequency of unilateral spatial agnosia from a right-sided lesion.

In a recent review of our material, out of 59 cases of unilateral spatial agnosia, we find in 51 instances right-sided lesions, in 4 instances bilateral lesions (with negligence bearing on the left part of the space), and 4 left-sided lesions (but in 3 cases with left-handed patients). However, with left-sided lesions, in any case more occipital than parieto-occipital, we have sometimes found a patient to have difficulty in closing his drawing on the right side, but the patient, far from neglecting this side, is particularly persistent in drawing the extreme right, without managing to execute it correctly.

Clinical associations show, too, the frequent association of this disorder with hemiasomatognosic phenomena. Brain (1941) concluded from this fact that the negligence of half of space corresponded with the negligence of body-half.

In our data of 415 cases of retrorolandic lesions, the opticognosic disturbances, most frequently noticed in association with unilateral spatial agnosia, were disturbances of topographical notions (60.41 per cent), agnosia of physiognomies (28.88 per cent), errors in Popellreuter's test (26.19 per cent), loss of topographical memory (22.22 per cent), while the least frequent associations concerned nonrecognition of simple images, colors, distances, and relief.

If we now consider these observations as a whole, contrasting the group with unilateral agnosia with the group without unilateral spatial agnosia, it appears to us that certain observations deserve closer attention.

Thus, sensory disorders are present in 81.35 per cent of the cases with unilateral spatial agnosia, while they are encountered in only 36.69

per cent of cases which do not have this difficulty. In the same way, visual field defects are noted in 75.59 per cent of the cases in the first group, as against 53.95 per cent of those in the second, constructive apraxia 94.73 per cent as against 47.44 per cent, somatognosic disturbances 57.62 per cent as against 21.78 per cent, metamorphopsias and directional and vestibular disorders 87.23 per cent as against 51.21 per cent, oculomotor disorders 85.41 per cent as against 26.83 per cent. Finally, a higher proportion of disturbances in consciousness is found in the group with unilateral spatial agnosia (54.23 per cent) than in those who do not show this last (26.96 per cent). We may add that general indifference is associated in 64.28 per cent of these cases with unilateral inattention, while it exists in only 19.31 per cent of the others.

A negative correlation appears, on the contrary, when one considers the frequency of aphasia (7.77 per cent of the observations with unilateral spatial agnosia as aganist 40.11 per cent of those without this symptom), alexia (3.38 per cent as against 33.99 per cent), ideatory or ideomotor apraxia (1.69 per cent as against 13.29 per cent).

A priori, and calling attention to the importance and the frequency of sensory disorders, hemianopia, oculomotor disorders, directional and vestibular disorders, clouding of consciousness and general indifference, the facts we have confirmed would therefore favor those who see in these facts of unilateral inattention only a combination of sensory defects and alterations in the general mental functioning. We must also emphasize that massive lesions are most often responsible for this symptomatic aspect (however we may note that in a third of our cases the lesion affects only one lobe). But we must remark that there are cases, although they are exceptional, of unilateral spatial agnosia without oculomotor or vestibular disorders (or at least not discovered by our means of investigation) without hemianopia and with perfect lucidity. Simple factors of anatomical contiguity could then be envisaged for consideration of the clinical context.

However, it appears to us difficult to envisage them in this way, and we believe there is a more intimate link between these factors and the occurrence of unilateral spatial agnosia. But it seems impossible, faced with the frequency, or even the constancy, of injury to the minor hemisphere, to call it the result of a simple conjunction of defects without its own originality. As we have seen, in our cases only one observation is an exception to this rule of lesional lateralization, since the other three patients with a spatial agnosia for the right side of space were left-handed.

As for those disturbances bearing on topographical relationships (inability to orientate on a plan, geographical map, or drawing of a labyrinth), these depend principally on parieto-occipital lesions situated for the most part in the minor hemisphere. These disturbances are, moreover, frequently associated with the other symptoms or lesions of the parieto-temporo-occipital junction of this hemisphere. Out of 40 observations in which we found this disorder, the location of the lesion on the right side could be confirmed in 29 cases; 8 times the lesions were situated on the left (3 left-handed patients), and 3 times they were bilateral. Association with unilateral spatial agnosia was noted in 29 cases.

If the researches of Semmes, Weinstein, Ghent, & Teuber (1955) confirm the parietal lesional localization with these disturbances of topographical notions (test called trying to find one's way, starting from maps visually and haptically presented), they do not show any hemispherical preference in the lesions.

Loss of topographical memory (inability to orient in exterior space, to describe and to visualize familiar itineraries and places): most of the anatomical cases concern bilateral lesions. Some have maintained that the left occipital lobe is dominant for this function. But in the last few years, the work done by Paterson & Zangwill (1944), and McFie, Piercy, & Zangwill (1955) favors a right hemispheric localization.

After observation of two patients with this disorder after removal of the epileptogenic zone in the posterior part of the right hemisphere, carried out by Dr. Penfield, we can confirm this hemispherical lateralization while specifying a topography which is principally occipitotemporal (Wada & Rasmussen, 1960). We shall also bear in mind the observation made by Pomme & Janny (1954), in which the excision of the gyrus angularis region of the minor hemisphere, very localized (3 cm. in diameter), and performed in order to extract a deep tumor, caused a loss of topographical memory, which, moreover, lasted only 15 days. In the whole of our clinical material, reviewed with Angelergues, the surgical verifications and clinical findings allow us to establish almost certainly a right hemispherical localization in 9 cases out of 15. Further, we may point out that, in the cases which have been checked, the occipital lobe was always injured as well.

Agnosias for things. We must consider the question of the lesional lateralization of these disturbances according to 3 varieties of disorders: agnosia for inanimate objects and images, agnosia for faces, agnosia for colors.

Agnosias for objects and images. For this type of agnosia, we possess only a minimum of anatomicoclinical observations of which we can make use. The lesions are, in general, bilateral, the patient deteriorated or even demented, and often aphasic. Thus the value of many of the observations upon object agnosia is open to question.

However, von Stauffenberg (1918) was able to conclude from his general studies that, in spite of the usual bilaterality of the lesions, psychic blindness is the more severe, the more the lesion involves the left hemisphere.

Nielsen (1937) drew attention more firmly to the role of the dominant hemisphere. We have ourselves, along with de Ajuriaguerra (1956), described an important case in this respect, since in this case the object agnosia was very typical and was due to a left occipital lobectomy, in a right-handed patient. This observation was all the more interesting for in spite of the object and image agnosia, alexia and color agnosia, this patient recognized faces perfectly, even on amateur snapshots.

If it is certain that object agnosia is most often found as part of a very complex syndrome, because of the habitual bilateral location of the lesion, it can occur therefore, and in this case with a much greater selectivity, in lesions limited to the dominant hemisphere.

Agnosias for animate objects (Prosopagnosia). The description of this type of agnosia is of relatively recent date (Bodamer, 1947). If observations of it have been multiplied these last years, from the anatomical point of view, we are still short of absolutely decisive evidence. However, although certain writers postulate bilateral lesions, we feel that the bulk of the observations are in favor of a right-hemispherical injury. Out of the 22 personal observations which have been gathered to date, the clinical signs, in particular visual field defects, the X-ray signs, and operative checking, allow us to say that the lesion is predominant, at least, in the posterior section of the right hemisphere in 16 cases, and is bilateral in 4 of our observations. Right-lesional unilaterality can almost certainly be confirmed. As for the region in question, it seems that the parieto-temporo-occipital junction is almost always involved. Moreover, in studying the symptomatic associations of this type of optical agnosia, it is to be noted that not only is the association with spatial agnosias extremely frequent, but also that the clinical context is very close to that of the spatial agnosias; however, vestibular and directional disorders appear nevertheless more frequently in prosopagnosia, while oculomotor disturbances are less frequent. Rarity of association with aphasia, alexia, and color agnosia is common to both these types of opticognosic syndromes.

Color Agnosia. Difficulties in recognizing colors do not seem to form a homogenous group. We cannot discuss this question here, for the distinctions proposed can be applied only with difficulty to all cases. We shall, therefore, consider them only globally, whether or not a more delicate psychophysiological analysis could have distinguished, among the observations made anatomically, the cases of true color agnosia and those of cortical color blindness.

Injury to the left hemisphere is particularly common. We know that the association of right hemianopia, of alexia, and of color agnosia forms the classic syndrome of occipital lesions of the dominant hemisphere.

In our series, out of 15 cases of difficulty in color recognition, in 9 the seat of the lesion was on the left, and in 4 it was bilateral. In the 2 cases resulting from a right-sided lesion, the disturbance was not marked in one case, and in the other the patient was left-handed.

As for the other clinical signs, these confirmed the location of the lesion in the left hemisphere.

Out of our 15 observations, alexia was present 11 times, constructive apraxia 11 times, acalculia and aphasia 9 times, object agnosia was found twice, and image agnosia 7 times. As for visual field defects, 10 times there was a complete or quadranopic right-sided defect; in the other cases, the visual field was bilaterally abnormal, except in one case of right hemianopia.

The frequency of these diverse symptoms associated with difficulty in recognizing colors is particularly interesting when compared with the frequency of these same symptoms in spatial agnosia. Alexia, intellectual deterioration, aphasia, and anarithmetria are frequently associated in the first group, rare in the second, while the opposite is noted when we consider somatognosic troubles, directional and vestibular disorders.

ACALCULIA

This term has been used to describe widely differing disorders. Without embarking upon a discussion of the complex problems set by these disorders, we feel that we can describe semeiologically 3 different aspects of acalculia: acalculia from figure or number alexia; acalculia in the restricted sense, or anarithmetria (loss of ability to perform arithmetical sums) and dyscalculia of the spatial type (inability to work out sums from neglect of part of the figures or from wrong positioning of these figures while retaining the principle of calculation).

In our material, these 3 groups were classified thus, according to the side of the brain damage:

Dyscalculia of the spatial type: 35 cases out of 113 right-sided lesions,
: 4 cases out of 191 left-sided lesions,

Figure alexia: 3 cases out of 146 right-sided lesions,
: 53 cases out of 143 left-sided lesions,

Anarithmetria: 25 cases out of 124 right-sided lesions,
: 91 cases out of 105 left-sided lesions.

The study of the associations of these 3 types of acalculia considered independently of the seat of the lesion goes in the same direction. Indeed, a significant association is found between dyscalculia of the spatial type and, in decreasing order, unilateral spatial agnosia, spatial agnosias in general, apraxia for dressing, constructive apraxia, unilateral asomatognosias, oculomotor disorders, object and image agnosias, somatosensory defects, directional and vestibular disorders, failure in Poppelreuter's test, prosopagnosia. Thus, this type of calculation difficulty seems really to be a disturbance of spatial relationships, showing in the manipulation of figures.

The statistically valid associations with figure alexia are, as was to be expected, alexia, aphasia, constructive apraxia, ideomotor apraxia, bilateral asomatognosias, failure in Poppelreuter's test, and color agnosia, that is to say that it belongs primarily to a context in which there are disturbances in verbal formulation with a very clear visual note.

As for anarithmetrias, we find more or less the same clinical context for figure alexia, but attention must be called to two points: on the one hand the greater frequency of aphasia, and on the other the association with apraxia for dressing. This last association, according to our data, indicates that injury of the minor hemisphere can also cause anarithmetria. Thus we find indicated anew the plurality of the mechanisms which can intervene in these disorders in arithmetical operations, although impairment of the verbal formulation is chiefly responsible.

Certainly anarithmetria can correspond to very different mechanisms (intellectual trouble, spatial agnosia, even disautomatization of the reading of figures), and any attempt at classification brings out the heterogeneity of the group.

On the other hand, the other two groups do seem to correspond to opposite hemispherical injuries, figure alexia naturally depending on lesions of the dominant hemisphere, while disorders of the spatial type can be integrated in the syndrome of the lesions of the minor hemisphere, already considered several times.

METAMORPHOPSIAS

These can be defined as modifications in the vision of forms, contours, outlines, and the number or the movement of objects or people, and which, in general, make their appearance in paroxysmal form. It is difficult to relate them to lesions of a particular territory, but it is, above all, injuries to the temporo-parieto-occipital regions which appear to produce them.

Penfield & Mullan (1959) describe analogous phenomena among visual illusions, concerning spatial interpretation, intensity of perception, and modifications of tempo and movement. Along with Mullan, this writer concludes that, according to the results of cortical stimulations, these illusions depend chiefly on the temporal cortex of the minor hemisphere.

It must be noted in this connection that these same writers indicate that visual illusions of the "feeling of familiarity" type depend on stimulations of the temporal cortex of the minor hemisphere (9 times out of 10), while the other types of visual illusions (unreality, strangeness), auditory illusions, feelings of fear were equally well produced by stimulations of the temporal lobe either right or left. One can therefore ask oneself whether the greater frequency of the "dreamy state" in right-temporal lesions, statistically valid, does not depend on this liaison between spatial illusions and the minor hemisphere, while the "dreamy state," properly speaking, does not possess definite lesional lateralization, as we have been able also to verify along with Audisio (1959) in studying all our "dreamy state" cases together.

Let us note, however, that in Bingley's series (1958), the frequency of the "dreamy state" was significantly higher with lesions of the minor temporal lobe, than with those of the major lobe, while hallucinations and visual illusions showed no significant association with lesional lateralization.

On the other hand, in our series of 415 cases of retrorolandic lesions, we find these metamorphosic episodes 26 times out of 154 cases of right-sided lesions (16.88 per cent), 17 times out of 206 left-sided cases (8.25 per cent), twice out of 55 bilateral lesions (3.63 per cent). If we eliminate left-handed patients, the percentage difference according to the lesioned hemisphere is 16.41 per cent (22 cases out of 134), as against 6.89 per cent (12 cases out of 174) and proves to be significant ($X^2 = 7$).

If we then consider the permanent directional and vestibular disorders in 215 cases of cortical lesions, these prove distinctly more frequent in right-sided lesions, 78 times out of 104 cases (75.96 per cent), than in left-sided lesions, 40 times out of 97 (45.97 per cent). We may also point out that while the percentage is more or less similar for cases with or without visual agnosias due to left-sided lesions, in right-sided lesions it becomes distinctly greater in the group with visual agnosia (in general of the spatial type), than in those without visual agnosia (94 per cent as against 57.4 per cent).

Teuber, Battersby, & Bender (1960) remark also that paroxysmal visual disorders in their brain-wounded patients appear in those with a posterior injury to the right hemisphere 13 times out of 15. Under the heading visual attacks, they include visual illusions as well as elementary hallucinations. These writers also remark that, out of the elementary visual hallucinations of the series we showed with Badaraco (1956), 14 of the 16 cases correspond to a lesion of the right hemisphere.

Finally, we must emphasize that difficulties in appreciating time, particularly the phenomenon of the shortening of time described by Potzl (1951) and Hoff (1955), are to be found in almost all cases with right peristriate lesions.

In the same way, Penfield & Mullan (1959) point out that they have not produced illusions bearing on the passing of time other than by stimulation of the nondominant hemisphere.

We have presented analytically the symptoms which, it appeared to us, ought to be connected with lesions of each hemisphere, and it remains to very briefly consider the symptomatic groupings produced by the cortical lesions.

The syndrome of the left temporal lesion is evidently centered on language disorders; if they are more or less isolated when the lesion is anterior, naturally, in the case of posterior temporal injuries, the syndrome may include apraxic elements as well (ideomotor apraxia, constructive apraxia), somatognosic elements (finger agnosia), and acalculia elements (here anarithmetria and figure alexia intervene).

Alexia will become more and more frequent if the lesion reaches the gyrus angularis and, above all, the occipital lobe. In this last case, the association of alexia and color agnosia is classic.

Finally, in large lesions of the posterior parts of the hemisphere, we find a particularly complex symptomatology: ideatory apraxia, autotopoagnosia, and object and image agnosia.

Conversely, lesions of the right hemisphere are centered on visuo-spatial disorders. Constructive apraxias are here extremely frequent. Apraxia for dressing is not exceptional. Contralateral somatognosic disturbances are frequently associated with spatial disturbances and especially with unilateral spatial agnosia.

The spatial note here marks the deficiencies encountered as much for constructive disabilities as for calculation disorders or for certain reading or writing deficiencies. The addition of directional and vestibular disturbances, of oculomotor troubles, in these different gnosopraxic alterations, must be emphasized.

It will be noted that it is chiefly parietal injury which determines the different symptoms in the minor hemisphere, while temporal injury appears above all the determining factor when the lesion is on the left side.

Considering the visual symptomatology, it is chiefly occipital lesions which determine this in the major hemisphere, while in the right hemisphere, it is parietal lesions which are principally responsible, with the possible exception of agnosia for faces, where the role of occipital injury must be borne in mind.

Further, right-sided lesions which cause gnosopraxic disorders seem more widespread than left-sided lesions observed in the presence of disorders of symbolic function; perhaps, moreover, we must only consider responsible for this state of affairs the fact that the lesion is more quickly discovered on the left side because of the difficulties caused by the aphasic symptoms.

We must also emphasize in a statistical context the results of psychometric studies, such as those of Weissemburg and McBride, already old ones, and especially the more recent studies of McFie & Piercy (1952) and of Andersen (1950, 1951), on patients with cortical lesions, variously seated. McFie & Piercy (1952), for example, in two successive studies, have shown that deficiencies in abstraction tests, verbal or nonverbal, were much more clearly marked with lesions of the dominant hemisphere, while with right-sided lesions, the deficiencies were noted in spatial and practical performances.

In the same way Reitan (1955) has found in two groups of patients with cerebral lesions a significant difference between the lowering of the verbal score in relation to the score performance according to the side of the lesion, left-sided lesions lowering the first, right-sided lesions the second.

With a special test (Trail making test), where one part (Part A) allows us to appreciate the capacity for understanding spatial configurations, the other (Part B) the capacity for perceiving and utilizing the symbolic material, Reitan & Tarshes (1959) find significant differences between the group of left-sided lesions, which chiefly impair the second of these capacities (B), and the group of right-sided lesions which chiefly impair the first (A).

We may also quote the verifications made by Milner (1958) with right and left temporal lobectomies carried out for epilepsy. Whereas if the excision is from the dominant hemisphere, she notices difficulties in verbal learning, which according to her do not represent a dysphasic disorder, right lobectomies cause a slight defect in visual recognition.

For Hoff (1953), who generally recognizes the same functional lateralizations as we do, it is possible to pass the symptom context and to consider the respective roles of the hemispheres. For this writer, the role of the left hemisphere is to construct new functional schemas in relation to superior activities and the highest human performances, while the task of the minor hemisphere consists in the preparation of foundations of superior realizations in providing the correct temporal notions and in ensuring the total knowledge of corporality and of its situation in space. More briefly, one could say that the dominant hemisphere has the responsibility for execution and that the minor hemisphere must create the necessary conditions for the realization of these activities.

Note again Wagner's formula: the right hemisphere is compared to the conductor, the left hemisphere both to the composer and to the orchestra.

According to his psychometric studies of patients with focal lesions of the brain, Andersen (1951) attempts also to classify the result of his researches in a functional formula, but he conversely compares the dominant hemisphere to a warehouse and the minor hemisphere to an executive office. One can say of the former, when it is lesioned, that it forgets what it must do, of the latter, in the same circumstances, that it no longer knows how it must do it.

Perhaps we have not yet reached a stage where our researches will allow such general conclusions, and other factors, particularly individual, intervene to make such formulae too absolute. More prudently, today's task should be to verify to which hemisphere a given group of symptoms corresponds, while from current studies, as much clinical as psychometrical, there stands out clearly the notion of a functional asymmetry of the hemispheres.

Moreover, a writer like Denny-Brown (1952, 1958), whose negative position toward a hemispherical lesional specificity for certain practicognosic disorders we have already seen, does retain the diversity of the gnosicopraxic symptomatology according to the side lesioned.

Only, for him, this dominance does not effectively exist other than for language difficulties and for true agnosias, and conceptual disorders, (though unable to be lateralized) which depend on the interhemispherical relationships with the language mechanisms. It is therefore only in cases of lesions of the dominant hemisphere that we will encounter, whether with or without evident aphasia, praxic disorders of the ideatory or ideomotor type, disorders in body recognition of the finger agnosia or autotopoagnosia type, visual gnosic disorders for things or space in its totality, that is to say practicognosic disorders linked with the conceptual organization of space, of objects, and of people. On the other hand, gestural or perceptive disorders affecting only half space or a half of the body, simple morphosynthesis deficiencies, are met with in the course of lesions of one or the other hemisphere. It seems, however, that in his last study Denny-Brown (1958) brings some corrections to this very coherent thesis, admitting that certain motor dexterities can be linked to a different cortical dominance from that recognized for the symbolic function they translate. Thus there would exist adextrous apraxias, which could be dependent on lesions of the minor hemisphere.

Thus without wishing to allocate functions to each hemisphere, we are able only to say that their lesions produce various syndromes, that the formation of concepts and verbal formulation are especially altered with left-sided lesions, that the manipulation of corporal and extra-corporal spatial data, the recognition of human faces, are disturbed with injuries to the other hemisphere.

Further, with Denny-Brown (1958), we are quite prepared to admit that disorders due to left-sided lesions affect the whole verbal field, exterior world, or body, but we think that disorders bearing only on one half of the body or half the field of vision are not, in right-handed patients at least, the appanage of one or the other hemisphere, but are produced by injuries to the so-called minor hemisphere.

Thus we suggest a different functional organization of the hemispheres, and the studies of Teuber (1960) and his co-workers on the subject of somatosensory disorders bring out valid arguments for such a conception, since already these studies reveal, on the level of the somatosensory function, a different representation according to the hemisphere injured. The study of sensory deficiencies in brain-wounded patients does indeed show that in the left parietal region the somatosensory representation is focalized and concerns both sides of the body. In the right hemisphere, on the other hand, the representation is more diffuse but affects one half of the body; furthermore, somatosensory disorders due to its injury occur as separate types, while those determined by left-sided lesions seem only to represent degrees of one and the same fundamental difficulty.

Hemispheric dominance, or at least a different organization of the hemispheres, seems thus established, when we consider the pathological facts. On the other hand, the anatomical and electrophysiological data only provide uncertain elements, even discordant, according to the writers, on the reality of this hemispheric diversity.

Prudence is also imperative in view of the facts of recuperation; functional restoration takes place equally in astonishing proportions, whether it is due to the "taking over" of functions by the other hemisphere or by zones of the same hemisphere, which had not so far had an activity of capital importance but potentially capable of carrying out this function.

The virtual absence of gnosic troubles in the series of brain-wounded patients studied by Teuber, Battersby, & Bender (1960), the absence of persistent aphasia even after a wide ablation of the language zones observed by Penfield & Roberts (1959), the recovery of the ability to read after a left occipital lobectomy in the cases studied by us with de Ajuriaguerra (1952, 1951), prove the importance of these facts of restoration and show that the hemispheric dominance cannot be considered in too absolute a manner.

Finally, the rarity of aphasia in children (and the experience of hemispherectomies carried out for lesions which occurred in early childhood is a patent example), its short duration when it does exist, its particular characteristics and the possibility of its appearance, with a right-sided lesion in a right-handed patient, forces us not to consider these facts of dominance in a rigid way and from a purely structural point of view.

It seems, therefore, to be a question of potentiality which social factors, thanks to the postnatal development of the child's brain, play a role by imposing themselves in some way upon the structural factors, in a way as yet poorly understood.

The problem is evidently linked to that of manual preference, whether this depends on structural or hereditary factors or, on the contrary, on sociological or cultural factors. The study of this question obviously cannot be begun here. From a review of the question, we have felt able to recognize there too a hereditary determination reinforced by the influences of the milieu (Hécaen, 1959).

Study of left-handed patients with postrolandic cerebral lesions demonstrates, on the other hand, that it is not possible to show a formal correlation between manual preference and hemispheric dominance.

But verifications with patients seem to us to furnish, furthermore, an indirect proof of the reality of the dominance, when we compare clinical pictures thus determined with those observed in right-handed patients with injuries to similar zones. Certainly the general formula is habitually respected: aphasia with the exception of expressive troubles, alexia especially from a left-sided lesion, object and image agnosia; ideatory and ideomotor apraxia determined solely from a left-sided lesion; unilateral asomatognosia, unilateral spatial agnosia, due principally to right-sided lesions. But we note, for example, bilateral asomatognosias, apraxias for dressing, troubles of spatial thought, and metamorphosias almost as frequently from lesions of one as from the other hemisphere.

Finally these syndromes take on a particular character: aphasia of the expressive type and amnesic aphasia are frequent, but verbal deafness is rare in left-handed patients. On the other hand, the disorders are of no great intensity, or are even slight, or appear transitorily or even paroxysmally.

It appears too, principally according to the comparative study of paroxysmal language disorders in left-handed and right-handed patients (Hécaen & Piercy, 1956), that it is possible to admit a lesser focalization with precise depositions in the left-handed patients than in the right-handed ones, whatever the "dominant" hemisphere. With Teuber, we must draw a parallel between this possibility of more diffuse representation of language mechanisms in the left-handed patient and what his studies reveal of the relative absence of focalization of the somatosensory representation on the minor hemisphere. At the origin of this diversity of somatosensory representation according to the hemisphere, Semmes, Weinstein, Ghent, & Teuber (1960) draw out the primary role of the lateralization of motor functions in children; concentration of the functions of language would then finally follow the differentiation of sensations.

The difference of organization of the representations would thus explain the hemispheric dominance, or rather the functional diversity. Dynamic patterns would organize themselves in each hemisphere, starting from the motor lateralization due to a hereditary transmission, susceptible, moreover, of being modified by the influences of the milieu.

Discussion Fourth Session

A.

DEREK DENNY-BROWN

Harvard University Medical School, Boston, Massachusetts

FOR THE CLINICIAN, the most remarkable feature of the changes in perception, resulting from unilateral parietal lobe lesions, is the phenomenon of extinction. It is associated with many of the disorders of perception, both simple or complex, and points to the existence of a perceptual rivalry derived from an essential total perceptual unity. Extinction operates at a low, physiological level of the perceptual process which we called "morphosynthesis," and which refers to the opposite half of corporeal and extracorporeal space.

Close analysis of the phenomenon of extinction reveals that it results from the defect of the process of spatial summation resulting from parietal lobe lesion. It can be overcome by increasing the area of the vulnerable stimulus. Thus the defect in touch, temperature, and pain sensation that renders them liable to extinction is their increased requirement for spatial summation under these circumstances. The unaffected stimulus extinguishes the stimulus from the affected side because it is a "smaller" touch, a "smaller" pain, or in broader terms, "less biologically significant" (Denny-Brown, Meyer, & Horenstein, 1952). It is also in these terms that a sensation is "lost" by reason of parietal lesion; not that it does not exist, but that it is biologically insignificant. Sensory defect of this type can be revived under some circumstances, for example in monkey experiments, where ablation of the parietal lobe of the second side revives "proprioceptive placing" lost as a result of injury to the first.

In the effects of right parietal lesion in a right-handed person, amorphosynthesis is found in terms of neglect and lack of awareness of left half of person, neglect and lack of awareness of left extracorporeal field. The relative accentuation of person or of extrapersonal space correlates with lesions in anterior parietal and in parieto-occipital areas respectively, with a large overlap in the intraparietal sulcus. A defect in morphosynthesis, in this sense, is but a wider aspect of defect in spatial summation, occurring at a physiological (as opposed to a psychological) level of perception and resulting in a corresponding physiological behavioral defect, reproducible in the experimental monkey. Such a defect is always associated with motor, behavioral release symptoms (postural change and facile labyrinthine effects).

Some, like Dr. Teuber and Dr. Critchley today, doubt this universal application of "extinction," pointing to the difficulty in demonstrating its presence in some circumstances when other evidence of parietal lobe defect is prominent. It is certainly true that late in recovery (and in some cases from the beginning) it is difficult or impossible to demonstrate extinction in terms of bilateral touch, bilateral pin prick, or bilateral visual stimuli, though other defects in perception in the affected side may still be present. In such cases, a more subtle test will, however, show that extinction is still operative. The consistent defect in weight discrimination in the two hands, described earlier today by Dr. Teuber, can have no other explanation. If such patients no longer presented extinction to bilateral, simultaneous stimulation of less complex kind, it is likely that some compensatory process (? learning) is offsetting its effect. Others have objected that extinction can be demonstrated in the sensory disturbances of peripheral lesions, or under some circumstances in the normal individual, and therefore belittle its relation to parietal lobe defect. If, however, perceptual rivalry is a fundamental feature of the perceptual process, the occurrence of extinction under these other circumstances is to be expected in some degree.

It is particularly the behavioral defects associated with right parietal lesion that convince me that spatial summation and extinction are the primary fault, for all of these are profoundly affected by events occurring at the time in the right, unaffected field. Neglect of the left half of body and extracorporeal space are paralleled by the confusion of parts of garments or in putting them on, in what Brain called "apraxia of dressing." Errors in route finding and drawing are due not only to neglect of left side, but to overpreoccupation with the right. Constructional apraxia from right-sided lesions is in this sense a preoccupation with small, irrelevant, usually right-sided parts; not just drawing the right side of a pattern, but a disarticulation and preoccupation in addition. The same can be found in the types of dyscalculia and dysgraphia resulting from right hemispheric lesion, where preoccupation with small parts of numerals or letters distorts or prevents perception. As we emphasized in our first paper with Meyer & Horenstein (1952), this fragmentation of perception results from amorphosynthesis and is not an agnosia as we understand that term.

Topographic agnosia is a disturbance of a seemingly different order, and we at first were inclined to class it as an agnosia, dependent on dominance. It, too, shows signs of inability to perceive the whole because of preoccupation with small parts, and we now doubt that it has any relation to dominance.

Dr. Hécaen's analysis of 415 cases of retrorolandic lesions is a magnificent contribution. Until now, we have had to proceed in terms of personal impressions and in relation to small groups of cases that had been studied intensively from special points of view. The advantage of a statistical analysis of a large series of cases, each studied by the same team of observers, is enormous.

In many respects, Dr. Hécaen's analysis confirms the impressions gained from smaller groups of cases, but there are some striking exceptions, and some additional new relationships are brought out. It has been obvious that the types of behavioral disorder we have called amorphosynthesis are particularly frequent in cases with right parietal lobe lesions, though we and others have found it at times in association with left hemispheric lesions in right-handed people (Denny-Brown & Banker, 1954). Dr. Hécaen puts the relationship at 21:3, 27:2, 51:1, for three different aspects of the process. These figures would correspond with our own impression.

Lesions of the *left* hemisphere present sensory aphasia, alexia, agnosia for objects and colors, and ideational apraxia, with some types of constructional apraxia and autotopoagnosia. We note that in characteristic form, all these disorders relate to both sides of the body and extrapersonal space. This is what we understand by *true agnosia,* for it relates to the whole perceptive field, whether right or left. We would insist on two further features, first, that true agnosia should be absolute in the sense not only that the percept for one class of propositional material is not formed, but that it does not exist in terms of current context of awareness. Thus, if the patient denies that he is blind, he can think of seeing only in terms of the past. Second, it should occur only in relation to a proposition (in Hughlings Jackson's sense). This second feature is most important to the neurophysiologist, for it helps to differentiate a type of difficulty that has arisen from methods of testing. Agnosia does not relate to a perception arrived at with difficulty, or in some distorted form, or even reached by another sense. If, owing to agnosia, the patient cannot recognize an object except by touch, or a face except by sound of voice or other sense, he is still lacking the visual concept of that object or face, which no longer exists in current context. This is the difference between amorphosynthesis and agnosia. So-called ideomotor and gestural types of apraxia are dependent on true agnosia, and we find these terms confusing and unhelpful. We group them all together under the general term "ideational apraxia," with the understanding that the defect is a diffuse type of agnosia (Denny-Brown, 1958). In such disorder, the patient cannot name a pencil or suggest a use for it when it is presented to him as an object, yet a moment later, given some paper and asked to write his name, picks up the pencil from among other objects and begins to write. He cannot light his pipe or wave goodbye when requested to do so, yet later is found lighting his pipe spontaneously and correctly when he needs it, or waving goodbye when spontaneously bidding a real farewell. The defect is in propositional behavior and has nothing whatever to do with synthesis of movement. If, under some other circumstance, agnosia is associated with some additional difficulty in physiological usage, we must suspect that an added, more elementary, function (morphosynthesis) is disturbed.

Nor am I happy about the use of "symbolic" to describe the lost activity (though we ourselves have used it in the past). Much of behavior that is instinctive and complex is morphosynthetic, yet nevertheless demonstrates equivalence of stimuli. It can be dependent on symbolic signals, as can conditioned responses of the minor hemisphere. The type of defect that is peculiar to the phenomenon of dominance is propositional, its most vulnerable aspect being the proposition "as if" in relation to some highly particularized situation. In contrast, "instinctive," "physiological," and emotional stimuli operate at a morphosynthetic level. For all these reasons, we doubt that "spatial agnosia" and "unilateral asomatagnosia" are agnosias and do not use these terms.

McFie, Piercy, & Zangwill (1950) and McFie & Zangwill (1960) postulate a fundamental difference in spatial function between the two hemispheres. Piercy, Hécaen, & de Ajuriaguerra (1960) conclude that the right hemisphere has a special role in constructional performance. I have a strong resistance to any such ideas, nevertheless recognizing the remarkable difference in symptomatology that Dr. Hécaen has further illuminated in the study he reports today. What is known of the physiology of the two cerebral hemispheres indicates that their nervous mechanism for behavioral reactions of physiological type is identical. Studies of hemispherectomy, lobar ablations, and large lesions in childhood have shown clearly that, up to the age of four years, dominance of hemispheric function is interchangeable, and for a few more years after that it is transferable. The functions that are interchangeable or transferable are all learned functions, acquired painfully and slowly, long after structural and physiological patterns are laid down. Studies of monkeys with split commissures show that each hemisphere can learn the simple conditioning of laboratory experiment. It has yet to be shown how the complex conditioning of verbal and other abstract recognition is acquired. But in any case, the experience of Lashley and our own experiments on parietal and temporal lobe ablations in monkeys (Denny-Brown & Chambers, 1958) convince us that visual recognition in the monkey is not the property of any single parietal or temporal area on either side. Recognition of this kind is equally disordered by bilateral parietal or bilateral temporal lesion and requires some sort of balance between these parts of the brain for its adequate performance.

The infrequency of neglect of person and of extrapersonal space, as a result of left parietal lobe lesions, is associated with less frequent abnormalities in response to such tests as size discrimination, as described by Dr. Weinstein, or two-point test as mentioned by Dr. Teuber. I do not agree that these are "basic sensory changes" as Dr. Teuber and his colleagues suggest. They involve complex judgments. If it can be substantiated that a larger area of more diffuse damage is necessary to produce them on the left side, this would still be far from the implication of a different pattern of anatomical organization. It could, for example, mean only that the unity of the perceptual process was biased toward the left hemisphere, with a corresponding need for loss of relatively more tissue to produce an equivalent degree of extinction. That amorphosynthesis is present, in a great many cases of left-sided lesion that do not show frank neglect of right side of person and extrapersonal space, is shown by the more frequent occurrence of the release symptoms that regularly accompany amorphosynthesis, namely, the tonic postural changes that we call avoiding, and labyrinthine symptoms. Pure agnosia, with or without aphasia, as seen, for example, in the early stage of degenerative disease, is not associated with such motor release symptoms. Also minor defects, in the form of failure to complete the right side of drawings or to use the right side of a piece of paper, show that a relative unilateral amorphosynthesis is present.

An important clue to this question is, I believe, presented by those cases where *bilateral* defect has resulted from *right* hemispheric lesion in right-handed patients. In Dr. Hécaen's analysis, bilateral asomatagnosia resulted from 2.7 per cent of right-sided lesions and 17.8 per cent of left-sided lesions. The bilateral defect is not just the sum of right and left defect, for unilateral asomatagnosia occurred in inverse proportion of cases (27:3). If asomatagnosia, in Dr. Hécaen's use of the term, is disturbed with approximately equal frequency with right-sided and left-sided lesions, and the difference is a preponderance of bilateral disturbance with left-sided lesions, and unilateral with right-sided, we can see that here is one explanation of the apparent bias of disorder. This symptom depends on spatial perception of body parts; it is a "mapping-function" in Dr. Young's sense. It is therefore of great interest that "topographic agnosia" (errors in route finding, in mapping surroundings) appeared in Dr. Hécaen's analysis with right-sided lesions in the proportion of 35:5, the same proportions as "unilateral asomatagnosia." In this case, the corresponding function that is disturbed in inverse relationship with left-sided lesions is not clear, though there is the implication that it is buried in some bilaterally applicable, more general disorder of perception. In relation to these two disorders then, we see there is a suggestion of a more complex, but not necessarily a different, function in the dominant hemisphere. Both involve concepts but not propositions, and as I said at the beginning, they are broken up by amorphosynthesis in a manner that interferes with a perception of a whole plan. Yet though they may apply to both sides of space or person, they could be essentially morphosynthetic in nature.

I have less difficulty than does Dr. Hécaen in accepting the possiblity that optimal topographic recognition requires both visual fields, for the greatest difference between perception of topography and of objects is the extent of field concerned. This would require a bilateral "mapping sense" in Professor Young's meaning, but not necessarily related to dominance. Since topographic sense and topographic memory are learned functions, I assume they need both occipitoparietal lobes in adult life. Therefore, loss of topographic sense from lesion of either side is acceptable from my point of view, (a one-ness without dominance) but here also there is the question of methodology of testing, for it is difficult to test topographic sense without making a propositional question. Reading a blueprint is a propositional activity and is likely to depend on the dominant hemisphere. Such defect would be likely to be found in left hemispheric lesions in a proportion inverse to that of topographic agnosia with right hemispheric lesions, (the missing bilateral symptom with predominantly left-sided lesions referred to above).

Constructional apraxia presents a more difficult problem. I have already mentioned that I feel that most, if not all the elements of "constructional apraxia," seen with right hemispheric lesions, can be accounted for by amorphosynthesis. The breaking up of the pattern into unrelated pieces is characteristic. In contrast, the constructional apraxia found with *left* hemispheric lesions shows aspects of agnosia. It was noted by Head that it then depended on "an inability to appreciate the general meaning of a situation," and Meyer-Gross felt it was necessary to postulate a "specific visual factor," separate from spatial or motor elements. I submit that this additional factor is the *visual propositional task.* The studies of McFie & Zangwill (1960) seem to me to bring out clearly that the constructional apraxia with left-sided lesions is a total difficulty in appreciating the whole task (a "conceptual spatial impairment," in the terms used by these authors). In our experience with left-sided lesions, the test often cannot be performed at all. It has an all-or-none feature. If any steps can be discerned in the development of agnosia, they are few and categorical, rather than the infinite series of piecemeal difficulties that are found with right-sided lesions. Thus in copying the outline of a house, the "particulars" of the pattern first fail to register, and only a stylized "universal" of a house is reproduced with difficulty, and eventually only an unrecognizable outline, or nothing. So, with the pattern of a star, there emerges a shapeless outline, or nothing. With a pattern of blocks, the result is a mass of blocks with no pattern, or a "catastrophic reaction." Dr. Hécaen notes the significant frequency of "catastrophic reaction" among those who showed some degree of constructional apraxia with left-sided lesion. How many other cases were there presenting *only a catastrophic reaction,* in the sense of a complete inability to begin any sort of pattern (a constructional agnosia)? This is the crucial question and is not clear in Dr. Hécaen's figures, which appear to count only those who produced defective construction or drawing. I submit that when both partial and complete test failures are counted as a constructional defect the difference between right and left lesions will disappear.

A similar difference is at least in part responsible for the lesser number with left-sided lesions who had apraxia in dressing; how many of them could not put their clothes on at all, much less put them on upside down, or only on the left side. Here the difficulty is in part an adextrous apraxia (Denny-Brown, 1958), which can only be clearly distinguished in left-handed people.

Though difficulty in appreciating the nature of the task is by our definition an agnosia, it is not necessarily associated with visual agnosia for objects, as ordinarily understood, which requires a more laterally placed lesion. The type of defect we are considering, therefore, does not correlate with the presence of visual object agnosia. We agree that the occurrence of aphasia in many patients with left hemispheric lesions is not an adequate explanation for the greater frequency of topographic disorders in the left half of personal and extrapersonal space, resulting from right-sided lesions. Eight per cent of aphasics showed such disorders on the right side, 40 per cent did not in Dr. Hécaen's series. It depends, of course, on what type of aphasia is present. The type of inability underlying classical constructional apraxia is an agnosia, and this also affects speech. With a left parietal lesion, the patient has a receptive speech defect of which he is unaware. In addition, he has a special difficulty in repeating what is said to him, the "central aphasia" of Goldstein (Stengle & Patch, 1955). From our point of view, these difficulties betray precisely the same type of disorder of perception that underlies the failure to construct a visual pattern. When such aphasic disorder is present, we would expect the patient to be untestable for visuospatial perceptive disorder.

For these various reasons, I would conclude that two additional factors are operating in relation to left parietal lesions, *first,* an asymmetry in relation to purely physiological function, and *second,* a disorder reflecting the operation of dominance. The first is an asymmetry in mapping function, such that both hemispheres, the left more particularly, are necessary for some types of complex maps. The resulting defect is bilateral topographic amorphosynthesis. The second is a much more complex propositional ("digital computer") function that is entirely left-sided in right-handed people, the defect of which results in a propositional pattern agnosia.

To put this in another way, we believe that all the elements of morphosynthesis are served as much by the left hemisphere as by the right hemisphere, perhaps to a more highly developed degree in the hemisphere relating to the preferred hand. The split commissure experiments in monkeys should continue to yield a great deal of further information about this function. In the dominant hemisphere, this function is overlaid and its defects obscured, by propositional function of a unitary, indivisible character that accounts for the phenomenon of dominance. Loss of recognition of faces is a very special disorder at low physiological level and, in our limited experience, requires a bilateral loss of form vision (amorphosynthesis). A more severe disturbance of this kind, produced by bilateral parieto-occipital lesions, is associated with visual disorientation, as in the case described by Smith & Holmes (1916), and presents striking differences from agnosia. The corresponding effect from severe left-sided lesions seems to be a total unresponsiveness (total agnosia). Asymbolia for pain is, in our view, also a bilateral amorphosynthesis and not an agnosia; for such patients that we have seen can feel pain and can discuss it, though it is not of any biological importance to them.

We therefore suspect that there are not only two levels of the perceptual process, but also two degrees of specialization of the one hemisphere, one a relatively greater intensity of bilateral physiologic function, the other a more complete unilateral dominance of "propositional function." Though in this last session we have discussed more particularly the asymmetry of symptomatology of right and left parietal lobe lesions, I should point out that the same order of difference was mentioned this morning in relation to temporal lobe symptomatology. Whereas a lesion of the left temporal lobe produces difficulty in retaining verbal material, in its use in speech, and a peculiar difficulty in listening, as Dr. Brenda Milner described, a lesion of the right temporal lobe affected nonverbal auditory discrimination. If one substitutes defect in temporal summation for spatial summation, the parallelism with the effects of left and right parietal lobe lesions becomes remarkable. One can see here the possibility of sequential, propositional programming versus simple sequence mapping as gnostic and physiological functions respectively. The much higher frequency of hallucinatory disorder from right temporal lesions than left may similarly reflect only a circumscribed specific defect in awareness (agnosia) associated with left-sided lesion. In our own experience, the associated behavioral disorder is the same for right and left temporal lesions, illustrating that both right and left temporal lobes have morphosynthetic function in temporal perception. I hope that perhaps this closer definition of agnosia may serve as a "working hypothesis" with which to explore the verbal aspects of dominance.

B.

Clinical Symptomatology in Right and Left Hemisphere Lesions[1]

ARTHUR L. BENTON

State University of Iowa College of Medicine, Iowa City, Iowa

DR. HÉCAEN has provided us with a comprehensive analysis of the complex problems bearing on the relationship between the functioning of one or the other cerebral hemisphere and behavior. As he has indicated, the range of questions in this area is so wide that most of them can be dealt with only in rather succinct fashion. In this discussion of his excellent review, I should like to consider only two or three of the many topics which he has covered.

THE DEFINITION OF "HANDEDNESS"

There can be no question that the relationship between handedness and cerebral dominance for language deserves continued scrutiny. Dr. Hécaen has sketched the developments since Broca first adduced evidence for the crucial importance of the left hemisphere exactly 100 years ago. The least controversial fact in this area is that the left hemisphere is dominant for language in the very great majority of right-handed persons. On the other hand, we now know that the second part of the classic formula (i.e., that the right hemisphere is dominant in sinistrals) does not hold. When hemispheric dominance is inferred from the occurrence of aphasia in left-handed patients with unilateral lesions, one finds that the crucial hemisphere is somewhat more likely to be the left, although there is certainly no dearth of cases of aphasia in sinistrals resulting from a right hemispheric lesion. In short, in

[1] The study of manual dexterity in self-classified right- and left-handed individuals which is reported in this discussion was supported by a research grant (B-616) from the National Institute of Neurological Diseases and Blindness, U. S. Public Health Service.

contrast to the situation obtaining with dextrals, the dominant hemisphere for language in sinistrals is essentially unpredictable.

This has been a provocative development, and it constitutes a real advance in knowledge. A rather neat formula, which was more or less accepted for perhaps 80 years, has been invalidated, and the true state of affairs has been shown to be rather complex and a little bewildering. Where do we go from here in the further exploration of the question of hemispheric dominance for language in general, and particularly in sinistrals? I think that a necessary first step is to take a closer look at the concept of "handedness," since this idea constitutes the fulcrum on which the major issue rests.

What do we mean by "handedness"? Operationally, it turns out to mean not one but a number of things. First and foremost, it is a verbal statement. In the clinic, this verbal statement is often a one-word answer to the simple question, "Are you (or is he) right-handed or left-handed?," addressed to the patient or his relatives. If the answer is consonant with expectations, the matter may be allowed to rest there. However, more specific questions may be asked, e.g., which hand is used in writing, in throwing, in turning a screwdriver, etc. In the clinic, this is likely to happen when the initial answer to the simple typological question is not in accord with expectations. In any case, such detailed questioning discloses that a good many people have mixed dominance with respect to hand preference. This is particularly characteristic of individuals who classify themselves as "left-handed," but it is also true to a degree of some individuals who classify themselves as "right-handed." The study of Humphrey (1951) showed this quite clearly.

In his investigation, Humphrey presented a 20-item questionnaire, concerned with hand preference in various activities (such as writing, drawing, throwing a ball, playing tennis, and using a screwdriver), to groups of Oxford University students who were self-classified as right-handed or left-handed. He found that in general the right-handed students reported strong preference for the use of the right hand in the various activities. However, a certain amount of interindividual variation in reported strength of right-hand preference was also present. The left-handed subjects showed a far less consistent picture. Interindividual variation was enormous. There were a number of individuals who reported using the right hand in a majority of the 20 activities and even some who reported a stronger preference for the use of the right hand than did some right-handed subjects.

The implications of Humphrey's findings are fairly obvious. "Left-handedness," as defined by self-classification, is a very mixed bag. It includes individuals who show stronger preference for the use of the right hand in various life activities than do some individuals who are classed by themselves and others as "right-handed." It is hardly surprising then that the hemispheric dominance for language of members of such a heterogeneous category is unpredictable.

A verbal statement (or a series of such statements) concerning hand preference is one operational definition of "handedness." Another operational definition is hand preference as actually observed, rather than as verbally reported. We usually assume that the two definitions amount to the same thing, i.e., that the verbal statements accurately reflect actual hand preference as the subject carries out daily life activities. Is this assumption correct? There is no reason to doubt that there is indeed a high degree of relationship between the verbal statements and actual practice. However, there is reason to doubt that the relationship is a perfect one. And when one considers that even a very high degree of relationship, as indexed by a correlation of .95, still leaves room for discrepancies between the two variables in individual cases, it is evident that there will be an occasional case in which the verbal statements of the subject or patient do not accurately reflect his actual hand preference. Thus another source of error is introduced into the handedness side of the handedness-cerebral dominance equation.

"Handedness" has still another operational meaning, beyond reported or actual preferential use in various activities. It also refers to the relative dexterity with which skilled acts are performed by each of the hands. Here again there is no reason to doubt that a positive correlation does exist between a person's hand preference and the relative smoothness or efficiency with which he performs the skilled movements involved in writing, cutting with a scissors, or using a screwdriver. But how close is the relationship? A recently completed study (Benton, Meyers, & Polder, 1961) in which this relationship was examined provides some indications.

We questioned essentially normal adult subjects about their handedness and first isolated a group of 50 subjects who stated that they were right-handed, that they were strongly (rather than moderately) right-handed, and that they used the right hand in writing, cutting with a scissors, and using a screwdriver. These subjects were then given a manual dexterity task (Crawford Small Parts Dexterity Test, Part I), which consists of picking up small pins with a tweezer, placing them in holes, and then picking up a small metal collar and placing it on the pin. This is a typical vocational selection test for jobs requiring fine manual dexterity. It involves accurate coordination of finger and hand movements, as well as control of arm movements. In our study, counterbalanced series of trials involving the right and the left hands were given, and a speed score for each hand was determined. An index of superiority of the right hand, in terms of the difference in speed between the two hands, was then computed.

Figure I shows the distribution of these "relative dexterity" scores in this group of self-defined "strongly right-handed" subjects. It will be seen that:

(1) There is a definite relative superiority of the right hand, as reflected in the mean "relative dexterity" score of +25.

(2) However, there is also considerable individual variation in performance. A majority of subjects show a marked superiority of the right hand, but there are others (16 per cent of the group) who show only a slight superiority, and still others (constituting 12 per cent of the group) who show either equal dexterity in the two hands or an actual superiority of the left hand.

Another group of 40 "left-handed" subjects was formed on the basis of their replies to the questions. These were subjects who stated that

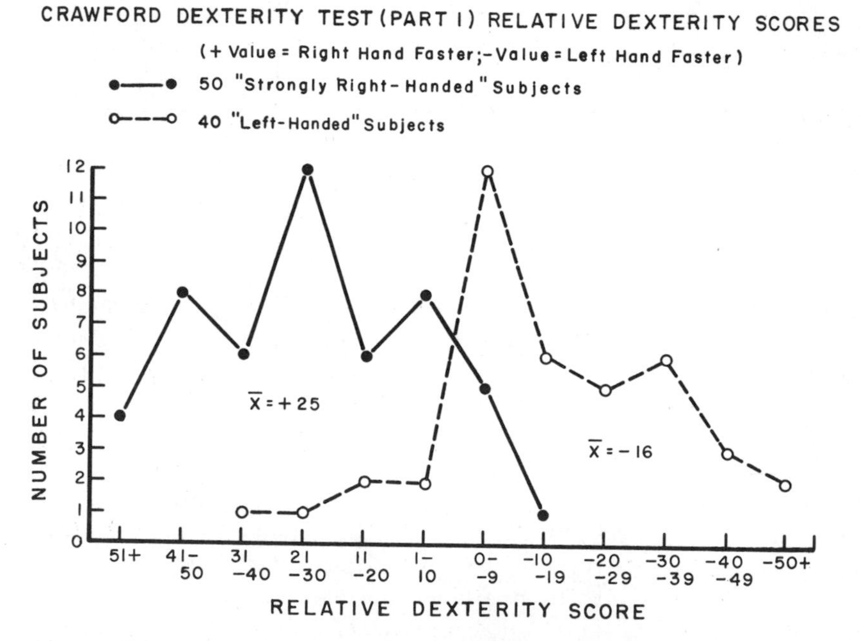

Fig. 1. Relative dexterity scores of self-classified right-handed and left-handed subjects on a "tweezer dexterity" test.

they were either strongly or moderately "left-handed." The distribution of the "relative dexterity" scores in this group is also shown in Figure 1. It will be seen that:

(1) There is a definite, relative superiority of the left hand, as reflected in the mean score of −16, and the two groups of subjects are clearly discriminable from each other, *as groups*.

(2) Individual variation in performance is marked—it could hardly be more pronounced. Fifty-five per cent of the subjects show the expected superiority in the left hand. At the other extreme, there are 6 subjects (15 per cent) who show a superiority in the right hand.

(3) Perhaps the finding of greatest interest is that there are people, classified by themselves or others as left-handed, who prove to be more right-handed on this dexterity task than some people, classified by themselves or others as strongly right-handed.

A more familiar task, cutting paper with a scissors along a straight or curved line, was also given to these subjects. Performance was scored in terms of both speed and "goodness of cut," and a dextrality index computed for each subject. The findings are shown in Figure 2. It will be seen that:

(1) The two groups differ markedly in trend, as indexed by the mean dextrality scores.

(2) There is some degree of interindividual variation among the right-handed subjects, the dextrality scores ranging from extreme superiority in the right hand to virtual ambidexterity.

(3) The left-handed subjects show a most extreme range of scores. Some of them show decided superiority of the right hand in cutting with a scissors.

(4) A noteworthy proportion of the left-handed subjects (15 per cent) show a higher degree of superiority of the right hand than is shown by the lowest 20 per cent of the right-handed subjects.

Findings such as these indicate quite clearly that our present methods of categorizing individuals with respect to handedness are much too imprecise and simply do not do justice to the facts. Strength of handedness, in terms of both preferential use and relative dexterity, should be quantitatively assessed; in addition, qualitative analysis of performances relating to handedness is called for. This is easy enough to do with normal subjects. Unfortunately, it is very difficult to make this type of assessment on brain-damaged patients. However, if we cannot make this type of assessment, we should be aware of the fact that our present descriptive habits are not adequate and possibly constitute a significant source of error in our determinations of the relationship between handedness and cerebral dominance.

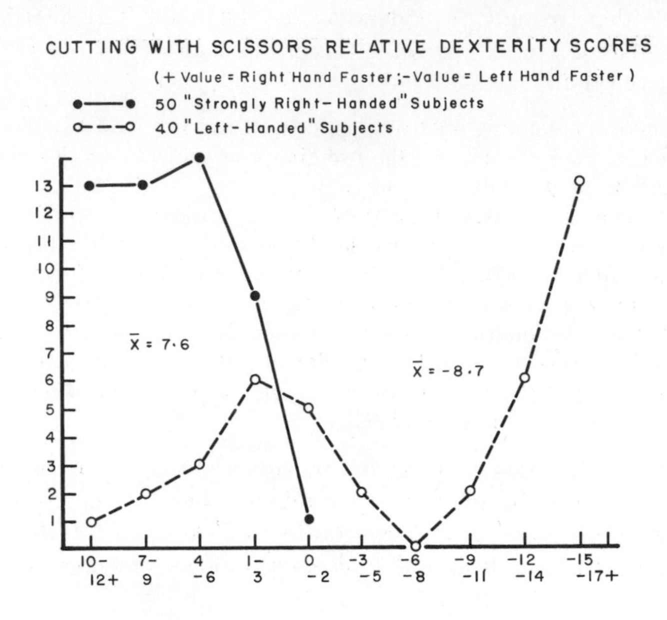

Fig. 2. Relative dexterity scores of self-classified right-handed and left-handed subjects in cutting paper with scissors.

CEREBRAL DOMINANCE AND PATTERN OF PSYCHOLOGICAL TEST PERFORMANCE

Dr. Hécaen has called attention to the series of psychometric studies which tend to indicate that, on a battery of tests in which separate scores are derived from the verbal and nonverbal components of the battery, patients with lesions of the right hemisphere will show more marked deficit on the nonverbal component while patients with lesions of the left hemisphere will show more marked deficit on the verbal component. Although, taken all in all, the results of these studies have been rather consistent in respect to these indications, they nevertheless have not been very impressive. First, fair-sized groups of patients with right and left hemispheric lesions are required to demonstrate the predicted difference in trends, indicating that individual variability is quite large. This in itself limits the clinical interest of the generalization. Secondly, the prediction that patients with lesions of the left hemisphere will show lower verbal scale scores than patients with lesions of the right hemisphere is hardly an exciting one, since we have been aware of this fact for decades. It is the prediction that patients with lesions of the right hemisphere will show greater deficit on nonverbal spatial tasks than will patients with lesions of the left hemisphere, which is of particular interest. But it is precisely with respect to this prediction that the findings of the psychometric studies have been weakest. Thus, while all of them show the predicted difference in trend of scores, i.e., in the verbal test-spatial test relationships, some of them show no difference in respect to spatial scores alone when the two groups of patients are compared.

This is true, for example, of the studies of Heilbrun (1956) and of Meyer & Jones (1957), the results of which are shown in Figure 3. It will be seen that in both studies the two groups of patients show the predicted intraindividual trend in "verbal" and "spatial" (or "nonverbal") scores. But we also see that, when the two groups are compared with respect to "spatial" or "nonverbal" scores alone, the predicted superiority of the patients with lesions of the left hemisphere is not apparent.[2]

There are a number of possible reasons for this failure to secure clear-cut differences in level of "spatial" test performance between patients with right and left hemispheric lesions. The particular factor to

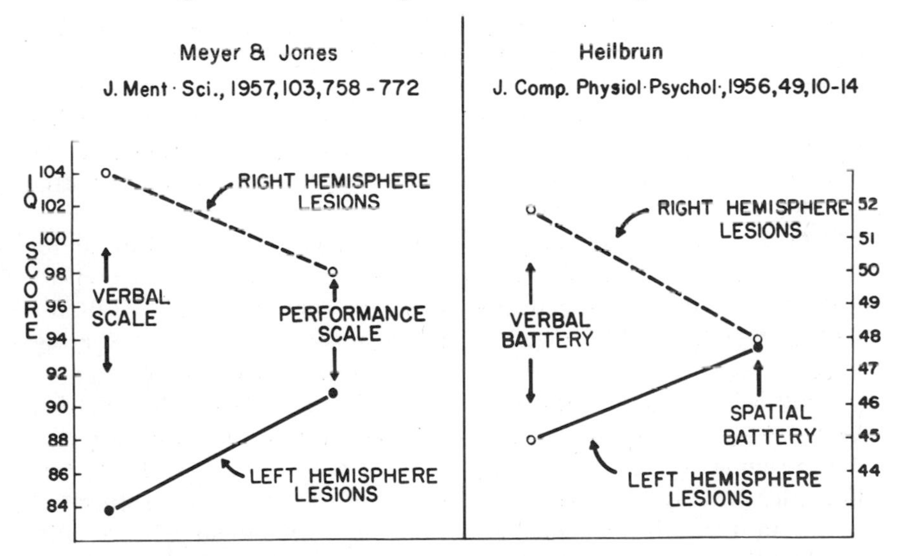

Fig. 3. Patterns of verbal and spatial test performance in patients with right and left hemispheric lesions.

[2] In the Meyer & Jones study, the difference between the two groups with respect to Performance Scale IQ is not significant.

which I should like to call attention is again one of a technical nature, namely, the rather free and easy manner with which we go about designating certain tasks as "verbal" tests and others as "nonverbal" or "spatial" tests. It is generally agreed that, when we speak of hemispheric dominance for language, we have in mind symbolic formulation and expression in the broadest sense, and not merely oral and written speech. In line with this, we assume that the patient who is truly aphasic suffers from an impairment in what used to be called "inner language," i.e., in verbal thinking and in the utilization of symbolic activity in problem-solving. From this, it follows that when language function is impaired in lesions of the dominant hemisphere, such impairment will be reflected not only on tasks of an obviously verbal nature, but also on any task in which verbal mediation facilitates performance.

On the whole, little attention has been paid to this consideration in selecting tests of a verbal and nonverbal (or spatial) nature to serve as a basis for comparing the performances of patients with lesions in one or the other hemisphere. Test makers generally designate any test which does not require an overt verbal response as a "nonverbal" test, without regard to the question of the relative importance of symbolic processes in mediating performance on the task. They are not to be criticized for this, since they have no particular concern about the question of hemispheric dominance for language and hence have no reason to avoid tasks which require symbolic intervention in performance. In fact, since a frequent aim is to devise nonverbal tests which will assess the same reasoning abilities as the more conventional verbal intelligence tests, the requirement of symbolic activity in task performance may be counted as an asset.

However, considering our purposes, we are hardly justified in taking the designation of these tests as "nonverbal" and "spatial" at face value, without reflecting on the degree to which they actually do call for language activity in the form either of overt verbal responses or mediating symbolic activity. But this is precisely what we do when we compare patients with lesions of the right or left hemisphere on the so-called Verbal Scale and Performance Scale of the Wechsler-Bellevue batteries. For example, the Picture Completion subtest of the Wechsler Performance Scale calls for verbal responses on the part of the subject. It is not unreasonable to assume, I think, that a patient with a mild word-finding disturbance could experience particular difficulty with the test. To take another example, the Picture Arrangement subtest of the same Scale may certainly be counted as a spatial and perceptual task, since it does involve spatial positioning of the cards and appreciation of the actions depicted in the pictures so that they can be arranged in the appropriate temporal sequence. But it is also likely that, at least in some subjects, performance is mediated by implicit verbalization which facilitates grasp of the meaning of the pictures. If such a subject suffers from impairment in "inner language" or "capacity for symbolic formulation," his performance will be impaired to some degree on this supposedly "nonverbal" task. Parenthetically, I might add that I cannot recall ever seeing a patient with sensory aphasia who performed adequately on the Picture Arrangement subtest.

This uncritical choice of tests may be one reason why the expected difference between patients with right and left hemispheric lesions, in respect to level of performance on a battery of spatial or nonverbal tests, is not always found. I doubt that this is the only reason, but eliminating this technical weakness in test selection should at least help to clarify the issue. The spatial tasks we give our patients should be as "pure" as possible, in the sense that the requirements for symbolic activity should be minimal. As with the handedness problem, it is much easier to point to the weakness than to remedy it. I know of no easy way to determine whether a task requires implicit verbalization or not. One would think that in general nonmeaningful material would be preferable to meaningful material, (e.g., the drawing of abstract designs rather than concrete objects) and that tests requiring verbal responses should be avoided. A possible method of test selection would be to choose those tests on which aphasic patients do as well as nonaphasic patients. One might come up with some surprising results.

UNILATERAL VS. BILATERAL SOMATOPERCEPTUAL DEFICIT

This question of the participation of symbolic activity in many performances which are ostensibly of a nonverbal nature leads to a consideration of a related problem which has been reviewed so well by Dr. Hécaen, namely, the somatoperceptual disorders resulting from lesions of one or the other hemisphere.

There is no arguing about the facts of the matter. Unilateral deficits *are* found more frequently in patients with lesions of the right hemisphere, and bilateral deficits *are* found more frequently in patients with lesions of the left hemisphere. The question is: How are these facts to be interpreted? The finding which particularly calls for explanation is the occurrence of bilateral somatoperceptual impairment in patients with lesions of the dominant hemisphere. As Dr. Hécaen has pointed out, this holds for such deficits as finger agnosia and for more general forms of autotopagnosia.

One way of approaching the problem is to invoke the concept of the body schema and to postulate that the operation of this organized mental model of the body is directly mediated by the posterior areas of the dominant hemisphere. Another approach is to consider these bilateral deficits as being of a different order from the unilateral deficits which may appear superficially to be of the same nature. Dr. Denny-Brown has advanced the view that these bilateral somatoperceptual deficits cannot be counted as being merely sensory or perceptual disturbances; they are, in his terms, "agnosias" which are determined by a basic impairment in "propositional awareness." Dealing specifically with right-left disorientation and finger agnosia (Benton, 1959), I have adopted the same position as Dr. Denny-Brown in this matter, although, on the one hand, I would reject the term "agnosia" to express the idea and, on the other hand, I have no hesitancy in thinking of "propositional awareness" as a symbolic process. I believe that when these bilateral deficits occur in patients with unilateral disease, they are conditioned by a basic impairment in symbolic understanding, symbolic operation, or symbolic expression.

At the present stage of our knowledge, evidence can be marshalled for and against this proposition, and the question remains unsettled. I can only report that my continuing personal experience has tended to confirm the idea. For example, we have just completed a comprehensive psychologic study of 100 patients with diverse types of brain damage and 100 control patients of comparable age and educational background. The findings in the brain-damaged patients vary from no deficit whatever, to extensive and severe impairment. There were five patients in the group who showed moderate to severe bilateral finger agnosia. Since three of the patients had diffuse disease, the specific question of the role of the dominant hemisphere cannot be evaluated. However, one can look at these patients from a purely behavioral standpoint and consider what their mental status is. Table 1 shows the performances of these patients on four key tests.

First, a "word fluency" test in which the patient is asked to say all the words he knows which begin with a particular letter of the alphabet, e.g., *B* or *R*. We consider this test to be a measure of facility of verbal association—a word-finding test, so to speak. The performances are expressed in terms of standard deviation scores, as compared with the mean score of the control group. It will be seen that the performances of four of the five patients are clearly defective.

The second test involved silent reading of paragraphs on about the sixth grade level of difficulty, with the patient answering questions concerning information in the paragraphs, with the text before him. The standard deviation scores show that all five patients performed on a grossly defective level.

The next test is the WAIS Similarities which requires the patient to state how two things are alike, e.g., dog and lion, coat and dress, etc. As indicated by the scale scores, not a single performance was within the average range.

Finally, since I have mentioned this test as probably involving some degree of symbolic activity in its performance, the patients' scores on Picture Arrangement are shown. Again it is seen that not a single performance was within the average range.

As a group, these five patients were far more severely impaired than the total group of brain-damaged patients. This is indicated by a comparison of their mean scores with those of the total group, as shown in the table.

TABLE I

Test Scores of Patients with Bilateral Finger Agnosia

Patient	Word Fluency (S.D. Score)	Paragraph Reading (S.D. Score)	WAIS Similarities (Scale Score)	WAIS Picture Arrangement (Scale Score)
1. R.B.	−2.5	−5.2	2	2
2. L.F.	−0.7	−5.2	4	2
3. O.H.	−2.8	−3.9	3	6
4. S.R.	−2.1	−5.2	6	2
5. H.Y.	−2.7	−5.2	6	6
Mean Score	−2.2	−4.9	4.2	3.6

Mean Scores for Total Groups

	Word Fluency	Par. Rdg.	Similarities	Pict. Arr.
Brain-Damaged	−1.0	−1.2	7.7	7.9
Control	—	—	10.0	9.6

One must concede that the fact that all five patients, with bilateral finger agnosia in this group, showed marked deficit in verbal thinking does not mean that the next case will show such impairment. Nor does this finding adequately account for the finger agnosia in these patients, since one can find patients who are equally impaired in respect to verbal abilities who do not show the body schema deficit. However, I do think that these observations constitute evidence that bilateral finger agnosia usually occurs within a setting of significant, generalized mental impairment with defective "propositional awareness" (to use Dr. Denny-Brown's term), rather than in isolation or in specific association with one, two, or three other behavioral deficits.

XI

Summary of the Conference

by RICHARD JUNG

University of Freiburg, Freiburg, Germany

WHEN I WAS ASKED to summarize this conference, I was somewhat surprised. It has been more than twenty years since I worked in this field, and then only for a short time with Kleist in Frankfurt. I soon discovered, however, that I had been chosen because I might qualify as an impartial outsider. I shall therefore try to summarize the proceedings, as best I can, in this capacity of an interested amateur. I hope you will allow me to add some reflections of my own concerning certain gaps in our knowledge—gaps which have become apparent to some of us in the course of this conference.

Let me consider first the reports given by the anatomists. The introductory paper by Professor von Bonin has provided convincing arguments for his negative conclusion, viz., that the minute differences between the human cerebral hemispheres and their various morphological asymmetries which he mentioned cannot account for the astounding differences in hemisphere function. At this time, morphology offers no explanation whatever for the facts of cerebral dominance. This negative conclusion need not exclude the possibility that more elaborate studies later on might disclose real differences between left and right cortices, whether in terms of cytoarchitecture or on some other cellular or subcellular level. At present, however, we can only assume that there must be functional differences in the learning capacity of the two hemispheres, differences which lack, so far, an obvious basis in structure.

In the paper which followed, Professor Young showed how an Aristotelian (teleologic) approach to the problem of hemisphere differentiation can be combined with comparative studies and with the application of various special cybernetic concepts, suggesting the existence of computing mechanisms in the brain. Although this approach may be unusual, and rather far removed from the problem of cerebral dominance, I found it most stimulating. In contrast to many of my colleagues, I am not convinced that mere statements of fact or descriptions of experimental results suffice in the advancement of our science. We also need to reflect on the context of our work and permit ourselves some degree of speculation, if we are to make progress. Professor Young made three points. First, he stressed the necessity for a map-like representation of the environment within the brain of lower forms. This cerebral representation is then employed in directing and controlling the behavior of the organism, enabling it to adapt to its environment. The second point involved a critique of Ramón y Cajal's view that the crossing of different cerebral pathways results from the inversion of the optical image and the chiasmal crossing. Professor Young added to this some intriguing findings and ideas concerning the horizontal and vertical visual coordinates in the octopus, but I will not attempt to discuss these observations here. The third point, and the one most pertinent to our subject, was the suggestion that the emergence of such a complex computing mechanism as the human brain may be associated with a reduction of bilateral learning and of bilateral mapping. Map-like, isomorphic representations found in brains with low degrees of complexity may be less important in brains of greater complexity, and hence gain relatively greater independence from direct environmental control. This may be but one aspect of the phylogenetic emergence of more and more complex neural mechanisms. We need not raise the question of whether Professor Young's comparisons of CNS structures with cybernetic mechanisms are appropriate. His ideas are justified by their heuristic value.

As did other anatomists who followed him, Professor Young stressed the probable role of dendritic systems. As a neurophysiologist, I must confess, however, that I was not able to follow all of the speculations on dendrites presented by the anatomists who spoke. These anatomical assumptions seem to me as conjectural as the tendency of many neurophysiologists to talk about "dendritic potentials," for which no real connection with dendrites has ever been shown. We know so little of the function of dendritic trees, of their membrane characteristics, and of their connections with other neurons and with the glial cells, that we must wait until we have decisive experiments.

Professor Bodian drew our attention to Coghill's view on the origin of central decussations: they may be needed to facilitate responses to sensory stimuli (impinging on one side of a bilaterally symmetrical body) by means of muscular activity which is concentrated on the opposite side. Professor Bodian also held out hopes that further advances in histology of the brain, by electromicroscopy, might provide a basis for the functional differences between hemispheres, for which Professor von Bonin was unable to give an anatomical explanation. The next speaker among those who dealt with anatomy, Dr. Scheibel, rightly stressed that the emergence of functional asymmetry in the human brain is associated with a number of other features which distinguish the brain of man from that of other forms: he emphasized the marked increase in number of cells as one goes from the anthropoid to the human brain. He also pointed out that a neural structure or mechanism may be used for one particular purpose, at some earlier stage in phylogeny, while serving quite different ends later on. He also stressed the increasing separation of afferent and efferent areas and the particular role of short-axon or Golgi II neurons. I should like to add here that the role of these cells remains an important, but entirely unsolved, problem. We simply do not know whether the Golgi II cells produce spikes or perhaps only slow potentials; the electrophysiology of these units requires further investigation by microelectrode techniques.

Dr. Kuypers was the first to mention the subject of temporal coding. In my opinion, this is a point which has not been sufficiently discussed at this meeting, although it seems pertinent to all acoustic and speech functions so important in interhemispheric relations. Following him, Dr. Nauta also mentioned the temporal characteristics of cortical events and the central problem of how the brain maintains the stability of behavior in time. In addition, he made some remarks concerning a bilaterally symmetrical system in relation to the cord. In his concluding remarks, Professor O'Leary, besides citing Voltaire, again drew attention to the short-axon cells and said that these are really the enigma of the cerebral cortex. I think this is a correct statement of our ignorance in this matter—a problem badly in need of scientific enlightenment. One may also safely say that the question of the first morning, "Why do we have two brains?" cannot be answered.

The afternoon of the first day was devoted to interhemispheric problems and the investigation of callosal function. The presentations were begun very successfully by Professor Sperry and by Drs. Myers and Downer.

In his introduction, Professor Sperry pointed out that the function of the corpus callosum has remained entirely obscure until recent years.

He cited McCulloch's jocular statement that the only function of this pathway seemed to be the transmission of epileptic seizures. This suggestion was taken quite seriously by some neurosurgeons, as you may know. They actually split the corpus callosum in some epileptics, only to find that the operation was not beneficial. The split-brain technique of Sperry and Myers has now finally revealed some functions of the callosal commissures in interhemispheric transfer.

Using rather elaborate techniques, Dr. Myers has found that these transfer mechanisms are not as similar in the monkey and the cat as might be believed, and that the functions of the callosum in transfer of learning, between the hemispheres, may be extremely complicated. For instance, one can teach such a split-brain animal various tasks by presenting one task to one eye and the other task to the other eye. Depending on the tasks employed, one can demonstrate absence of hemisphere interaction, facilitation of learning, or interference.

These presentations were rounded out by a very fine paper by Dr. Downer. He described his experiments on monkeys with split brains and with additional lesions, from which he obtained many new results, especially on visual and temporal-lobe mechanisms. His most impressive observation on the split-brain preparation concerned the role of unilateral temporal-lobe lesions. Following such lesions, he was able to obtain an optically-induced, reversible Klüver-Bucy syndrome in these split-brain animals by covering the eye connected with the intact temporal lobe, and thus limiting the visual input to the side with the temporal-lobe lesion. In addition, his experiments gave some clue to the functions of the anterior commissure as a connection between the temporal lobes. Anatomically this pathway is well known, but its function had not been demonstrated thus far. Dr. Downer's experiments also show, as anatomical findings had suggested, that no fibers cross between the two striate areas. However, I cannot agree altogether with Dr. Downer's sharp distinction between sensation and perception. Some hemispheric interaction may take place already at the level of the so-called primary receiving system. In the cat at least, there are some fibers crossing between the two striate and the two parastriate regions; parastriate connections are demonstrated electrophysiologically by Ajmone-Marsan and Widen down to the geniculate. There may be more connections in the visual system than we suspect. The experiments of Doty show that cats may still develop useful pattern vision, after the entire striate area had been removed at birth.

I would like to call special attention to the results of Dr. Ettlinger's investigation on interhemispheric relations in the somatosensory system. He has demonstrated transfer by way of the corpus callosum between the posterior parietal areas. He has also noted that skills involving the use of the hand are primarily under contralateral control. Dr. Ettlinger showed further how much can be gained by working with animals, as well as with brain-injured humans.

In the discussion that followed, Dr. Mishkin very clearly summarized the results of his own experiments and those of Dr. Myers: visual integration is better within one hemisphere than it is between hemispheres. Dr. Mishkin's own experiments showed especially well the importance of the inferior temporal lobes for visual function. He thus confirmed some old experiments by von Bonin and co-workers who had demonstrated the connection of these inferotemporal regions with the striate and parastriate areas.

Dr. Pribram elaborated the computer function further and tried to distinguish between analog and digital mechanisms. He proposed four brains instead of two. I at first did not quite understand which four brains he meant, but I believe his scheme was mainly concerned with the limbic system. He proposed that one side of the brain might provide stabilization in space and the other stabilization in time. Thus, the conception of time was again introduced. It is hoped that future experiments may clarify the bases of these functions. Dr. Pribram also made an important observation in showing that certain types of choice behavior may be lost after cerebral lesions, although other forms of behavior may be preserved. This corresponds to observations in clinical neurology; it may be related to Professor Denny-Brown's later comments concerning similar differences between spontaneous and commanded actions in apraxia.

I believe the split-brain experiments were the most novel part of this symposium. They tell us a story of marriage and divorce of the two brains. Before operation, the joined hemispheres apparently had led a rather happy married life and were able to solve their problems together. Following the split, the divorced hemispheres accomplished much less, failed in many tasks, and even deteriorated in their moral standards—as Dr. Downer's experiments with the indecent behavior of the Klüver-Bucy monkeys seemed to show.

These remarks might suffice to summarize the main parts of the first day. I am afraid that it leads to one rather negative conclusion, in spite of all the illuminating observations we have heard. Up to this point, nothing has been found in these animal experiments that would bear on cerebral dominance. I believe this shows clearly the limitation of animal experiments. It is evident that real hemispheric dominance does not occur in any of these infrahuman species. We have no evidence whatsoever for cerebral dominance in monkeys, not to mention the carnivores. In discussing this point, Dr. Jasper stressed the occurrence of handedness in animals. Dr. Pribram said that rudimentary dominance may occur in monkeys, but, as you heard, Dr. Mishkin had to refer to observations on man in order to bring his views on cross-connections between the visual and temporal areas into harmony with the conception of cerebral dominance. He proposed that the connections to one side were stronger than those to the other. In my opinion, preference for one side of the body, in animals, is very different from handedness. Many experiments show this. Cole and Glees have shown that hand preference in monkeys is rather evenly distributed, in contrast to the preponderant preference for the right hand in man. Besides, preference for a particular hand, right or left, is much less pronounced in the monkey. Similarly, J. M. Warren has shown that paw preferences in cats, and hand preferences in monkeys, are rather plastic: the "favoring" of one upper extremity over the other increases as a function of prolonged testing and is much more easily reversed than in man.

Thus, I think that we must distinguish between the preference for one hand in animals, and the dominance of one side of the brain in man. As I said, no evidence whatsoever has been presented that cerebral dominance really occurs in monkeys. As Professor Teuber later pointed out, both of the hemispheres of these animals apparently function as does the right hemisphere of the human. And everybody knows they have no speech.

Before concluding this discussion of the animal experiments, I must mention Dr. Lilly's report on the dolphin. Some people may think that the dolphin who is capable of a sort of speech, or language-like communication, may be an exception. Therefore, I asked Dr. Lilly if there is any evidence for dominance in the dolphin, and he assured me that there is none. Of course we must wait to see what else comes out of this work. When Dr. Lilly showed the beautiful brain of the dolphin, my impression was that the corpus callosum was rather small in comparison to that of man. Since Dr. Lilly believes that the dolphin is capable of sleeping with one hemisphere, with one eye closed, I do not believe that the prospect of finding cerebral dominance in the dolphin is very great. If the dolphins are really as clever as Dr. Lilly states, then they may be able to fool the neurophysiologists in future experiments, and we might not find what we are looking for. Then the last hope for finding hemispheric dominance in animals will be gone.

Since the first half of this symposium contained very important results but was not concerned with cerebral dominance, I propose to enlarge the title of our meeting to embrace all that had been covered by calling it, "Conference on Interhemispheric Relations and Cerebral Dominance."

This brings me to a consideration of the proceedings of the following day, the study of the human brain and neurology proper. Here, speech is evidently the most important factor connected with cerebral dominance. It was astonishing that speech was not mentioned until Dr. Critchley's presentation late in the morning. As you know, language—or if you prefer the Pavlovian term, "the second signalling system"—is essentially a learned function, an acquired behavior. Although speech is unique to human communication and therefore should depend on a species-specific innate faculty, it is entirely acquired in early age and determined solely by the language surround. Every human baby will learn either Chinese or English or German, if raised in the appropriate linguistic milieu, be it of European or Negro or Mongolian race, but no ape will do it. So innate factors for special language seem negligible, but innate faculties for speech in general remain a privilege of man and of the dominant hemisphere of his brain.

As you know, no monkey or ape has learned human speech, although some people have tried hard to educate them. Yet the cortical substrate in the "language areas" is present in the ape's brain as in the human brain. The cytoarchitectural speech areas in apes are very well developed and similar to those in man, but they are apparently used for other purposes. A similar differentiation in function seems to occur between the left and right speech areas in man which are identical morphologically. From all this it may be inferred that—in spite of some innate factors for the function of cortical speech areas—the hemispheric difference is mainly acquired by learning, and the species difference is mainly a functional one.

The fact that a learned function, such as speech, was located in a circumscribed region of the brain impressed the neurologists of the last one hundred years so much that practically all the work on cerebral localization has come out of the demonstrations of Broca. We are very grateful to Dr. Critchley for bringing aphasia into the discussion. Before considering speech further, however, let me speak about some of the important papers which were presented in the morning.

Professor Teuber first showed us some essential differences in sensorimotor and intellectual function, inferred from different hemispheric lesions. He demonstrated that there was a preponderance of visual seizures and hallucinations associated with lesions in the right hemisphere. This fits very nicely with Penfield's results and some observations I had made during the war, although I had dismissed them at that time as sheer coincidence. Professor Teuber further recounted the elaborate and important investigations of sensory function of the hand, following lesions in the right or left hemisphere. Detailed psychophysical tests were used in these studies. The procedures and controls employed make these investigations much more valuable than the usual clinical observations. The results showed that the sensory functions of the right hand were more focally represented (in the sensorimotor region of the opposite hemisphere) than were the corresponding functions of the left hand (which were more widely dispersed and less lateralized).

In additional studies based on the same population of patients, Professor Teuber showed considerable autonomy in the function of the hemispheres (e.g., for tactile pattern discrimination learning), interaction (as in auditory localization studies), and interference (as in studies of bimanual hefting of weights). Thus, depending on the task employed, one could gain evidence for independent action of a hemisphere, facilitating interaction between hemispheres, or mutual interference (as in the phenomena of visual or tactile "extinction"). I will not go into further detail. I only wanted to point out that this is the type of investigation needed to overcome the difficult selection problems involved in the assessing of clinical material.

Dr. Weinstein reported on two studies. In one, rather selective losses were shown after left hemispheric lesions; in the other, after those of the right. In the first study, the investigators assessed changes in performance on the Army General Classification Test given to more than sixty men shortly before, and over five years after, a penetrating brain wound had been sustained. Thus was grasped the rare opportunity to compare tests before and after cerebral lesions in man. The results showed a selective drop in test performance after left parietotemporal lesions, but not after lesions elsewhere in the brain. This difference was found even after aphasic patients were excluded from consideration. Still there remained the difficult question of the validity of such tests—whether the absence of a drop in score really means intact intelligence. Dr. Weinstein himself showed, in his description of the second study (based on the same groups of patients), that a tactile size discrimination test showed more results for men with right than with left hemispheric lesions. Thus, there are certain nonverbal (and nonvisual) functions that are more severely impaired by lesions in the so-called nondominant hemisphere.

Quite similar results emerged from Dr. Milner's summary of her earlier work, and from observations she had made together with Professor Penfield. She demonstrated differences in the behavioral effects of left- and right-sided epileptogenic lesions of the human brain; there were corresponding differences in the momentary effects of cortical stimulation, left or right, in conscious patients during craniotomy. Dr. Milner found that, in the majority of these patients, various visuospatial tasks are more affected by right hemispheric lesions, while verbal learning and verbal memory are more affected by lesions of the left cerebral hemisphere. Clearly, right as well as left hemispheres, in man, seem to differ in their functional organization from the corresponding structures in lower forms. In her more recent studies involving auditory tests, Dr. Milner again noted such hemispheric differences. She found deficits on nonverbal auditory discriminations after right (nondominant) temporal lobectomy, but not after left. On a test presenting different digits (e.g., 7, 5, 8 and 9, 4, 6), simultaneously to the two ears, there was greater accuracy of report for the right ear in normal adults, in normal children down to age five, and in most of her epileptic patients. However, for patients with speech localized in the right hemisphere, accuracy of report (on simultaneous stimulation with such verbal material) was greater for the left ear. One might say then, that under these conditions of conflicting binaural stimulation, verbal material reaching the ear opposite the dominant temporal lobe tends to be "favored." Evidently, here again we are faced with differences not found in studying the cerebral hemispheres of infrahuman forms. It will be recalled that Dr. Neff who spoke in the discussion has not found hemispheric differences in his studies on the temporal lobes of animals.

In his critical discussion of these presentations, Dr. Wolff used an approach aimed at assessing the "highest integrative functions" of the human brain. His own results showed little or no difference in this respect in the outcome of lesions in the right or left hemisphere. He proposed seven criteria as essential for the assessment of clinical material, and insisted, rightly, on the importance of premorbid character and adaptability. I consider these criteria—particularly the mass of cerebral tissue loss—extremely valuable; they should always be applied when comparing the effects of removals from right and left temporal lobes. On the average, neurosurgeons remove more tissue from the right than from the left frontal or temporal cortex, since they must be more careful when operating on the left side. Dr. Wolff's material and its discussion recalls the old dichotomy between those who, like himself, propose a holistic view of cortical organization, and those who prefer to stress specific localization of cortical function. He has shown that the amount of brain tissue removed bears an important and direct relation to impairment of what he defines as the highest integrative functions of the brain. This is a point which must be remembered, although it is difficult to assess by his tests, and does not invalidate the differences in functional losses after left and right hemispheric lesions.

Closing this discussion, Dr. Critchley gave us an elegant historical review of early work on aphasia and of the development of the concepts of cerebral dominance during the last century. He also pointed out that Dax senior had conceived of speech-dominance in the left hemisphere 150 years ago, although he never published his idea, so that the concept antedates Broca by fifty years. He also reminded us of Hughlings Jackson's view and discussed the special role of the minor hemisphere which, as you know, is an old conception of Jackson's, who ascribed some role in vocalization to the right hemisphere.

The main paper in the afternoon was that of Dr. Hécaen on the symptoms of right and left hemispheric lesions. His statistical evaluation of a large amount of material representing mixed diagnoses showed quite clearly the importance of special symptoms associated with right-sided lesions. As signs of right hemispheric damage, he mentioned especially unilateral neglect and somatognostic disturbances, apraxia of dressing, as well as certain forms of constructive apraxia which differ in nature after right-sided and left-sided lesions. He retained the term "agnosia" in a broad sense for fundamental sensory disturbances of a higher order. These problems were also discussed by Professor Denny-Brown.

It seems evident from Dr. Hécaen's observations, and from those of most of the other speakers, that one cannot call one hemisphere dominant as such. Dominance manifests itself only for special functions: in the left hemisphere, dominance exists for language (sometimes also in left-handers), including reading and calculation. In the right hemisphere, dominance seems to exist for certain spatial and practic functions and some special gnostic performances, such as those disturbed in prosopagnosia. By contrast, object-agnosia occurs more often in left or bilateral occipito-parietal lesions. To characterize hemispheric functions further, Dr. Hécaen cited Wagner's metaphor comparing the right hemisphere to the conductor, the left to the composer and orchestra of a complex musical performance, although he was careful to say that this is not a valid general conclusion. I will not attempt a detailed discussion of this material which has just been so ably discussed by other speakers. I only want to point out that even an approach which employs mixed material of such widely different brain diseases as tumors and vascular lesions may provide valuable results. One need not always be too fussy about combining clinical material of various diagnoses. But the value of single, well-selected, and completely studied clinical cases will also stand; it will always remain the cornerstone of cortical symptomatology.

In the presentation that followed, Professor Denny-Brown dealt with parietal functions. He discussed his interpretations of extinction and perceptual rivalry and presented a synthesis which might account for many of the parietal syndromes. Although Dr. Hécaen employed "agnosia" in the usual sense of the term, Professor Denny-Brown sees in the catastrophic failure of some patients with left-sided lesions a type of reaction that he would call "agnosia." This is, of course, a terminological difference which one must remember when one discusses agnosia. Professor Denny-Brown further mentioned that apraxia may be dependent upon agnosia as in constructional apractic disturbances. He also stressed an important point for apractic investigations and for Dr. Pribram's examinations in monkeys: A patient may be capable of accomplishing a given task by doing it spontaneously, whereas he could not do it on command.

In the final paper, Professor Benton discussed the problem of defining handedness. He showed that the concept is not a simple one; many behavioral techniques are needed before "handedness" can be diagnosed in any precise sense, even for clinical purposes. In addition, Professor Benton discussed the results of Dr. Hécaen in the light of the various possible ways of assessing handedness, and the uncertain relations between handedness and cerebral dominance.

This, then, has been a very brief synopsis of the special results presented at this symposium. I would now like to take a few minutes to focus on some gaps in our knowledge; some of these gaps I mentioned previously in passing. I shall deal with only four points, two arising from neurophysiologic investigations of cortex and two from clinical studies.

Let us first consider physiological mechanisms, basic to cortical function in two related hemispheres. All that can be said with certainty is that we are as ignorant about the intricate callosal mechanisms of transfer as we are about the basis of memory in general or about the function of the famous Golgi II cells, mentioned several times. Similarly, we know very little about inhibitory mechanisms that may be at play between the right and left brain.

Inhibition, therefore, is my first point. I do not like to go into detail, but I think that inhibitory mechanisms should have been mentioned a little more prominently in this symposium. If inhibition did not occur in the cortex, we would all be epileptics, and if it did not occur between the two hemispheres, we would not develop skilled voluntary movements. For a neurophysiologist, it seems evident that interhemispheric coordination and all of the functions which have been discussed, including transfer of training, can only occur with a considerable amount of inhibition. The present evidence for interhemispheric inhibition is based on rather crude experiments with electrical stimulation and seems rather scanty. Some years ago, our group in Freiburg showed that callosal volleys cause inhibition in cortical neurons. When one fires a callosal volley to the motor cortex by stimulating the opposite symmetrical cortex with low frequency electric shocks, inhibition of single neurons occurs after every shock (Fig. 1b, c). The same

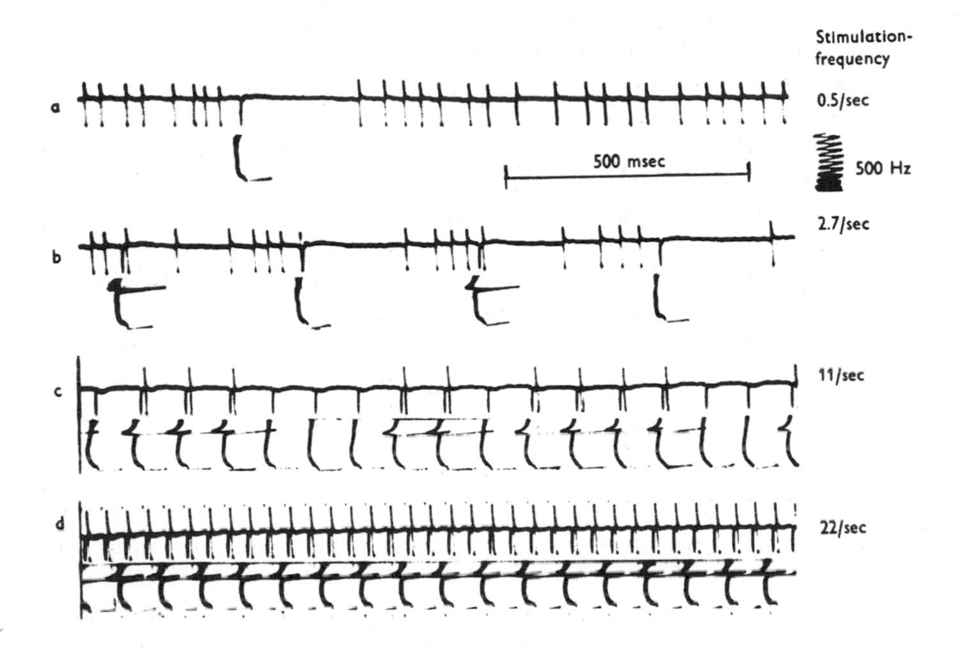

cortical neurons may be driven to a regular discharge by the same stimuli at higher frequency (Fig. 1d). This may have some importance in relation to functions involved in transfer.

Second: Large gaps remain, moreover, in our knowledge of the coordination of left and right visual (and paravisual) areas and their function in unifying the two visual half-fields in perception. Some progress has been made on neuronal integration in the primary visual cortex, but the interhemispheric connections of the striate and parastriate areas have not yet been investigated sufficiently. Here we need more combined experimentation by neurophysiologists and neuroanatomists, particularly since we possess the Nauta method which permits us to trace small-caliber fibers in spite of their small amounts of myelin.

Third: Several speakers mentioned time factors in cortical function and their disturbances after right-sided lesions. The nature of such time-recording functions, however, is not yet clear, either in terms of physiology or neurology. You will recall Dr. Hécaen's comments that, in right-sided lesions, disturbances in the time sense may occur more often than after lesions of the supposedly dominant hemisphere. Although such disturbances in time sense as the "Zeitrafferphänomen" (time-lapse effect) in right temporal-lobe lesions have been demonstrated long ago by the Viennese school, by Poetzl, Hoff and others, they need more detailed study. These were only casual observations, and it seems that these "Zeitraffer" (time-lapse) and "Zeitlupe" (slow motion) experiences arose from atypical temporal-lobe seizures. A combination of EEG studies with the application of psychophysical techniques may lead further, since methods are now available for testing time judgments more carefully than has been done up to now.

Fourth: A clinical problem which needs further investigation is the greater vulnerability of the left hemisphere to atrophy and epilepsy. Especially the left temporal lobe seems to be more prone to atrophy and to seizures than is the right. When comparing temporal-lobe epilepsy of the two hemispheres, nearly all investigators have found it to be more common on the left side, and when studying pneumoencephalograms, it is usually found that atrophy is more marked in the left hemisphere. I think that these differences in atrophic processes between the two sides may also account for some of the minute asymmetries which Professor von Bonin has demonstrated for the two hemispheres. This problem also merits further investigation. The enigmatic preference of left-sided temporal epileptic foci remains an unsolved question. Although we have heard from Professor Teuber that hallucinatory epileptic seizures are more common with right-sided foci, the opposite is true for temporal-lobe seizures in general, which are more often found with left-sided foci. These findings cannot simply be the result of a clinical selection on the basis of the more prominent symptoms of left-sided lesions, because these foci were diagnosed by the EEG and not by clinical symptoms.

There are many more questions which remain open and will have to be further investigated. The problems of hemispheric difference and cerebral dominance will demand the joint efforts of many generations of scientists: animal experiments, clinical observations, and psychophysical experiments will have to be used, preferably in combination. These tasks require the work of neuroanatomists, neurophysiologists, neurologists, psychologists, and many others. Such co-operative work will be essential for clarifying the functions of interhemispheric connections. These hopes for future research conclude my comments regarding the scientific part of the meeting.

Since I am the last speaker, I would like to express thanks, both for myself and for all of the guests who were invited to this meeting and who enjoyed the hospitality of the Johns Hopkins University. We are most grateful to the committee members who organized and to the sponsors who facilitated this most stimulating conference, and particularly to Professor Bordley, who did so much of the work in preparing for it.

REFERENCES CITED

Ades, H. W. Central auditory mechanisms. In: *Handbook of Physiology, Sec. 1.* Vol. I, p. 585. American Physiological Society, Washington, D.C., 1959.

Adrian, E. D. Sensory messages and sensation. The response of the olfactory organ to different smells. *Acta Physiol. Scand.,* **29:** 5, 1953.

———. The basis of sensation. Some recent studies of olfaction. *Brit. Med. J.,* **1:** 287, 1954.

Ajuriaguerra, J. de & Hécaen, H. La restauration fonctionnelle après lobectomie occipitale. *J. de Psychol.,* **44:** 510–46, 1951.

———, ———, & Angelergues, R. Les apraxies; variétés cliniques et latéralisation lésionnelle. *Rev. Neurol. (Par.),* **102:** 28–57, 1960.

Akert, K., Woolsey, C. N. Diamond, I. T., & Neff, W. D. The cortical projection area of the posterior pole of the medial geniculate body in *Macaca mulatta. Anat. Rec.,* **134:** 242, 1959.

Alajouanine, T. & Lhermitte, F. Les troubles des activités espressives du langage dans l'aphasie, leurs relations avec les apraxies. *Rev. Neurol. (Par.),* **102:** 604–29, 1960.

Alema, G. & Donini, G. cité par Peria, Rosadini, et Rossi, 1960.

Amassian, V. & Waller, H. J. Spatiotemporal patterns of activity in individual reticular neurons. In: *Reticular Formation of the Brain,* p. 69. Boston, Little, Brown, 1958.

Andersen, A. L. The effect of laterality localization of brain damage on Wechsler-Bellevue indices of deterioration. *J. Clin. Psychol.,* **6:** 191–94, 1950.

———. The effect of laterality localization of focal brain lesions on the Wechsler-Bellevue subtests. *ibid.,* **7:** 149–53, 1951.

Apter, J. T. Projection of the retina on superior colliculus of cats. *J. Neurophysiol.,* **8:** 123, 1945.

———. Eye movements following strychninization of the superior colliculus of cats. *ibid.,* **9:** 73, 1946.

Arseni, C., Voinesco, J., & Goldenberg, M. Considérations clinico-statistiques sur le syndrome pariétal dans les tumeurs cérébrales. *Rev. Neurol., (Par.),* **99:** 623–38, 1958.

Aresu, M. La superficie cerebrale nell'uòmo. *Arch. Ital. Anat. Embriol.,* **12:** 380–433, 1914.

Armstrong, J. A. An experimental study of the visual pathways in a reptile. *(Lacerta vivipara). J. Anat.,* **84:** 146–67, 1950.

Audisio, M. *Essai sur l'Historique et de la Séméiologie de l'État de Rêve.* Paris, Thèse, 1959.

Bastian, H. C. On the specific gravity of different parts of the human brain. *J. Ment. Sci.,* **56:** 29, 1866.

Bates, J. A. V. & Ettlinger, G. Posterior bi-parietal ablations in the monkey. *Arch. Neurol. Psychiat.,* **3:** 177–92, 1960.

Battersby, W. S. The regional gradient of critical flicker frequency after frontal or occipital lobe injury. *J. Exp. Psychol.,* **42:** 59–68, 1951.

———, Bender, M. B., Pollack, M., & Kahn, R. L. Unilateral "spatial agnosia" ("inattention") . *Brain,* **79:** 68–93, 1956.

Bender, M. B. Extinction and precipitation of cutaneous sensations. *Arch. Neurol. Psychiat.,* **54:** 1–9, 1945.

BENTON, A. L. *Right-left Discrimination and Finger Localization.* New York, Paul B. Hoeber, Inc., 1959.

———, MEYERS, R. & POLDER, G. J. Some aspects of handedness. To be published.

BINGLEY, T. Mental symptoms in temporal lobe epilepsy and temporal lobe gliomas. *Acta. Neurol. Belg.,* Sup. 120, p. 33, 1958.

BINGLEY, T. Mental symptoms in temporal lobe epilepsy and temporal lobe gliomas, with special reference to laterality of lesion and the relationship between handedness and brainedness. *Acta Psychiat. Scand.,* **33:** 151, 1958.

BLAKE, L. The effect of lesions of the superior colliculus on brightness and pattern discrimination in the cat. *J. Comp. Physiol. Psychol.,* **52:** 272, 1959.

BLUM, J. S., CHOW, K. L., & PRIBRAM, K. H. A behavioral analysis of the organization of the parieto-temporo-preoccipital cortex. *J. Comp. Neurol.,* **93:** 53–100, 1950.

BOCCA, E. Clinical aspects of cortical deafness. *Laryngoscope,* **68:** 301–309, 1958.

———, CALEARO, C., CASSINARI, V., & MIGLIAVACCA, F. Testing "cortical" hearing in temporal lobe tumors. *Acta Otolaryng. (Stockh.),* **45:** 289–304, 1955.

BODAMER, J. Die Prosop-agnosie. *Arch. Psychol. Z. Neurol.,* **179:** 6–54, 1947.

BOK, S. T. *Histonomy of the Cerebral Cortex.* Amsterdam, Elsevier Press, 1959.

BONIN, G. v. On a curious asymmetry in the Chinese brain. *Chin. Med. J.,* July, 1924.

———, GAROL, H. W. & MCCULLOCH, W. S. The functional organization of the occipital lobe. *Biol. Symp. (Visual Mechanisms),* **8:** 165–92, 1942.

BOTEZ, M. I. & WERTHEIM, N. Expressive aphasia and amusia, following right frontal lesion in a right-handed man. *Brain,* **82:** 186–202, 1959.

BOYCOTT, B. B. & YOUNG, J. Z. Reactions to shape in *Octopus vulgaris* Lamark. *Proc. Zool. Soc. London,* **126:** 491–547, 1956.

BOYD, R. Tables of the weights of the human body and internal organs in the sane and insane of both sexes at various ages arranged from 2,114 post-mortem examinations. *Phil. Trans.,* **151:** 241–62, 1861.

BRAIN, R. Visual disorientation with special reference to the lesions of the right cerebral hemisphere. *Brain,* **64:** 244–72, 1941.

BRAUNE, C. W. Die Gewichtsverhältnisse der rechten zur linken Hirnhälfte beim Menschen. *Arch. Anat. u. Physiol., Anat. Abstr.,* p. 253, 1891.

BRAZIER, MARY A. B. *The Central Nervous System and Behavior.* (Transactions of the Third Conference, 1960) . New York, The Josiah Macy, Jr. Foundation, 1960.

BREMER, BRIHAYE, & ANDRE-BALISAUX. Physiologie et pathologie du corps calleux. *Arch. Suisses Neurol. Psychiat.,* **78:** 31–87, 1956.

BROADBENT, D. E. The role of auditory localization in attention and memory span. *J. Exp. Psychol.,* **47:** 191–96, 1954.

BROCA, P. Sur la faculté du langage articulé. *Bull. Soc. d'Anthropol. (Paris),* Vol. 6, 1865.

———. Instructions craniologiques et craniométriques de la Société d'Anthropologie de Paris. *Ibid.* pp. 534–36, 1875.

BRYDEN, M. P. Tachistoscopic recognition of nonalphabetical material. *Canad. J. Psychol.,* **14:** 78–86, 1960.

BUCY, P. C. & KLUVER, H. Anatomic changes secondary to temporal lobectomy. *Arch. Neurol. Psychiat.,* **44:** 1142–46, 1940.

BUSER, P. & DUSSARDIER, M. Organisation des projections de la rétine sure le lobe optique, étudiée chez quelques Téléostéens. *J. Physiol. (Par),* **45:** 57–60, 1953.

———. *Die Structur des Chiasma opticum nebst einer allgemeinen Theorie der Kreuzung der Nervenbahnen.* Leipzig, 1899.

———. Estructure del kiasma optico y teoriá general de los entrecruzamientos de los viás nervosas. *Rev. Trimestra. Microg.,* *3:* 15, 1898.

———. Contribucion al concocimiento de la retina y centros opticos de los cefalópodos. *Trab. Lab. Invest. Biol. Univ. Madr.,* **15:** 1–82, 1917.

———. *Histologie du Système Nerveux de l'Homme et des Vertèbres.* Vol. II. Instituto Ramon y Cajal, Madrid, 1955.

——— & Sanchez, D. Contribucion al conocimiento de los centros nerviosos de los insectos. *Trab. Lab. Invest. Biol. Univ. Madr.,* **13:** 1–164, 1915.

Chesher, E. C. Some observations concerning the relation of handedness to the language mechanism. *Bull. Neurol. Inst., N.Y.,* **4:** 556–62, 1936.

Chorazyna, H. & Stepien, L. Impairment of auditory recent memory produced by cortical lesions in dogs. *Acta. Biol. Exp.,* **21:** 177–87, 1961.

Chow, K. L. Effects of partial extirpations of the posterior association cortex on visually mediated behavior in monkeys. *Comp. Psychol. Monogr.,* Vol. 20, No. 3, 1951.

Cohen, L. Perception of reversible figures after brain injury. *Arch. Neurol. Psychiat.,* **81:** 765–75, 1959.

Conrad, K. Über aphasische Sprachstörungen bei hirnverletzten Linkshändern. *Nervenarzt,* **20:** 148–54, 1959.

Critchley, M. Phenomenon of tactile inattention with special reference to parietal lesions. *Brain,* **72:** 538–61, 1949.

———. *The Parietal Lobes.* London, Edward Arnold, 1953, distributed by Williams & Wilkins Co., Baltimore.

Crosby, E. C. & Henderson, J. W. The mammalian midbrain and isthmus regions. Part II, B. *J. Comp. Neurol.,* **88:** 53, 1948.

———, ———, & Yoss, R. E. The mammalian midbrain and isthmus regions. Part II, D. *ibid.,* **97:** 357, 1952.

Cunningham, D. J. Contribution to the surface anatomy of the cerebral hemispheres. Dublin, Royal Irish Acad. *Cunningham memoirs,* **7:** 372, 1892.

Curtis, H. J. Intercortical connections of corpus callosum as indicated by evoked potentials. *J. Neurophysiol.,* **3:** 407–22, 1940.

——— & Bard, P. Intercortical connections of corpus callosum as indicated by evoked potentials. *Amer. J. Physiol.,* **126:** 473, 1939.

Denny-Brown, D. The nature of apraxia. *J. Nerv. Ment. Dis.,* **126:** 9–33, 1958.

——— & Banker, B. Amorphosynthesis from left parietal lesion. *Arch. Neurol. Psychiat.,* **71:** 302–13, 1954.

——— & Chambers, R. A. The parietal lobe and behavior. *Res. Publ. Assoc. Res. Nerv. Ment. Dis.,* **36:** 35–117, 1958.

———, Meyer, J. S., & Horenstein, S. The significance of perceptual rivalry resulting from parietal lesion. *Brain,* **75:** 433–71, 1952.

Diamond, I. T. & Neff, W. D. Ablation of temporal cortex and discrimination of auditory patterns. *J. Neurophysiol.,* **20:** 300–15, 1957.

———, Chow, K. L., & Neff, W. D. Degeneration of caudal medial geniculate body following cortical lesion ventral to auditory area II in cat. *J. Comp. Neurol.,* **109:** 349–62, 1958.

Dide, M. Les désorientations temporo-spatiales et la prépondérance de l'hémisphère droit dans les agnoso-akinésies proprioceptives. Encéphale., **33:** 276–94, 1938.

Doty, R. W. & Rutledge, L. T. "Generalization" between cortically and peripherally applied stimuli eliciting conditional reflexes. *J. Neurophysiol.,* **22:** 428–35, 1959.

Downer, J. L. deC. Role of corpus callosum in transfer of training in Macaca mulatta. *Fed. Proc.,* **17:** 37, 1958.

———. Changes in visually guided behavior following midsaggital division of optic chiasma and corpus callosum in monkey (Macaca mulatta) . *Brain,* **82:** 251–59, 1959.

Dubois, E. On the relation between the quantity of brain and the size of the body in vetebrates. *Proc. Kon. Ned. Akad. Wetenschap.,* **16:** 647–68, 1914.

Duensing, F. Raumagnostische und ideatorisch apraktische Störung des gestaltenden Handelns. *Deutsch Z. Nervenheills.,* **170:** 72–94, 1953.

Eberstaller, O. Zur Oberflächenanatomie der Grosshirnhemisphären. *Wien. Med. Blaetter,* **7:** 479–82, 542–82, 644–46, 1884.

Ebner, F. F. & Myers, R. E. Inter- and intrahemispheric transmission of tactile gnosis in normal and corpus callosum-sectioned monkeys. *Fed. Proc.,* **19:** 292, 1960.

———. Corpus callosum and the interhemispheric transmission of tactual learning, *J. Neurophysiol.* **25:** 380–391, 1962.

ECONOMO, C. v. & HORN, L. Ueber Windungsrelief, Masse und Rindenarchitektonik der Supratemoralfläche, ihre individuellen und ihre Seitenunterschiede. *Z. Neurol. Psychiat.,* **130:** 678–757, 1930.

ETTLINGER, G. Visual discrimination with a single manipulandum following temporal ablations in the monkey. *Quart. J. Exp. Psychol.,* **3:** 164–74, 1959.

———. The description and interpretation of pictures in cases of brain lesion. *J. Ment. Sci.,* **106:** 1337–46, 1960.

———. Lateral preferences in monkeys. *Behavior,* accepted for publication 1961.

———, WARRINGTON, E. & ZANGWILL, O. L. A further study of visual spatial agnosia. *Brain,* **80:** 335–61, 1957.

EVANS, J. P. A study of the sensory defects resulting from excision of cerebral substance in humans. *Res. Publ. Assoc. Res. Nerv. Ment. Dis.,* **15:** 331–66, 1935.

FOIX, C. Contribution à l'étude de l'apraxie idéomotrice. *Rev. neurol. (Par.),* **1:** 285–98, 1916.

———. Sur une variété de troubles bilatéraux de la sensibilité par lésion unilatérale du cerveau. *ibid.,* **29:** 322–31, 1922.

FOX, C. A., FISHER, R. R., & DESALVA, S. J. The distribution of the anterior commissure in monkey (Macaca mulatta). *J. Comp. Neurol.,* **89:** 245–78, 1948.

GANS, A. Das Handzentrum in der linken hinteren Zentralwindung. *Z. Neurol. Psychiat.,* **75:** 689, 1922.

———. Das Handzentrum in der hinteren zentraien Windung bei Javanern. *ibid.,* **85:** 66, 1923.

GAZE, R. M. The representation of the retina on the optic lobe of the frog. *Quart. J. Exp. Physiol.,* **43:** 209–14, 1958.

———. Regeneration of the optic nerve in amphibia. *Int. Rev. Neurobiol.,* **2:** 1–40, 1960.

GENTILLI, C. *Il Lobo Parietale.* Bologna, Cacciari, 1955.

GERSHUNI, V. A. & BLINKOV, S. M. Personal communication to author, 1960.

GHENT, L., SEMMES, J., WEINSTEIN, S., & TEUBER, H.-L. Tactile discrimination after unilateral brain injury in man. *Amer. Psychologist,* **10:** 408, 1955.

———, WEINSTEIN, S., SEMMES, J., & TEUBER, H.-L. Effects of unilateral brain injury in man on learning of a tactual discrimination. *J. Comp. Physiol. Psychol.,* **48:** 478–81, 1955.

———, ———, ———, & ———. Learning of a tactile pattern discrimination after brain injury. Paper read at meeting of Eastern Psychological Association, Philadelphia, April, 1955.

GLICKSTEIN, M. & SPERRY, R. W. Intermanual somesthetic transfer in split-brain rhesus monkeys. *J. Comp. Physiol. Psychol.,* **53:** 322–27, 1960.

——— & ———. Intermanual transfer in split-brain monkeys after somatic cortical ablation. *Amer. Psychologist,* **15:** 485, 1960b.

GLONING, I., GLONING, K., & HOFF, A. Die Störung von Zeit und Raum in der Hirnpathologie. *Wien Z. Nervenheilk.,* **10:** 346–77, 1955.

GOLDBERG, J. M., DIAMOND, I. T., & NEFF, W. D. Auditory discrimination after ablation of temporal and insular cortex in cat. *Fed. Proc.,* **16:** 47, 1957.

GOODGLASS, H. & QUADFASEL, F. A. Language laterality in left-handed aphasics. *Brain,* **77:** 521–48, 1954.

GRAFSTEIN, B. Organization of callosal connections in suprasylvian gyrus of cat. *J. Neurophysiol.,* **22:** 504–15, 1959.

GRUNEBERG, H. The causes of asymmetries in animals. *Amer. Nat.,* **69:** 323–43, 1914.

GUILLAIN, G., ALAJOUANINE, T., & GARCIN, R. Un cas d'apraxie idéomotrice bilatérale coïncidant avec une aphasie et une hémiparésie gauche chez une gauchère; troubles bilatéraux de la sensibilité profonde. *Rev. Neurol. (Par.),* **2:** 116–24, 1925.

HALSTEAD, W. C. *Brain and Intelligence. A Quantitative Study of the Frontal Lobes.* Chicago, University of Chicago Press, 1947.

HANSTROM, B. *Vergleichende Anatomie des Nervensystems der wirbellosen Tiere unter Berücksichtigung seiner Funktion.* Berlin, 1928.

HARLOW, H. F. The formation of learning sets. *Psychol. Rev.*, **56:** 51–65, 1949.

HEAD, H. *Studies in Neurology.* London, Oxford Medical Publications, 1920.

HEBB, D. O. Intelligence in man after large removals of cerebral tissue: defects following right temporal lobectomy. *J. Gen. Psychol.*, **21:** 437–46, 1939.

HÉCAEN, H. Dominance hémisphérique et préférence manuelle. *Evolution Psychiatrique,* **1:** 1–50, 1959.

——— & AJURIAGUERRA, J. DE. L'apraxie de l'habillage. Ses rapports avec la planotopokinésie et les troubles de la somatognosie. *Encéphale,* **34:** 113–44, 1945.

——— & ———. *Méconnaissance et Hallucinations Corporelles.* Paris, Masson & Co., 1952.

——— & ———. *Les troubles mentaux au cours des tumeurs intracraniennes.* Vol. 1. p. 153. Paris, Massons et Cie, 1956.

——— & ———. Agnosie visuelle pour les objets inanimés par lésion unilatérale gauche. *Rev. Neurol. (Par.),* **94:** 222–23, 1956.

———, ———, & MASSONNET, J. Les troubles visuo-constructifs par lésion pariéto-occipitale droite. Rôle des perturbations vestibulaires. *Encéphale,* **1:** 122–79, 1951.

———, ———, & DAVID, M. Les déficits fonctionnels après lobectomie occipitale. *Mschr. Psychiat. Neurol.,* **123:** 239–91, 1952.

———, ANGELERGUES, R., BERNHARDT, C., & CHIARELLI, J. Essai de distinction des modalités cliniques de l'agnosie des physionomies. *Rev. Neurol. (Par.),* **96:** 125–44, 1957.

———, PENFIELD, W., BERTRAND, C., & MALMO, R. The syndrome of apractognosia due to lesions of the minor cerebral hemisphere. *Arch. Neurol. Psychiat.,* **75:** 400–34, 1956.

——— & GARCIA-BADARACCO, J. Séméiologie des hallucinations visuelles en clinique neurologique. *Acta Neurol. Latinoam.,* **2:** 23–58, 1956.

——— & GIMENO ALAVA, L. L'apraxie idéo-motrice unilatérale gauche. *Rev. Neurol. (Par.),* **102:** 648–53, 1960.

——— & PIERCY, M. Paroxysmal dysphasia and the problem of cerebral dominance. *J. Neurol. Neurosurg. Psychiat.,* **19:** 194–201, 1956.

HEILBRUN, A. B. Psychological test performance as a function of lateral localization of cerebral lesion. *J. Comp. Physiol. Psychol.,* **49:** 10–14, 1956.

HERON, W. Perception as a function of retinal locus and attention. *Amer. J. Psychol.,* **70:** 38–48, 1957.

HERRICK, C. J. *The Tiger Salamander.* Chicago, The University of Chicago Press, 1948.

HOADLEY, M. D. & PEARSON, K. Measurement of internal diameter of skull in relation to "pre-eminence" of left hemisphere. *Biometrika,* **21:** 94–123, 1929.

HOFF, H. Les relations entre le lobe pariétal droit et gauche. *Vème Congrès international de Neurologie, Lisbonne.* **1:** 195–213, 1953.

HUBEL, D. H. & WIESEL, T. N. Receptive fields of single neurons in the cat's striate cortex. *J. Physiol.,* **148:** 574–91, 1959.

HUMPHREY, M. E. Consistency of hand usage. *Brit. J. Educ. Psychol.,* **21:** 214–25, 1951.

——— & ZANGWILL, O. L. Dysphasia in lefthanded patients with unilateral brain lesions. *J. Neurol. Neurosurg. Psychiat.,* **15:** 184–93, 1952.

INGELMARK, B. E. Über die Längenasymmetrie der Exstremitäten . . . Eine neue röntgenologische Registriermethode. *Upsala Läkarrfornings Förhandlingar,* **51:** 17–82, 1947.

JACOBSOHN-LASK, L. Die Kreuzung der Nervenbahnen und die bilaterale Symmetrie des tierischen Körpers. *Abh. Neurologie, Psychiatrie, Psychologie,* **26:** 1–125, 1924.

JAMES, W. *Principles of Psychology, I.* pp. 489–90, 177–79. New York, Dover Publications, Inc., 1950.

JERGER, J. F. Observations on auditory behavior in lesions of the central auditory pathway. *Arch. Otolaryng.,* **71:** 797–806, 1960.

——— & Mier, M. The effect of brain stem lesions on auditory responses of humans. Paper read at First Annual Meeting of Psychonomic Society, Chicago, September, 1960.

Jerison, H. J. & Neff, W. D. Effect of cortical ablation in the monkey on discrimination of auditory patterns. *Fed. Proc.,* **12:** 73–74, 1953.

Kimura, Doreen. Visual and auditory perception after temporal-lobe damage. Unpublished doctoral thesis, McGill University, 1960.

———. Cerebral dominance and the perception of verbal stimuli. *Canad. J. Psychol.,* **15:** 166–71, 1961a.

———. Some effects of temporal-lobe damage on auditory perception. *ibid.,* **15:** 156–65, 1961b.

Kleist, K. *Gehirnpathologie.* 1408 pp. Leipzig, Barth, 1934.

Klüver, H. Visual functions after removal of the occipital lobes. *J. Psychol.,* **11:** 23, 1941.

——— & Bucy, P. C. "Psychic blindness" and other symptoms following bilateral temporal lobectomy in rhesus monkeys. *Amer. J. Physiol.,* **119:** 352–53, 1937.

——— & ———. Preliminary analysis of functions of temporal lobes in monkeys. *Arch. Neurol. Psychiat.,* **42:** 979, 1939.

Kodama, K. Beitrage zur Anatomie des Zentralnervensystems der Japaner. VIII. Insula Reilii. *Folia Anat. Jap.,* **12:** 423–44, 1934.

Kohl, G. F. & Tschabitscher, H. Uber einen Fall von Amusie. *Wien. Z. Nervenheilk.,* **6:** 219–30, 1953.

Köhler, W. Zur Theorie des Sukzessivvergleichs und der Zeitfehler. *Psychol. Forsch.,* **4:** 115–75, 1923.

Kopsch, F. v. Mitteilungen über das Ganglion opticum der Cephalopoden. *Int. Mschr. Anat. Physiol.,* **16:** 33–52, 1899.

Krueger, E. G., Price, P. A., & Teuber, H.-L. Tactile extinction in parietal lobe neoplasm. *J. Psychol.,* **38:** 191–202, 1954.

Kruger, L. & Porter, P. A behavioral study of the functions of the Rolandic cortex in the monkey. *J. Comp. Neurol.,* **109:** 439–70, 1958.

Kuypers, H. G. J. M. Central cortical projections to motor and somatosensory cell groups. *Brain,* **83:** 161, 1960.

———. Some projections from the pericentral cortex to the pons and lower brain stem in monkey and chimpanzee. *J. Comp. Neurol.,* **110:** 221, 1958.

———, Fleming, W. R., & Farinholt, J. W. Descending projections to spinal motor and sensory cell groups in the monkey: cortex vs. subcortex. *Science,* **132:** 38, 1960.

Lange, J. Agnosien und Apraxien. In: *Handbuch der Neurologie,* Bumke & Foerster, Ed. **6:** 807–960, 1936.

Langworthy, O. R. A description of the central nervous system of the porpoise (Tursiops truncatus). *J. Comp. Neurol.,* **54:** 437–88, 1932.

Lansdell, H. C. Two selective deficits found to be lateralized in temporal neurosurgery patients. Paper read at 32nd Annual Meeting of Eastern Psychological Association, Philadelphia, 1961.

Lashley, K. S. Coalescence of neurology and psychology. *Proc. Amer. Phil. Soc.,* **84:** 461–70, 1941.

Lende, R. A. & Woolsey, C. N. Sensory and motor localization in cerebral cortex of porcupine. *J. Neurophysiol.,* **19:** 544, 1956.

Lettvin, J. Y., Maturana, H. R., McCulloch, W. S., & Pitts, W. H. What the frog's eye tells the frog's brain. *Proc. I.R.E.,* **47:** 1940–51, 1959.

Liepmann, H. Das Krankheitsbild der Apraxia (motorischen Asymbolie). *Mschr. Psychiat. Neurol.,* **8:** 15–44, 102–32, 182–97, 1900.

Lilly, J. C. *Man and Dolphin.* Garden City, Doubleday, 1961.

——— & Miller, A. M. Sounds emitted by the bottlenose dolphin—the audible emissions underwater or in air of captive dolphins are remarkably complex and varied. *Science,* **133:** 1689–93, 1961a.

——— & ———. Vocal exchanges between dolphins. Bottlenose dolphins "talk" to each other with whistles, clicks, and a variety of other noises. *Science,* **134:** 1873–76, 1961b.

——— & ———. Production of human speech sounds by the bottlenose dolphin. (Manuscript), 1962a.

——— & ———. Operant conditioning of the bottlenose dolphin with electrical stimulation of the brain. *J. Comp. Physiol. Psychol.,* **55:** 73–79, 1962b.

LOEB, J. Die Sehstörungen nach Verletzung der Grosshirnrinde. *Pflügers Arch. Ges. Physiol.,* **34:** 67–172, 1884.

LORENTE DE NO, R. Cerebral cortex; architecture, intracortical cortical connections, motor projections, etc., In: *Physiology of the Nervous System,* 2nd ed., J. F. Fulton, 1943.

LUNN, V. *Om Legemsbevidstheden. Belyst Ved Nogle Forstyrrelser af den Normale Oplevelsesmaade.* Copenhagen, Ejnar Munksgaard, 1948.

LURIA, A. R. Personal communication, 1960.

MCCULLOCH, W. S. Personal communication.

——— & GAROL, H. W. Cortical origin and distribution of corpus callosum and anterior commissure in the monkey (Macaca mulatta). *J. Neurophysiol.,* **4:** 555–63, 1941.

MCFIE, J. & PIERCY, M. F. Intellectual impairment with localized cerebral lesions. *Brain,* **75:** 292–311, 1952.

———, ———, & ZANGWILL, O. L. Visual spatial agnosia associated with lesions of the right cerebral hemisphere. *Brain,* **73:** 167–90, 1950.

——— & ZANGWILL, O. L. Visual-constructive disabilities associated with lesions of the left cerebral hemisphere. *Brain,* **83:** 243–60, 1960.

MACH, E. *The Analysis of Sensation.* New York, Dover Publications, 1959.

MARTIN, R. *Lehrbuch der Anthropologie.* 3rd ed., 3 vols. Stuttgart, G. Fischer, 1957–60.

MASON, J. W. Personal communication. 1961.

MATURANA, H. R., LETTVIN, J. Y., MCCULLOCH, W. S., & PITTS, W. H. Anatomy and physiology of vision in the frog *(Rana pipiens). J. Gen. Physiol.,* **43:** 129–75, 1960.

MATZKER, J. *Ein binauraler Hörsynthese-Test zum Nachweis zerebraler Hörstörungen.* p. 117. Stuttgart, Thieme, 1958.

MEIKLE, T. H., JR. Personal communication. 1961.

——— & SECHZER, J. A. Interocular transfer of brightness discrimination in "split-brain" cats. *Science,* **132:** 734–35, 1960.

MEYER, V. & JONES, H. G. Patterns of cognitive test performance as functions of the lateral localization of cerebral abnormalities in the temporal lobe. *J. Ment. Sci.,* **194:** 758–72, 1957.

MEYER, V. & YATES, H. J. Intellectual changes following temporal lobectomy for psychomotor epilepsy. *J. Neurol. Neurosurg, Psychiat.,* **18:** 44–52, 1955.

MILNER, B. Intellectual functions of the temporal lobes. *Psychol. Bull.,* **51:** 42–62, 1954.

———. Psychological defects produced by temporal lobe excision. *Res. Publ. Assoc. Res. Nerv. Ment. Dis.,* **36:** 244–57, 1958.

———. The memory defect in bilateral hippocampal lesions. *Psychiat. Res. Rep. Amer. Psychiat. Assoc.,* **11:** 43–58, 1959.

———. Impairment of visual recognition and recall after right temporal lobectomy in man. Paper read at First Annual Meeting of Psychonomic Society, Chicago, 1960.

MISHKIN, M. & PRIBRAM, K. H. Visual discrimination performance following partial ablations of the temporal lobe: I Ventral vs. lateral. *J. Comp. Physiol. Psychol.,* **47:** 14–20, 1954.

MOONEY, C. M. Closure with negative after-images under flickering light. *Canad. J. Psychol.,* **10:** 191–99, 1956.

———. Closure as affected by configural clarity and contextual consistency. *ibid.,* **11:** 80–88, 1957.

MORLAAS, J. *Contribution à l'Étude de l'Apraxie.* A. Legrand, Ed. Paris, Thèse, 1928.

MOZELL, M. M. & PFAFFMAN, C. The afferent neural processes in odor perception. *Ann. N. Y. Acad. Sci.,* **58:** 96, 1953.

MULLAN, S. & PENFIELD, W. Illusions of comparative interpretation and emotion. *Arch. Neurol. Psychiat.*, **81**: 269–84, 1959.

MYERS, R. E. Corpus callosum and interhemispheric communication: enduring memory effects. *Fed. Proc.*, **16**: 398, 1957.

———. Function of corpus callosum in interocular transfer. *Brain,* **79**: 358–63, 1959.

———. Failure of intermanual transfer in corpus callosum-sectioned chimpanzees. *Anat. Rec.*, **136**: 358, 1960a.

———. Interhemispheric interconnections between occipital poles of the monkey brain. *ibid.*, **136**: 249, 1960b.

———. Corpus callosum and visual gnosis. In: *Brain Mechanisms and Learning,* A. Fessard, *et al.* Eds. Oxford, Blackwell, 1961.

——— & HENSON, C. O. Role of corpus callosum in transfer of tactuokinesthetic learning in chimpanzee. *Arch. Neurol Psychiat.*, **3**: 404–409, 1960.

——— & SPERRY, R. W. Interocular transfer of a visual form discrimination habit in cats after section of the optic chiasma and corpus callosum. *Anat. Rec.*, **115**: 351–52, 1953.

NEFF, W. D. Behavioral studies of auditory discrimination. *Ann. Otol.,* **66**: 505–13, 1957.

———. Neural mechanisms of auditory discrimination. In: *Sensory Communication,* W. A. Rosenblith, Ed. pp. 259–78. M.I.T. Press and New York, John Wiley & Sons, 1961.

NIELSEN, J. M. Unilateral cerebral dominance as related to mind blindness: minimal lesion capable of causing agnosia for objects. *Arch. Neurol. Psychiat.*, **38**: 108–35, 1937.

———. *Agnosia, Apraxia, Aphasia; Their Value in Cerebral Localization.* 2nd ed. New York, Paul B. Hoeber, Inc., 1946.

ODOR, H. G. Functions of the temporal lobe in monkey (Macaca mulatta). Master's thesis, University of Chicago, 1959.

OGLE, S. W. On dextral pre-eminence. *Med.-chir. Trans.*, **35**: 279–301, 1871.

O'LEARY, J. Structure of the area striata of the cat. *J. Comp. Neurol.*, **75**: 131–64, 1941.

ORBACH, J. & CHOW, K. L. Differential effects of resections of somatic areas I and II in monkeys. *J. Neurophysiol.*, **22**: 195–203, 1959.

PARSONS, B. S. *Left-handedness.* New York, The Macmillan Co., 1924.

PATERSON, A. & ZANGWILL, O. L. Disorders of visual space perception associated with lesions of the right cerebral hemisphere. *Brain,* **67**: 331–58, 1944.

PENFIELD, W. Functional localization in temporal and deep sylvian areas. *Res. Publ. Assoc. Res. Nerv. & Ment. Dis.*, **36**: 210–26, 1958.

——— & EVANS, J. Functional defects produced by cerebral lobectomies. *Res. Publ. Assoc. Res. Nerv. Ment. Dis.*, **13**: 352–77, 1934.

——— & ROBERTS, L. *Speech and Brain Mechanisms.* Princeton, Princeton University Press, 1959.

PERIA, L., ROSADINI, G., & ROSSI, G. F. Determination of side of cerebral dominance with amobarbital. *Arch. Neurol.*, **4**: 173–81, 1961.

PFEIFER, R. A. Pathologie der Horstrahlung und der corticalen Horsphare. In: *Handb. d. Neurol.*, ed. by O. Bumke & O. Foerster, **6**: 533–626, 1936.

PIERCY, M., HÉCAEN, H., & AJURIAGUERRA, J. DE. Constructional apraxia associated with unilateral cerebral lesions. Left- and right-sided cases compared. *Brain,* **83**: 225–42, 1960.

POLYAK, S. *The Vertebrate Visual System.* Chicago, University of Chicago Press, 1957.

POMME, B. & JANNY, P. Trouble de la mémoire topographique consécutif à une intervention sur l'hémisphère non dominant. *Rev. Neurol. (Par.),* **91**: 307–308, 1954.

POPPELREUTER, W. *Die psychischen Schädigungen durch Kopfschuss im Kriege 1914–16; die Störungen der niederen und höheren Sehleistungen durch Verletzungen des Okzipitalhirns.* Vol. I. Leipzig, Voss, 1917.

POTZL, O. *Die Optisch-agnostichen Storungen.* Leipzig, F. Deuticke, 1928.

———. Weiteres über des Zeitraffer Erlebnis. *Wien. A. Nervenheilk.*, **4**: 9–39, 1951.
POWELL, T. P. S. & COWAN, W. M. Personal communication.
PRIBRAM, K. H. Toward a science of neuropsychology: (Method and data) . In: *Current Trends in Psychology and the Behavioral Sciences.* pp. 115–42. Pittsburgh, University of Pittsburgh Press, 1954.
———. Neocortical function in behavior. In: *Biological and Biochemical Bases of Behavior.* pp. 151–72. Madison, University of Wisconsin Press, 1958.
———. Regional physiology of CNS, The search for the engram—Decade of Decision. In: *Progress in Neurology and Psychiatry.* In Press. New York, Grune & Stratton, 1961.
——— & BAGSHAW, M. Further analysis of the temporal lobe syndrome utilizing fronto-temporal ablations. *J. Comp. Neurol.*, **99**: 347–75, 1955.
PROBLETE, R., RUBEN, R. J. & WALKER, A. E. The Propagation of after-discharge between temporal lobes. *J. Neurophysiol.*, **22**: 538–53, 1959.
REISEN, A. H., KURKE, M. I., & MELLINGER, J. C. Interocular transfer of habits learned monocularly in visually naive and visually experienced cats. *J. Comp. Physiol. Psychol.*, **46**: 166–72, 1953.
REITAN, R. M. Certain differential effects of left and right cerebral lesions in human adults. *J. Comp. Physiol. Psychol.*, **6**: 474–77, 1955.
——— & TARSHES, E. L. Differential effects of lateralized brain lesions on the trail-making test. *J. Nerv. Ment. Dis.*, **129**, 257–62, 1959.
RETZIUS, G. *Das Menschenhirn.* P. A. Norstedt u. Soner, 1896.
———. Zur Morphologie der Insula Reilii. *Biol. Unters. N F.*, **10**: 15–20, 1902.
RIOPELLE, A. J. & ADES, H. W. Visual discrimination performance in rhesus monkeys following extirpation of prestriate and temporal cortex. *J. Genet. Psychol.*, **83**: 63–77, 1953.
ROBINSON, J. S. & VONEIDA, T. J. Interocular perceptual integration in cats with optic chiasma and corpus callosum sectioned. *Amer. Psychologist*, **16**: 447–48, 1961.
ROSE, J. E. & WOOLSEY, C. N. The relations of thalamic connections, cellular structure, and evocable electrical activity in the auditory region of the cat. *J. Comp. Neurol.*, **91**: 441, 1949.
——— & ———. Cortical connections and functional organization of the thalamic auditory system of the cat. In: *Biological and Biochemical Bases of Behavior*, H. F. Harlow & C. N. Woolsey, Eds. pp. 127–50. Madison, University of Wisconsin Press, 1958.
——— & MOUNTCASTLE, V. B. *Handbook of Physiology*, Sec. 1, Vol. I: Neurophysiology, ed. by H. W. Magoun. American Physiology Society, Washington, D.C., 1959.
———, GALAMBOS, R., & HUGHES, J. R. Microelectrode studies of the cochlear nuclei of the cat. *Bull. Johns Hopkins Hosp.*, **104**: 211, 1959.
ROSENZWEIG, M. R. Representations of the two ears at the auditory cortex. *Amer. J. Physiol.*, **167**: 147–58, 1951.
———. Cortical correlates of auditory localization and of related perceptual phenomena. *J. Comp. Physiol. Psychol.*, **47**: 269, 1954.
RUCH, T. C., FULTON, J. K., & GERMAN, W. J. Sensory discrimination in monkey, chimpanzee, and man after lesions of the parietal lobe. *Arch. Neurol. Psychiat.*, **39**: 919–37, 1938.
RUSSELL, J. R. & REITAN, R. M. Psychological abnormalities in agenesis of the corpus callosum. *J. Nerv. Ment. Dis.*, **121**: 205–14, 1955.
SAETVEIT, J. G., LEWIS, D., & SEASHORE, C. G. *Revision of the Seashore Measures of Musical Talents. Univ. Iowa Stud. Aims Progr. Res. No. 65.* Iowa City, University of Iowa Press, 1940.
SANCHEZ-LONGO, L. P. & FORSTER, F. M. Clinical significance of impairment of sound localization. *Neurology*, **8**: 119–25, 1958.
———, ———, & AUTH, T. L. A clinical test for sound localization and its application. *Neurology*, **7**: 655–63, 1957.

SCHEIBEL, M. E. & SCHEIBEL, A. B. Structural substrates for integrative action in the brain stem reticular core. In: *Symposium on Reticular Formation.* H. Jaspar, ed. Boston, Little, Brown, 1958.

SCHRIER, A. M. & SPERRY, R. W. Visuomotor integration in split-brained cats. *Science,* **129:** 1275–76, 1959.

SCHWARTZBAUM, J. S. & PRIBRAM, K. H. The effects of amygdalectomy in monkeys on transposition along a brightness continuum. *J. Comp. Physiol. Psychol.,* **53:** 396–99, 1960.

SCOVILLE, W. B. & MILNER, B. Loss of recent memory after bilateral hippocampal lesion. *J. Neurol. Neurosurg. Psychiat.,* **20:** 11–21, 1957.

SEMMES, J., WEINSTEIN, S., GHENT, L., & TEUBER, H. L. Spatial orientation in man after cerebral injury: analyses by locus of lesion. *J. Psychol.,* **39:** 227–44, 1955.

———, ———, ———, & ———. Performance on complex tactual tasks after brain injury in man: analysis by locus of lesion. *Amer. J. Psychol.,* **67:** 220–40, 1954.

———, ———, ———, & ———. *Somatosensory Changes after Penetrating Brain Wounds in Man.* Vol. 1. p. 91. Cambridge, Harvard University Press, 1960.

SHANKWEILER, D. P. Performance of brain-damaged patients on two tests of sound localization. *J. Comp. Physiol. Psychol.,* **54:** 375–81, 1961.

SHARPLESS, S. & JASPER, H. Habituation of the arousal reaction. *Brain,* **79:** 655–80, 1956.

SHERRINGTON, C. S. Experimental note on two movements of the eye. *J. Physiol.,* **17:** 27–29, 1894.

SINHA, S. P. The role of the temporal lobe in hearing. Unpublished Master's thesis, McGill University, 1959.

SMITH, K. U. Learning and the association pathways of the human cerebral cortex. *Science,* **114:** 117–21, 1951.

SMITH, S. & HOLMES, G. A case of bilateral motor apraxia with disturbance of visual orientation. *Brit. Med. J.,* **1:** 437–41, 1916.

SPERRY, R. W. Corpus callosum and interhemispheric transfer in the monkey (Macaca mulatta) . *Anat. Rec.,* **131:** 297, 1958.

———. Physiological plasticity and brain circuit theory. In: *Biological and Biochemical Bases of Behavior.* pp. 401–24. Madison, University of Wisconsin Press, 1958.

———. In: *The Central Nervous System and Behavior,* Transactions of the first Macy Conference, M. A. B. Brazier, Ed. New York, Josiah Macy, Jr. Foundation, 1959.

———. Cerebral organization and behavior. *Science,* **133:** 1749–57, 1961.

———, STAMM, J. S. & MINER, N. Relearning tests for interocular transfer following division of optic chiasma and corpus callosum in cats. *J. Comp. Physiol. Psychol.,* **49:** 529–33, 1956.

SPRAGUE, J. M., CHAMBERS, W. W., & STELLAR, E. Attentive, affective, and adaptive behavior in the cat. *Science,* **144:** 165, 1961.

STAMM, J .S. & SPERRY, R. W. Function of corpus callosum in contralateral transfer of somesthetic discrimination in cats. *J. Comp. Physiol. Psychol.,* **50:** 138–43, 1957.

STAUFFENBERG, W. Klinische und anatom. Beiträge zur Kenntnis der aphasischen, agnostischen und apraktischen symptome. *Z. Ges. Neurol. Psychiat.,* **93:** 71, 1918.

STEBBINS, R. C. & EAKIN, R. M. The role of the "Third Eye" in reptilian behavior. *American Museum Novitates 1870,* **1:** 40, 1958.

STENGEL, E. Morphologische und cytoarchitektonische Studien über den Bau der unteren Frontalwindung . . . *Z. Neurol. Psychiat.,* **130:** 631–77, 1930.

——— & PATCH, I. C. L. "Central" aphasia associated with parietal symptoms. *Brain,* **78:** 401–16, 1955.

STEPIEN, L. C., CORDEAU, J. P., & RASMUSSEN, T. The effect of temporal lobe and hippocampal lesions on auditory and visual recent memory in monkeys. *Brain,* **83:** 470–89, 1960.

STIER, E. *Untersuchangen über Linkshändigkeit* . . . p. 252. Jena, G. Fischer, 1911.

STÖER, W. F. H. Das optische system beim Wassermolch. (Triturus taeniatus) . *Acta Morph. Neerl. Scand.,* **3:** 178–95, 1940.

SUTHERLAND, N. S. Visual discrimination of orientation and shape by the octopus. *Nature,* **179:** 11–13, 1957.
———. Visual discrimination of the orientation of rectangles by *Octopus vulgaris* Lamark. *J. Comp. Physiol. Psychol.,* **51:** 452–58, 1958.
TALBOT, S. A. & MARSHALL, W. H. Physiological studies on neural mechanisms in visual localization and discrimination. *Amer. J. Ophthal.,* **24:** 1255, 1941.
TERRACE, H. S. The effects of retinal locus and attention on the perception of words. *J. Exp. Psychol.,* **58:** 382–85, 1959.
TERZIAN, H. & DALLE ORE, G. Syndrome of Kluver and Bucy reproduced in man by bilateral removal of the temporal lobes. *Neurology,* **5:** 373–80, 1955.
——— & CECOTTO, C. cité par Donini, 1959.
TEUBER, H.-L. Some alterations in behavior after cerebral lesions in man. In: *Evolution of Nervous Control.* pp. 157–94. American Association for Advancement of Science, Washington, D.C., 1959.
———. Perception. In: *Handbook of Physiology,* Vol. III, pp. 1595–1668. American Physiological Society, Washington, D.C., 1960.
——— & BENDER, M. B. Alterations in pattern vision following trauma of occipital lobes in man. *J. Gen. Psychol.,* **40:** 37–57, 1949.
———, BATTERSBY, W. S. & BENDER, M. B. Performance of complex visual tasks after cerebral lesions. *J. Nerv. Ment. Dis.,* **114:** 413–29, 1951.
———, ———, ———. *Visual Field Defects after Penetrating Missile Wounds of the Brain,* p. 143. Cambridge, Harvard University Press, 1960.
——— & DIAMOND, S. Effects of brain injury in man on binaural localization of sounds. Paper read at 27th Annual Meeting of the Eastern Psychological Association, Atlantic City, 1956.
——— & WEINSTEIN, S. Performance on a formboard-task after penetrating brain injury. *J. Psychol.,* **38:** 177–90, 1954.
——— & ———. General and specific effects of cerebral lesions. *Amer. Psychol.,* **10:** 408–09, 1955.
——— & ———. Ability to discover hidden figures after cerebral lesions. *Arch. Neurol. Psychiat.,* **76:** 369–79, 1956.
——— & ———. Equipotentiality versus cortical localization. *Science,* **127:** 241–42, 1958.
THURNAM, J. On the weight of the brain and the circumstances affecting it. *J. Ment. Sci.,* Apr. 1866.
TRAVIS, A. M. Neurological deficiencies after ablation of the precentral motor area in Macaca mulatta. *Brain,* **78:** 155, 1955.
TREVARTHEN, C. B. Simultaneous learning of two conflicting problems by split-brain monkeys. *Amer. Psychologist,* **15:** 485, 1960.
———. Studies on visual learning in split-brain monkeys. Unpublished doctoral dissertation, California Institute of Technology, 1961.
TSCHIRGI, R. Spatial perception and central nervous system symmetry. *Arq. Neuro-psiquiat.,* **16:** 364–66, 1958.
TUNTURI, A. R. A study on the pathway from the medial geniculate body to the acoustic cortex in the dog. *Amer. J. Physiol.,* **147:** 311–19, 1946.
VALKENBURG, C. T. v. Experimental and pathologico-anatomical researches on the corpus callosum. *Brain,* **36:** 119–65, 1913.
VOGT, O. & VOGT, C. Personal communication.
VONEIDA, T. J. & SPERRY, R. W. Central nervous pathways involved in conditioning. *Anat. Rec.,* **139:** 283, 1961.
WADA, J. A. & RASMUSSEN, T. Intracarotid injection of sodium amytal for the lateralization of cerebral speech dominance. Experimental and clinical observations. *J. Neurosurg.,* **17:** 266–82, 1960.
WAGMAN, I. H., KRIEGER, H. P., & BENDER, M. B. Eye movements elicited by surface and depth stimulation of the occipital lobe of Macque mulatta. *J. Comp. Neurol.,* **109:** 169, 1958.

WAGNER, H. *Massbestimmungen der Oberfläche des grossen Gehirns.* Wigand, Cassel und Göttingen, 1864.

WAGNER, W. Aphasie, Apraxie, Agnosie. *Fortschr. Neurol. Psychiat.,* **14:** 219–47, 1942.

WALSH, E. G. An investigation of sound localization in patients with neurological abnormalities. *Brain,* **80:** 222–50, 1957.

WEIL, A. Measurements of cerebral and cerebellar surfaces. *Amer. J. Phys. Anthropol.,* **13:** 69–90, 1929.

WEINBERG, R. Die Gehirnform der Polen, *Z. Morphol. Anthropol.,* **8:** 123–214, 279–424, 1905.

WEINSTEIN, E. A. & KAHN, R. L. *Denial of Illness: Symbolic and Physiological Aspects.* Springfield, Ill., Charles C. Thomas, 1955.

WEINSTEIN, S. Time error in weight judgment after brain injury. *J. Comp. Physiol. Psychol.,* **48:** 203–207, 1955.

———. Weight judgment in somesthesis after penetrating injury to the brain. *J. Comp. Physiol. Psychol.,* **47:** 31–35, 1954.

———. Tactile size judgment after penetrating injury to the brain. *J. Comp. Physiol. Psychol.,* **48:** 106–09, 1955a.

———. Time error in tactile size judgment after penetrating brain injury. *J. Comp. Physiol. Psychol.,* **48:** 322–23, 1955c.

———. The effect of traumatic brain injury on speed of finger oscillation. Paper read at meeting of Eastern Psychological Association, Atlantic City, April, 1959.

———, SEMMES, J., GHENT, L., & TEUBER, H.-L. Roughness discrimination after penetrating brain injury in man: analysis according to locus of lesion. *J. Comp. Physiol. Psychol.,* **51:** 269–75, 1958.

———, ———, ———, & ———. Spatial orientation in man after cerebral injury: analyses according to concomitant defects. *J. Psychol.,* **42:** 249–63, 1956.

———, ———, ———, & ———. Tactile size discrimination after penetrating brain injury to man. Paper read at meeting of Eastern Psychological Association, Philadelphia, April, 1958b.

——— & SERSEN, E. A. Tactual sensitivity as a function of handedness and laterality. *J. Comp. Physiol. Psychol.,* **54:** 665–69, 1961.

———, & TEUBER, H.-L. Effects of penetrating brain injury on intelligence test scores. *Science,* **125:** 1036–37, 1957.

——— & ———. The role of preinjury education and intelligence level in intellectual loss after brain injury. *J. Comp. Physiol. Psychol.,* **50:** 535–39, 1957.

———, ———, GHENT, L., & SEMMES, J. Complex visual task performance after penetrating brain injury in man. *Amer. Psychologist,* **10:** 408, 1955.

WEISKRANTZ, L. & MISHKIN, M. Effects of temporal and frontal cortical lesions on auditory discrimination in monkeys. *Brain,* **81:** 406–14, 1958.

WELLS, M. J. Proprioception and visual discrimination of orientation in *Octopus. J. Exp. Biol.,* **37:** 489–99, 1960.

WEN, I. C. A study of the occipital region of the Chinese fetal brain. *J. Comp. Neurol.,* **57:** 477–506, 1933.

WHITTERIDGE, D. Central control of eye movements. In: *Handbook of Physiology, Sec. 1.* American Physiological Society, Washington, D.C., **II:** 1089, 1960.

WOO, T. L. On the asymmetry of the human skull. *Biometrika,* **22:** 324–52, 1931.

WOOLSEY, C. N. & WALZL, E. M. Topical projection of nerve fibers from local regions of the cochlea to the cerebral cortex of the cat. *Bull. Johns Hopkins Hosp.,* **71:** 315, 1942.

———, MARSHALL, W. H., & BARD, P. Representation of cutaneous tactile sensibility in the cerebral cortex of the monkey as indicated by evoked potentials. *Bull. Johns Hopkins Hosp.,* **70:** 399, 1942.

———, SETTLAGE, P. H., MEYER, D. R., SENCER, W., HAMUY, T. P., & TRAVIS, A. M. Patterns of localization in precentral and "supplementary" motor areas and their relation to the concept of a premotor area. *Res. Publ. Assoc. Res. Nerv. & Ment. Dis.,* **30:** 238, 1950.

WUNDT, H. *Vorlesungen über die Menschen und Tierseele,* 6 ed. Leipzig, 1919.
YOUNG, J. Z. The photoreceptors of Lampreys. II The functions of the pineal complex. *J. Exp. Biol.,* **12:** 254–70, 1960.
———. The visual system of *Octopus*. Regularities in the retina and optic lobes of Octopus in relation to form discrimination. *Nature,* (Lond.) **186:** 836–39, 1960.
ZANGWILL, O. L. *Cerebral Dominance and Its Relation to Psychological Function,* p. 31. Edinburgh, Oliver & Boyd, 1960.

Index